Contents

Note for parents, tutors, teachers and other adult helpers
A pull-out answers section (pages A1 to A8) appears in the centre of this book, between pages 26 and 27 (Paper 4). This provides answers to all the questions, along with guidance on marking the papers. Remove the pull-out section before the child begins working through the practice papers.

Verbal Reasoning Progress Paper 1

MARK
✓ OR ✗

Q. 1–5

jumbled words with clues

Each question has a word in CAPITALS. The letters in this word have been mixed up. Use the clue to work out what the word is. Write it on the line.

Example NIBOR   (a bird).   ___ROBIN___

1	MAD (a beaver builds it)	_____	1 ☐
2	STEAKFARB (a meal)	_____	2 ☐
3	ROUSTERS (clothing)	_____	3 ☐
4	LIFES (insects)	_____	4 ☐
5	FEARFIG (an animal)	_____	5 ☐

Q. 6–10

odd ones out

Two words in each question do **not** belong with the rest. Underline these **two** words.

Example horrid   nasty   <u>kind</u>   mean   unfriendly   <u>helpful</u>

6	red	green	colour	orange	paint	yellow	6 ☐
7	foal	dog	puppy	kitten	cat	calf	7 ☐
8	trapezium	triangle	square	rectangle	circle	parallelogram	8 ☐
9	bicycle	car	van	lorry	taxi	sledge	9 ☐
10	armchair	settee	table	chair	desk	stool	10 ☐

Q. 11–15

word grids

Fit each set of words into the grid beside them. The words should read across and down.

11

c	a	n

one
day
ado
eye
ace
~~can~~

12

a	g	o

tot
~~ago~~
bay
yet
bat
age

13

i	r	e

~~ire~~
let
pal
net
are
pin

11 ☐
12 ☐
13 ☐

14

a	r	e

nap
ten
ore
not
pen
~~are~~

15

e	w	e

wed
red
par
~~ewe~~
pew
awe

14 ☐
15 ☐

MARK [   ]

MARK
✓ OR ✗

Q. 16–20

spot the word

A four-letter word is hidden in each of these sentences. You will find the hidden word at the end of one word and the beginning of the next. Underline the hidden word and then write it on the line.

Example Daniel <u>end</u>ed his speech with a joke. __lend__

16 "I think you were adding up the wrong numbers," Suzy told me.

_____ 16 ☐

17 Esther often goes with her friend to play tennis. _____ 17 ☐

18 Max painted the table after he had painted the chairs. _____ 18 ☐

19 Theseus said he would go alone to fight the hideous Minotaur.

_____ 19 ☐

20 Eggs often go bad in very warm weather. _____ 20 ☐

Q. 21–25

position problems

This is a diagram of a street. The odd house numbers are on one side and the even numbers on the other side. Five children (Adam, Bilal, Claire, David and Ella) live in the street.

Read the questions and write the answers on the lines. You may write notes on the diagram if this will help you.

1	3	5	7	9

Main Street

2	4	6	8	10

21 Adam lives in a house with an even number above 9.
What is the number of Adam's house? _____ 21 ☐

22 Bilal lives in a house with an odd number that is the square of 3.
What is the number of Bilal's house? _____ 22 ☐

23 Claire lives next door to Bilal.
What is the number of Claire's house? _____ 23 ☐

24 David lives in the house two doors along from Adam.
What is the number of David's house? _____ 24 ☐

25 Ella lives opposite the house that is two to the left of David.
What is the number of Ella's house? _____ 25 ☐

MARK ☐

MARK
✓ OR ✗

Q. 26–30 letter codes	Answer these letter analogies. Use the alphabet to help you. A B C D E F G H I J K L M N O P Q R S T U V W X Y Z

26 A is to B as C is to _____ .   26 ☐

27 Z is to Y as F is to _____ .   27 ☐

28 D is to G as T is to _____ .   28 ☐

29 MN is to OP as FG is to _____ .   29 ☐

30 X is to B as Q is to _____ .   30 ☐

Q. 31–35 symbol codes

The word **SHEARED** is written as ▲ ▼ ► ◄ ● ► ■ in code. Use the same code to work out the hidden words.

31 ▲ ► ► ■   _____   31 ☐

32 ■ ◄ ● ►   _____   32 ☐

33 ● ► ◄ ■   _____   33 ☐

34 ▼ ◄ ● ■   _____   34 ☐

35 ► ◄ ● ▲   _____   35 ☐

Q. 36–40
missing
three-letter
words

Use the clue to work out the five-letter word. The missing three letters also form a word. Write the three-letter word on the line.

Example S _ _ _ T (to begin) _TAR_

36 S _ _ _ K (to talk)   _____   36 ☐

37 C _ _ _ E (a large box)   _____   37 ☐

38 S _ _ _ K (a nasty smell)   _____   38 ☐

39 G _ _ _ N (got bigger)   _____   39 ☐

40 P _ _ _ L (found in an oyster shell)   _____   40 ☐

MARK ☐

MARK
✓ OR ✗

Q. 41–45

true statements

Read the information in each question. Circle the **only** statement (A, B, C, D or E) that has to be true, based on this information.

41 Sara is my sister. My name is Dan. We live with our parents.

A Dad's name is Dan.
B Dan has no grandpa.
C Sara has a brother.
D Sara's other sister is Maria.
E They have a large garden.

41 ☐

42 Hussein likes books. Usman reads a lot. Usman is Hussein's father.

A Hussein can read.
B Hussein just likes looking at the pictures.
C Hussein's dad can read.
D Usman's cousin is a librarian.
E Hussein's mother reads a lot.

42 ☐

43 Carly's dad has a butcher's shop. Carly is a plumber. Carly's mum is a secretary.

A Carly's mum can repair burst pipes.
B Carly's dad is called Trevor.
C Carly's dad likes eating steak.
D Carly's mum keeps secrets.
E Carly's dad sells meat.

43 ☐

44 Molly's mother is in the army. She travels all over the world. She comes home to her family three times a year.

A Molly's mum is the captain of a ship.
B Molly travels all over the world.
C Molly's dad comes home every four months.
D Molly's mum never sees her daughter.
E Molly sees her mum three times a year.

44 ☐

45 Harry watches a lot of TV. He likes comedy shows best. Mandy is Harry's sister. She hates all TV programmes.

A Harry's mother is called Mandy.
B Mandy loves watching the news on TV.
C Harry's favourite TV programmes are funny.
D Harry's sister has a lot of hobbies.
E Harry's sister likes documentaries better than comedy shows.

45 ☐

MARK ☐

MARK
✓ OR ✗

Q. 46–50

complete the sentence

Underline **one** word in the brackets to make the sentence sensible.

Example The yacht sailed into the (shop hospital <u>harbour</u> cinema matchbox).

46 The dog lay on the mat and gnawed on a (cat floor emu bone chair). | 46 ☐

47 Our car broke down and had to be taken to the (nursery doctor park zoo garage). | 47 ☐

48 Potatoes are my favourite (fruit pasta bread pets vegetable). | 48 ☐

49 The table was laid, ready for (sanding varnishing lunch painting dancing). | 49 ☐

50 Britain is entirely surrounded by (water wasps trees fences lettuce). | 50 ☐

Q. 51–55

interpreting tables

Here is a table showing the rainfall in Birmingham and Bristol over a twelve-month period. Look at the table and then answer the questions. Measurements are to the nearest centimetre.

	Rainfall in cm	
Month	**Birmingham**	**Bristol**
Jan	17	5
Feb	14	4
Mar	13	4
Apr	9	4
May	9	4
June	8	5
July	10	6
Aug	14	6
Sep	12	5
Oct	13	7
Nov	16	5
Dec	19	6
Total	154	61

51 Which month has the highest rainfall in Bristol?

_____ | 51 ☐

52 Which month has the highest rainfall in Birmingham?

_____ | 52 ☐

53 What is the total of the four months that have the lowest rainfall in Bristol?

_____ cm | 53 ☐

54 Which month is driest in Birmingham?

_____ | 54 ☐

55 Over the twelve months, which city is drier? _____ | 55 ☐

MARK ☐

Q. 56–60

join two words to make one

Circle **one** word from **each** group, which together will make a longer word.

Example (pond (dam) river)   (era down (age))

56 (zip weigh but)	(tonne gram ton)	56 ☐
57 (van car round)	(go come tor)	57 ☐
58 (super great marvel)	(louse market shop)	58 ☐
59 (suit look foot)	(tie over ball)	59 ☐
60 (eye make-up brow)	(foot touch sight)	60 ☐

Q. 61–65

letters for numbers

If **A** is **1**, **B** is **4**, **C** is **5**, **D** is **10** and **E** is **15**, work out these calculations. Give the answer as a letter.

Example C + D = ▨   ___E___

61	$3 \times C = $ ▨	_____	61 ☐
62	$E - C = $ ▨	_____	62 ☐
63	$A \times C = $ ▨	_____	63 ☐
64	$A + B = $ ▨	_____	64 ☐
65	$E \div C = B - $ ▨	_____	65 ☐

Q. 66–70

antonyms

Underline two words, **one** from **each** set of brackets, that have the **opposite** meaning.

Example (happy kind grin)   (sad face cheerful)

66 (in up down)	(there gone out)	66 ☐
67 (bulb sun light)	(dark night day)	67 ☐
68 (ugly lean fall)	(fat think meat)	68 ☐
69 (out shout move)	(hiss bawl whisper)	69 ☐
70 (shut open down)	(wide hear close)	70 ☐

MARK ☐

MARK
✓ OR ✗

...tart in the shaded square in each grid. Find out how the items in the grid are related to one another. Then fill in the missing item.

71

6	12	18
48	⬛	
42	36	30

72

42	49	56
35	⬛	7
	21	14

73

100		80
30	⬛	70
40	50	60

71 ☐

72 ☐

73 ☐

74

	÷	×
−	⬛	−
×	÷	+

75

7	8	15
	⬛	23
99	61	38

74 ☐

75 ☐

Q. 76–80
mixed-up groups

Two groups of three words have been mixed up in each question. Work out which would be the **middle** word in each group if they were in the correct order. Underline these **two** words.

Example city   <u>adolescent</u>   village   <u>town</u>   infant   adult

76	seven	first	third	five	three	second	76 ☐
77	higher	low	high	lowest	lower	highest	77 ☐
78	cat	melon	horse	apple	mouse	blackberry	78 ☐
79	bottom	shout	middle	top	whisper	say	79 ☐
80	fifteenth	five	tenth	fifth	ten	fifteen	80 ☐

Q. 81–85
analogies

Complete these analogies. Write the answers on the lines.

Example Arrive is to depart as come is to _____go_____.

81   March is to May as October is to _December_.   81)

82   Six is to sixty as eight is to _eighty_.   82 \

83   Fish is to swim as bird is to _fly_.   83)

84   Eat is to hungry as drink is to _thirsty_.   84 |

85   Sheep is to mutton as cow is to _beef_.   85

MARK [   ]

MARK
✓ OR ✗

Q. 86–90

odd ones out

One word in each question does **not** belong with the rest. Underline this word.

Example horrid   nasty   <u>kind</u>   mean   unfriendly

86	daughter	wife	sister	aunt	niece	son	86 ☐
87	mastiff	tabby	setter	spaniel	corgi	dachshund	87 ☐
88	seven	nineteen	fourth	fifty	eight	twenty	88 ☐
89	tiger	leopard	lion	panther	hyena	lynx	89 ☐
90	piece	fragment	whole	part	portion	bit	90 ☐

Q. 91–95

mixed-up sentences

Two words must swap places for each sentence to make sense. Underline these **two** words in each sentence.

Example The <u>bone</u> growled softly as he approached the <u>dog</u>.

91	The letters brought the postman to our house.	91 ☐
92	Our milkman bit the dog as he opened the front gate.	92 ☐
93	Mum asked Olga to help with her homework.	93 ☐
94	The warm made the room very fire.	94 ☐
95	A cloud of flames arose from the smoke of the bonfire.	95 ☐

Q. 96–100

alphabetical order

Number the words in each line in alphabetical order. Use the alphabet to help you.

Example HIGH   LOUD   TAKE   FAIL   MEAL
                    [2]   [3]   [5]   [1]   [4]

A B C D E F G H I J K L M N O P Q R S T U V W X Y Z

96	WELL	TELL	BELL	SELL	DELL	96 ☐
	☐	☐	☐	☐	☐	
97	GREEN	VIOLET	PURPLE	ORANGE	BLUE	97 ☐
	☐	☐	☐	☐	☐	
98	BREEZE	BRIGHT	BRAVE	BROTHER	BRUSH	98 ☐
	☐	☐	☐	☐	☐	
99	TREE	PROUD	FRIGHT	CRINGE	BRAIN	99 ☐
	☐	☐	☐	☐	☐	
100	START	STAMP	STAIR	STABLE	STALE	100 ☐
	☐	☐	☐	☐	☐	

MARK ☐

END OF TEST

PROGRESS PAPER 1 TOTAL ☐

MARK
✓ OR ✗

Q. 1–5

sorting information

Read the information below carefully. Then answer the questions.

My name is James. I will be 20 in nine years' time. My brother Henry will be 11 then and my sister Eve will be 18. Dad is two years older than Mum who will then be 41.

1	How old am I now?	_____ years old	1
2	How old is Henry now?	_____ years old	2
3	How old is Eve now?	_____ years old	3
4	How old is Mum now?	_____ years old	4
5	How old is Dad now?	_____ years old	5

Q. 6–10

letter sequences

Write the next two items in each sequence. Use the alphabet to help you.

Example AB   CD   EF   GH   __IJ__   __KL__

A B C D E F G H I J K L M N O P Q R S T U V W X Y Z

6	C	F	I	L	_____	_____	6
7	BC	EF	HI	KL	_____	_____	7
8	CDE	GHI	KLM	OPQ	_____	_____	8
9	KL	IJ	GH	EF	_____	_____	9
10	I	L	O	R	_____	_____	10

Q. 11–15

which word

One word in each question **cannot** be made from the word in CAPITALS. Underline this word. You may only use each letter once.

Example AIRPORT   rip   <u>park</u>   trio   pair   roar

11	TERRIBLE	tribe	rite	enter	reel	biter	11
12	CURTAINS	stain	strain	rust	carts	station	12
13	SERPENT	repent	parent	trees	present	tense	13
14	TRIANGLE	learn	tinge	gear	tearing	ranger	14
15	ASSEMBLE	bless	least	beams	measles	seals	15

MARK [   ]

MARK
✓ OR ✗

Q. 16–20
make a word

Look at how the second word is made from the first word in each pair. Complete the third pair in the same way. Write the answers on the lines.

Example (rat rates)   (mop mopes)   (fin ___fines___)

16 (on one)   (mat mate)   (past _____)   16 ☐
17 (post poster)   (fast faster)   (quick _____)   17 ☐
18 (tot pop)   (slit slip)   (totter _____)   18 ☐
19 (bat bare)   (scab scare)   (dip _____)   19 ☐
20 (duty dusty)   (rut rust)   (cot _____)   20 ☐

Q. 21–25
word categories

Below this table are 10 words. Write each word in the correct column.

21 flowers	22 vegetables	23 dogs	24 counties	25 countries

onion   boxer   Durham   Poland   broccoli
daffodil   Italy   gladiolus   terrier   Berkshire

21 ☐
22 ☐
23 ☐
24 ☐
25 ☐

Q. 26–30
jumbled words in sentences

The letters of the words in CAPITALS have been mixed up. Write the **two** correct words on the lines.

Example The TERWA was too cold to WSIM in. ___WATER___ and ___SWIM___

26 The OXF chased the SHEN around the farmyard.
_____ and _____   26 ☐

27 He burned his FRINGES when he picked up the hot STOAT.
_____ and _____   27 ☐

28 The decorator spilled the INAPT all over the PETCAR.
_____ and _____   28 ☐

29 Those NURNESR won a LAMED at the Olympics.
_____ and _____   29 ☐

30 He opened the STAGE so that he could drive his ARC up to the house.
_____ and _____   30 ☐

MARK ☐

MARK
✓ OR ✗

Q. 31–35

match the codes

The words below have been written in code. Which code belongs to which word? Write the answers on the lines.

TIME	EMIT	ITEM	MITE	TAME
4286	2968	8642	2468	6428

31 The code for TIME is _____ .

32 The code for EMIT is _____ .

33 The code for ITEM is _____ .

34 The code for MITE is _____ .

35 The code for TAME is _____ .

31
32
33
34
35

Q. 36–40

word connections

Underline the **one** word that fits with **both** pairs of words in brackets.

Example (heart club) (ruby emerald)   jewel brain <u>diamond</u> card brooch

36 (dahlia snowdrop) (lifted elevated)   upwards crocus rose flower heavy

37 (leash rein) (iron tin)   dog shower clothes beans lead

38 (house bungalow) (even level)   hotel hilly odd flat apartment

39 (below underneath) (miserable sad)   beneath low grumpy cellar tunnel

40 (game challenge) (same equal)   tennis match different plus ground

36
37
38
39
40

Q. 41–45

jumbled words in grids

The letters in each grid make **two** four-letter words. The letters must stay in the same columns. Work out where each letter goes.

Example

w	a	l	k
s	w	i	m
s	a	i	k
w	w	l	m

41

42
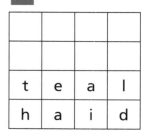

43
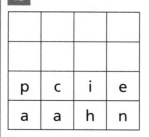

44
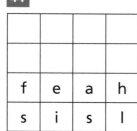

45
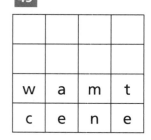

41
42
43
44
45

MARK ⬜

Q. 46–50

time problems

Study this train timetable. Then answer the questions below.

Station		Train A	Train B	Train C	
Ashlow	departs	07:13	08:17		
Barston	arrives	07:25		09:33	
Craigow	arrives	07:50	08:54		
Deston	arrives	07:59		10:03	
Earlstown	arrives	08:12	09:16	10:16	12:10

46 Trains A and B both take 59 minutes to travel the same journey. What time does Train B arrive at Barston? _____ 46 ☐

47 What time does Train B arrive at Deston? _____ 47 ☐

48 All four trains take 12 minutes to travel from Ashlow to Barston. What time does Train C leave Ashlow? _____ 48 ☐

49 How many minutes less than Train A does Train C take to complete the whole journey? _____ min 49 ☐

50 Which train takes the longest time to travel from Ashlow to Earlstown? Train _____ 50 ☐

Q. 51–55

analogies

Underline **one** word in **each** set of brackets to complete these analogies.

Example Arrive is to (<u>depart</u> plane speed) as come is to (run hurry <u>go</u>).

51 Top is to (up down bottom) as narrow is to (thin wide short). 51 ☐

52 Grass is to (mow lawn green) as sky is to (cloudy blue sun). 52 ☐

53 Shoal is to (fish shovel whales) as pack is to (luggage puppies dogs). 53 ☐

54 Always is to (sometimes usually never) as often is to (seldom now go). 54 ☐

55 Tadpole is to (kipper swim frog) as caterpillar is to (butterfly grub bird). 55 ☐

Q. 56–60

word meanings

Each of these words can have **two** meanings. Write the numbers of the two meanings in the table below.

Example		**56**		**57**		**58**		**59**		**60**	
organ		hail		hide		over		cow		blunt	
11	12										

56 ☐
57 ☐
58 ☐
59 ☐
60 ☐

Meanings 1 to conceal 2 concluded 3 to subdue 4 to greet
5 saying what you really mean 6 above 7 not sharp
8 animal skin 9 wintry rain 10 a female animal
11 a musical instrument 12 part of the body

MARK ☐

MARK
✓ OR ✗

65

Odd ones out

One word in each question does **not** belong with the rest. Underline this word.

Example horrid   nasty   <u>kind</u>   mean   unfriendly

61	table	chair	wardrobe	cooker	bed	sideboard	61
62	robin	starling	ostrich	sparrow	eagle	swift	62
63	bread	butter	cream	milk	yoghurt	cheese	63
64	trawler	warship	pedalo	liner	lifeboat	cruiser	64
65	netball	bowls	darts	tennis	cricket	rugby	65

Q. 66–70

antonyms

Underline the **two** words in each question that have the **opposite** meaning.

Example <u>happy</u>   kind   grin   <u>sad</u>   face   cheerful

66	water low shallow cold deep empty wet swim	66
67	top over throw high tunnel under across cellar	67
68	scribble mucky understand untidy bedroom neat dirty	68
69	assault fight battle attack peace compliment insult shout	69
70	illness trivial great serious angry apologise miner stop	70

Q. 71–75

mixed-up sentences

Two words must swap places for each sentence to make sense. Underline these **two** words in each sentence.

Example The <u>bone</u> growled softly as he approached the <u>dog</u>.

71	The river over the bridge had to be closed.	71
72	The plane used the carpenter to smooth the wood.	72
73	I shouted at her to crossroad at the busy stop.	73
74	Please money as much give as you can.	74
75	Month is the second February of the year.	75

MARK [   ]

MARK
✓ OR ✗

Q. 76–80

interpreting graphs

This chart shows the number of children in Years 3 to 6 at a school. Study the chart. Then answer the questions.

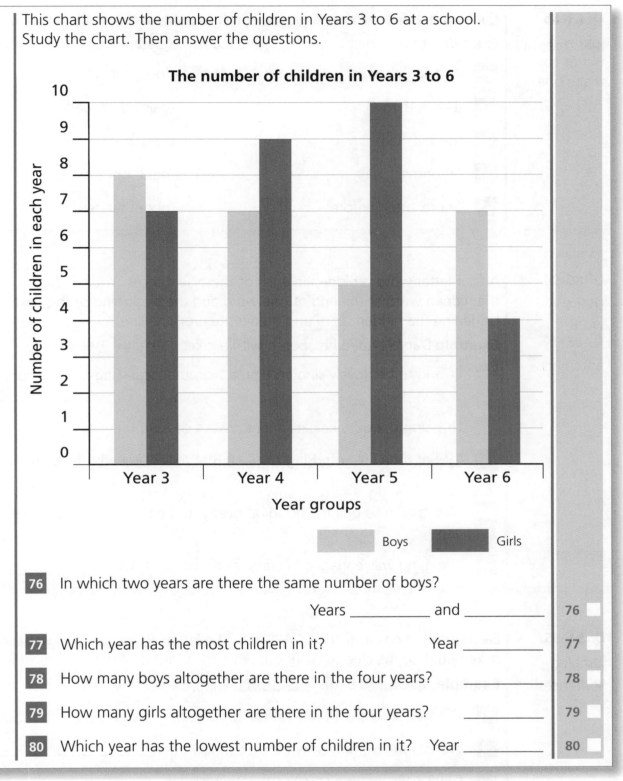

The number of children in Years 3 to 6

Number of children in each year

Year groups

Boys ▢ Girls ▢

76 In which two years are there the same number of boys?

Years _____ and _____   76 ▢

77 Which year has the most children in it?   Year _____   77 ▢

78 How many boys altogether are there in the four years?   _____   78 ▢

79 How many girls altogether are there in the four years?   _____   79 ▢

80 Which year has the lowest number of children in it?   Year _____   80 ▢

MARK ▢

MARK
✓ OR ✗

Q. 81–85

join two words to make one

Circle **one** word from **each** group, which together will make a longer word.

Example (pond (dam) river)   (era   down (age))

81	(fire leg arm)	(foot gun chair)	81 ☐
82	(bar rod row)	(gain knee oar)	82 ☐
83	(by hill half)	(pass near past)	83 ☐
84	(wrong all rail)	(right gone way)	84 ☐
85	(more after before)	(noon tar tea)	85 ☐

Q. 86–90

spot the word

A four-letter word is hidden in each of these sentences. You will find the hidden word at the end of one word and the beginning of the next. Underline the hidden word and then write it on the line.

Example Daniel <u>end</u>ed his speech with a joke.   <u>lend</u>

86 Owing to her lovely singing Emma won the local song competition.

_____   86 ☐

87 Lin's dog doesn't like cats and is always chasing them. _____   87 ☐

88 "What rope are you using to climb that rock?" asked the instructor.

_____   88 ☐

89 "It's raining so pull the hood up over your head," my friend advised.

_____   89 ☐

90 The gang was engaged in crime all round the town. _____   90 ☐

Q. 91–95

jumbled words with clues

Each question has a word in CAPITALS. The letters in this word have been mixed up. Use the clue to work out what the word is. Write it on the line.

Example NIBOR   (a bird)   <u>ROBIN</u>

91 OSCID   (where you can dance)   _____   91 ☐

92 SLIME   (a very long way)   _____   92 ☐

93 GERRYUS   (where you visit the doctor)   _____   93 ☐

94 EVLITSEINO   (what you watch)   _____   94 ☐

95 QUOITEUB   (a shop)   _____   95 ☐

MARK ☐

MARK
✓ OR ✗

Q. 96–100
word grids

Fit each set of words into the grid above them. The words should read across and down.

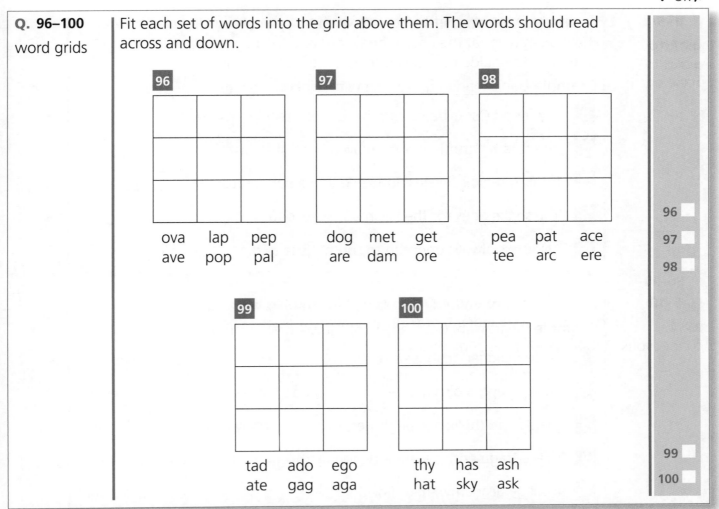

96 |
97 |
98 |

99 |
100 |

START HERE

MARK
✓ OR ✗

Q. 1–5

spot the word

A four-letter word is hidden in each of these sentences. You will find the hidden word at the end of one word and the beginning of the next. Underline the hidden word and then write it on the line.

Example Daniel <u>ended</u> his speech with a joke.   <u>lend</u>

1 My friend Oscar trains with his football team every week. _____ | 1 ☐

2 The caramel truffles were enjoyed by all the class. _____ | 2 ☐

3 If this reservoir freezes now it could be dangerous. _____ | 3 ☐

4 The snake goes for the kill in a split second. _____ | 4 ☐

5 "North is always opposite to south," she said. _____ | 5 ☐

Q. 6–10

word connections

Underline the **one** word that fits with **both** pairs of words in brackets.

Example (heart club) (ruby emerald)   jewel brain <u>diamond</u> card brooch

6 (shovel digger) (choose select)   make pick grab excavate sell | 6 ☐

7 (alter adapt) (coins money)   modify notes pound change destroy | 7 ☐

8 (pale faint) (brilliance brightness)   skinny bulb light small candle | 8 ☐

9 (piece fragment) (separate disconnect)   split peace whole part bit | 9 ☐

10 (college academy) (herd flock)   group set litter crowd school | 10 ☐

Q. 11–15

complete the sentence

Underline **one** word in **each** set of brackets to make the sentence sensible.

Example The (plumber <u>electrician</u> baker) repaired the (<u>light</u> loaf sink) so that we could (lamp hear <u>see</u>) again.

11 The (whale goldfish diver) swam round and round its (saucer teacup bowl) and kept the (sharks children weeds) happy. | 11 ☐

12 I (were weren't wasn't) too (sad poorly happy) when the late (bus cabbage rocket) made me miss the opening of the show. | 12 ☐

13 Rebecca likes (mining gardening reading) and goes to the (hospital library jail) every (century decade week). | 13 ☐

14 The (scooter train bicycle) stopped at the (station pool newsagent) to let the (tigers acrobats passengers) get off. | 14 ☐

15 Lexi told her (foot mother budgie) that the (taxi restaurant penguin) had (fallen flown arrived). | 15 ☐

MARK ☐

MARK
✓ OR ✗

Q. 16–20
word categories

Underline the **general** word in each row, which is the word that includes all the others.

Example banana   apple   <u>fruit</u>   raspberry   pear   kiwi

16	van car bus lorry ambulance vehicle	16 ☐
17	turkey poultry chicken duck pheasant goose	17 ☐
18	hat cap bowler beret trilby beanie	18 ☐
19	hyphen comma apostrophe colon bracket punctuation	19 ☐
20	circle square polygon rectangle shape octagon	20 ☐

Q. 21–25
word meanings

Each of these words can have **two** meanings. Write the numbers of the two meanings in the table below.

Example		**21**		**22**		**23**		**24**		**25**	
organ		mean		train		safe		band		drive	
11	12										

Meanings   1 secure   2 intend   3 a group of musicians
   4 to educate   5 a place to keep money   6 miserly
   7 the road up to a house   8 a flat strip of cloth
   9 to operate a vehicle   10 transport on rails
   11 a musical instrument   12 part of the body

21 ☐
22 ☐
23 ☐
24 ☐
25 ☐

Q. 26–30
word chains

Turn the word on the left into the word on the right. You can only change one letter at a time. Each change must result in a real word.

Example LID   <u>LED</u>   BED

26	D I N	_____	B A N	26 ☐
27	S I T	_____	H A T	27 ☐
28	D I G	_____	L O G	28 ☐
29	M A D	_____	B I D	29 ☐
30	L O W	_____	R A W	30 ☐

MARK ☐

MARK
✓ OR ✗

Q. 31–35

change a word

One word is incorrect in each sentence. Underline this word. Write the correct word on the line.

Example Climbing over that wall is not <u>aloud</u>.   <u>allowed</u>

31 The doctor told me to take two of the tables each day.

_____   31 ☐

32 What you have just said is absolute nuisance.   _____   32 ☐

33 The bugler broke into the house when the owners went on holiday.

_____   33 ☐

34 The dog jumped into the pound and swam to the other side.

_____   34 ☐

35 In autumn the loaves fall from the trees.   _____   35 ☐

Q. 36–40

mixed-up groups

Two groups of three words have been mixed up in each question. Work out which would be the **middle** word in each group if they were in the correct order. Underline these **two** words.

Example city   <u>adolescent</u>   village   <u>town</u>   infant   adult

36	wren	monkey	shrew	emu	elephant	eagle	36 ☐
37	trickle	chapter	river	stream	page	book	37 ☐
38	thinner	sea	lake	thinnest	thin	pool	38 ☐
39	second	week	hour	minute	year	day	39 ☐
40	midnight	grey	white	dusk	black	dawn	40 ☐

Q. 41–45

always has

Look at the word in **bold**. Underline **one** option in the brackets. It must describe what the word in bold **always has**.

Example A **lake** always has (boats   <u>water</u>   ducks   swimmers   fish).

41 **Money** always has (paper   metal   a bank   value   an account   a wallet).   41 ☐

42 A **box** always has (a lid   hinges   a Jack   volume   wheels   wood).   42 ☐

43 A **bookcase** always has (books   ornaments   clutter   shelves   legs).   43 ☐

44 **Water** is always (hot   cold   clean   dirty   wet   deep   green).   44 ☐

45 A **pair** always has (fruit   socks   double   two   three   trousers).   45 ☐

MARK ☐

MARK
✓ OR ✗

Q. 46–50

move a letter

Take **one** letter from the first word and put it in the second word to make two new words. Write the letter you have moved and the two new words in the table below.

	First word	Second word	Letter moved	New first word	New second word
Example	slope	feat	s	lope	feast
46	cause	bond			
47	store	rifle			
48	pretty	gain			
49	coast	sets			
50	zone	pries			

46
47
48
49
50

Q. 51–55

missing three-letter words

Use the clue to work out the five-letter word. The missing three letters also form a word. Write the three-letter word on the line.

Example S _ _ _ T   (to begin)   TAR

51 S _ _ _ L   (to take something from someone else)   _____

52 S _ _ _ E   (a large pebble)   _____

53 C _ _ _ Y   (a sweet)   _____

54 B _ _ _ E   (a woman getting married)   _____

55 G _ _ _ M   (to shine)   _____

51
52
53
54
55

Q. 56–60

letters for numbers

If **A** is **1**, **B** is **2**, **C** is **3**, **D** is **5** and **E** is **10**, work out these calculations. Give the answer as a letter.

Example C + B = _D_

56 B × C = D + ▓   _____

57 D – C = ▓   _____

58 E ÷ D = ▓   _____

59 A + B + C = D + ▓   _____

60 A × B × C × D = 3 × ▓   _____

56
57
58
59
60

MARK [ ]

MARK
✓ OR ✗

Q. 61–65
add a letter

Read the clue in brackets. Add **one** letter to the word in CAPITALS to make a new word that matches the clue. Write the new word on the line.

Example CANE   (lifts heavy objects)   <u>CRANE</u>

61 PLAN   (flatland)   _____   61 ☐

62 TANK   (be grateful)   _____   62 ☐

63 SALE   (not fresh)   _____   63 ☐

64 AMPLE   (an example or specimen)   _____   64 ☐

65 IDEA   (perfect)   _____   65 ☐

Q. 66–70
position
problems

This is a diagram of a five-storey block of flats. Families A, B, C, D and E live here. Work out where each family lives. Write the letter of the family on the correct floor in the diagram.

Family B lives three floors above Family E.

Family E has no stairs to climb in order to get home.

Family D lives two floors below Family C.

Family C has to climb the most stairs.

Family A has to climb one flight of stairs to get home.

	Floor	Family		
66	4th floor			66 ☐
67	3rd floor			67 ☐
68	2nd floor			68 ☐
69	1st floor			69 ☐
70	Ground floor			70 ☐

MARK [   ]

MARK
✓ OR ✗

Q. 71–75

word codes

Work out these codes. The code used in each question is different. Use the alphabet to help you.

A B C D E F G H I J K L M N O P Q R S T U V W X Y Z

Example If DWU is the code for BUS, what does EQCEJ mean? __COACH__

71 If IBQQZ is the code for HAPPY, what does KPZGVM mean?

_____ 71 ☐

72 If VKTGF is the code for TIRED, what does YGCTA mean?

_____ 72 ☐

73 If RSZKD is the code for STALE, what does EQDRG mean?

_____ 73 ☐

74 If ITGGP is the code for GREEN, what does AGNNQY mean?

_____ 74 ☐

75 If CHEUD is the code for ZEBRA, what does WLJHU mean?

_____ 75 ☐

Q. 76–80

join two words to make one

Circle **one** word from **each** group, which together will make a longer word.

Example (pond (dam) river) (era down (age))

76 (over under below)   (stand sit crouch)   76 ☐

77 (more plus extra)   (usual normal ordinary)   77 ☐

78 (cot divan bed)   (age time blanket)   78 ☐

79 (shower sink bath)   (cubicle swim room)   79 ☐

80 (eat sup drink)   (pose glass dinner)   80 ☐

MARK ☐

MARK
✓ OR ✗

Q. 81–85

odd ones out

One word in each question does **not** belong with the rest. Underline this word.

Example horrid   nasty   <u>kind</u>   mean   unfriendly

81	Sheffield	England	London	Leeds	Coventry	Exeter	81 ☐
82	lollipop	coffee	sherbet	toffee	humbug	gobstopper	82 ☐
83	violin	cello	guitar	trumpet	harp	viola	83 ☐
84	tortoise	lizard	viper	chameleon	rabbit	crocodile	84 ☐
85	Himalayas	Andes	Pennines	Rockies	Alps	Thames	85 ☐

Q. 86–90

jumbled words in sentences

The letters of the words in CAPITALS have been mixed up. Write the **two** correct words on the lines.

Example The TERWA was too cold to WSIM in. ___WATER___ and ___SWIM___

86 Binoy scored three GAOLS in the CATHM.

_____ and _____   86 ☐

87 I read the GAPES as fast as I could to FISHIN the book.

_____ and _____   87 ☐

88 He pricked his finger on the SORE and hoped it would not leave a CARS.

_____ and _____   88 ☐

89 The CHEATER told the children to be QUITE.

_____ and _____   89 ☐

90 Annie likes to KIPS and play out in the DANGER.

_____ and _____   90 ☐

MARK ☐

MARK
✓ OR ✗

Q. 91–95

time problems

Here is part of a railway timetable. It shows morning trains from Airevale to Condale, stopping at Burdale on the way.

Circle your answer to each question.

Train	Airevale	Burdale		Condale
	depart	arrive	depart	arrive
A	08:10	08:30	08:35	09:05
B	09:15	09:30	09:35	10:05
C	10:05	10:30	10:35	11:00
D	11:00	11:20	11:35	12:05
E	12:05	12:25	12:30	13:05

91 Which train stops longest at Burdale?   A B C D E   91 ☐

92 Mohammed's journey took one hour, on which train?   A B C D E   92 ☐

93 Which is the fastest train from Burdale to Condale?   A B C D E   93 ☐

94 Which train takes exactly twice as long to travel the second part of the journey as the first?   A B C D E   94 ☐

95 Which is the fastest train from Airevale to Burdale? A B C D E   95 ☐

Q. 96–100

alphabetical order

Answer the questions. Use the alphabet to help you.

A B C D E F G H I J K L M N O P Q R S T U V W X Y Z

96 Which letter comes after the third vowel?   _____   96 ☐

97 If all the vowels were removed, what would be the 15th letter? _____ 97 ☐

98 Apart from 'hi', what other word of two consecutive letters is found in the alphabet?   _____   98 ☐

99 If you read the alphabet backwards, what word of three consecutive letters can you find?   _____   99 ☐

100 Reading the alphabet backwards, what is the fourth vowel? _____ 100 ☐

MARK ☐

END OF TEST

PROGRESS PAPER 3 TOTAL ☐

Q. 1–5

interpreting graphs

This graph shows the number of DVDs sold in a shop in one week last year. Study the graph. Then answer the questions.

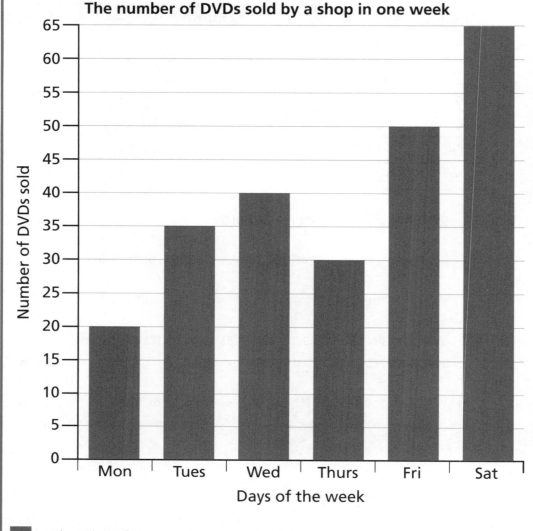

The number of DVDs sold by a shop in one week

1 What day of the week was busiest? _____ 1 ☐

2 What was the least busy day? _____ 2 ☐

3 Which two days' sales together equalled Saturday's sales?

_____ and _____ 3 ☐

4 If each DVD cost £9.95, how much money was taken on the Monday of that week? £ _____ 4 ☐

5 How many DVDs were sold altogether on the Monday and Saturday?

_____ 5 ☐

MARK ☐

Progress Papers
Answers

Verbal Reasoning 1

Schofield & Sims

Progress Papers in Verbal Reasoning 1

Notes for parents, tutors, teachers and other helpers

This pull-out book contains correct answers to all the questions in **Progress Papers in Verbal Reasoning 1**, and is designed to assist you, the adult helper, as you mark the child's work. Once the child has become accustomed to the method of working, you may wish to give him or her direct access to this pull-out section.

When marking, put a tick or a cross in the tinted column on the far right of the question page. **Only one mark is available for each question**. Sub-total boxes at the foot of each page will help you to add marks quickly. You can then fill in the total marks at the end of the paper. The total score is out of 100 and can easily be turned into a percentage. The child's progress can be recorded using the **Progress chart** on page 52.

The child should aim to spend between 40 and 75 minutes on each paper, but may need more time, or more than one session, to complete the paper. The child should try to work on each paper when feeling fresh and free from distraction.

How to use the pull-out answers

This booklet contains answers to all the questions in the book, as well as footnotes to help with marking. Where the child has answered a question incorrectly, take time to look at the question and answer together and work out how the correct answer was achieved.

By working through the tests and corresponding answers, the child will start to recognise the clues that he or she should look for next time. These skills can then be put into practice by moving on to the next paper, as the difficulty increases incrementally throughout the series.

When a paper has been marked, notice if there are any topics that are proving particularly tricky. You may wish to complete some targeted practice in those areas, by focusing on that particular topic as it appears in each paper. For example, if a child has struggled with word meanings, but answered all other questions accurately, you may wish to target only word meanings questions in your next practice session. The **Topics chart** at the back of the book makes it easy to tailor practice to the child's individual needs.

This book of answers is a pull-out section from
Progress Papers in Verbal Reasoning 1

Published by **Schofield & Sims Ltd**, Dogley Mill, Fenay Bridge, Huddersfield HD8 0NQ, UK

Telephone 01484 607080

www.schofieldandsims.co.uk

First published in 2016

Author: **Patrick Berry**

Patrick Berry has asserted his moral right under the Copyright, Designs and Patents Act, 1988, to be identified as the author of this work.

Design by **Oxford Designers and Illustrators**

ISBN 978 07217 1279 6

Printed in the UK by **Wyndeham Grange Ltd**, Southwick, West Sussex

British Library Catalogue in Publication Data:
A catalogue record for this book is available from the British Library.

Progress Paper 1

1	DAM*	
2	BREAKFAST*	
3	TROUSERS*	
4	FLIES*	
5	GIRAFFE*	
6	colour	paint
7	dog	cat
8	triangle	circle
9	bicycle	sledge
10	table	desk

11 (across) ado can eye
(down) ace day one

12 (across) bat ago yet
(down) bay age tot

13 (across) pal ire net
(down) pin are let

14 (across) not are pen
(down) nap ore ten

15 (across) par ewe wed
(down) pew awe red

16	read
17	hero
18	leaf
19	goal
20	soft
21	10
22	9
23	7
24	6
25	1
26	D
27	E
28	W
29	HI
30	U
31	SEED
32	DARE
33	READ
34	HARD
35	EARS

Paper 1 – continued

36	PEA
37	RAT
38	TIN
39	ROW
40	EAR
41	C
42	C
43	E
44	E
45	C
46	bone
47	garage
48	vegetable
49	lunch
50	water
51	October
52	December
53	16cm
54	June
55	Bristol

56	but	ton
57	car	go
58	super	market
59	foot	ball
60	eye	sight

61	E
62	D
63	C
64	C
65	A

66	in	out
67	light	dark
68	lean	fat
69	shout	whisper
70	open	close

71	24 (+6)
72	28 (+7)
73	90 (–10)
74	+ (repeating pattern)
75	160 (add the previous number)

Paper 1 – continued

76	five	second
77	higher	lower
78	cat	apple
79	middle	say
80	tenth	ten

81	December
82	eighty
83	fly
84	thirsty
85	beef
86	son
87	tabby
88	fourth
89	hyena
90	whole

91	letters	postman
92	milkman	dog
93	Mum	Olga
94	warm	fire
95	flames	smoke

96	5 4 1 3 2
97	2 5 4 3 1
98	2 3 1 4 5
99	5 4 3 2 1
100	5 4 2 1 3

*spellings must be correct

Verbal Reasoning Progress Paper 2 • Answers

Progress Paper 2

1	11 years old
2	2 years old
3	9 years old
4	32 years old
5	34 years old

6	O	R
7	NO	QR
8	STU	WXY
9	CD	AB
10	U	X

11	enter
12	station
13	parent
14	ranger
15	least

16	paste
17	quicker
18	popper
19	dire
20	cost

21	daffodil	gladiolus
22	onion	broccoli
23	boxer	terrier
24	Durham	Berkshire
25	Poland	Italy

26	FOX	HENS*
27	FINGERS	TOAST*
28	PAINT	CARPET*
29	RUNNERS	MEDAL*
30	GATES	CAR*

31	2468
32	8642
33	4286
34	6428
35	2968

36	rose
37	lead
38	flat
39	low
40	match

Paper 2 – continued

41	mine	your*
42	head	tail*
43	pain	ache*
44	fish	seal*
45	went	came*

46	08:29
47	09:03
48	09:21
49	4 min
50	Train D

51	bottom	wide
52	green	blue
53	fish	dogs
54	never	seldom
55	frog	butterfly

56	4 9
57	1 8
58	2 6
59	3 10
60	5 7

61	cooker
62	ostrich
63	bread
64	pedalo
65	darts

66	shallow	deep
67	over	under
68	untidy	neat
69	compliment	insult
70	trivial	serious

71	river	bridge
72	plane	carpenter
73	crossroad	stop
74	money	give
75	month	February

76	Years 4 and 6
77	Year 4
78	27
79	30
80	Year 6

Paper 2 – continued

81	arm	chair
82	bar	gain
83	by	pass
84	rail	way
85	after	noon

86	also
87	sand
88	pear
89	very
90	meal

91	DISCO*
92	MILES*
93	SURGERY*
94	TELEVISION*
95	BOUTIQUE*

96	(across) pal ova pep (down) pop ave lap†
97	(across) dog are met (down) dam ore get†
98	(across) pea arc tee (down) pat ere ace†
99	(across) aga tad ego (down) ate gag ado†
100	(across) hat ash sky (down) has ask thy†

*spellings must be correct

†across and down words can also be the other way round

A4

Schofield & Sims • Progress Papers • Verbal Reasoning 1

Progress Paper 3

1 cart
2 melt
3 snow
4 fort
5 this

6 pick
7 change
8 light
9 part
10 school

11 goldfish bowl children
12 wasn't happy bus
13 reading library week
14 train station passengers
15 mother taxi arrived

16 vehicle
17 poultry
18 hat
19 punctuation
20 shape

21 2   6
22 4   10
23 1   5
24 3   8
25 7   9

26 BIN
27 SAT or HIT
28 DOG
29 BAD
30 ROW or LAW

Accept any accurate response to word chain questions.

31 (tables) tablets*
32 (nuisance) nonsense*
33 (bugler) burglar*
34 (pound) pond*
35 (loaves) leaves*

36 monkey   eagle
37 chapter   stream
38 thinner   lake
39 week   minute
40 midnight   grey

Paper 3 – *continued*

41 value
42 volume
43 shelves
44 wet
45 two

46 u   case   bound
47 t   sore   trifle
   or s   tore   rifles
48 r   petty   grain
49 a   cost   seats
50 z   one   prizes

51 TEA
52 TON
53 AND
54 RID
55 LEA

56 A
57 B
58 B
59 A
60 E

61 PLAIN
62 THANK
63 STALE
64 SAMPLE
65 IDEAL

66 C
67 B
68 D
69 A
70 E

71 JOYFUL
72 WEARY
73 FRESH
74 YELLOW
75 TIGER

76 under   stand
77 extra   ordinary
78 bed   time
79 bath   room
80 sup   pose

Paper 3 – *continued*

81 England
82 coffee
83 trumpet
84 rabbit
85 Thames

86 GOALS   MATCH*
87 PAGES   FINISH*
88 ROSE   SCAR*
89 TEACHER   QUIET*
90 SKIP   GARDEN*

91 D
92 E
93 C
94 B
95 B

96 J
97 S
98 no
99 fed
100 E

*spellings must be correct

Progress Paper 4

1	Sat	
2	Mon	
3	Tues and Thurs	
4	£199	
5	85	
6	wolf	hens*
7	coat	shoe*
8	lose	gain*
9	fast	slow*
10	huge	tiny*
11	VWXYZ	
12	VWYZX	
13	ZXYWU	
14	VYZXU	
15	WYVXU	
16	butter	
17	scar	
18	pets	
19	sitting	
20	meat	
21	gain	loss
22	feminine	masculine
23	fine	coarse
24	divide	multiply
25	departure	arrival
26	AT	
27	OT	
28	BE	
29	TE	
30	EN	
31	FILE	MILE
32	POST	PORT
	or POST	PAST
	or CAST	PAST
33	FARE	PARE
34	COLD	CORD
35	TALE	SALE
	or MILE	MOLE
	or PILE	POLE

Accept any accurate response to word chain questions.

Paper 4 – continued

36	7.5 or $7\frac{1}{2}$	3.75 or $3\frac{3}{4}$
37	33	41
38	60	48
39	6.25	3.125
40	62	126
41	feel	
42	hate	
43	dash	
44	deny or test	
45	your	
46	weep	
47	huge	
48	teaching	
49	held	
50	evil	
51	spend	
52	robot	
53	yarns	
54	stray	
55	dates	
56	water	
57	engine	
58	bakers	
59	my	
60	terrier	
61	depth	
62	wings	
63	a top	
64	pages	
65	an orbit	
66	unknown	
67	unknown	
68	false	
69	true	
70	false	
71	puncture	tyre
72	angel	angle
73	him	I
74	describe	prescribe
75	submarine	trawler

Paper 4 – continued

76	LEAP	
77	PLEAD	
78	PEALED	
79	DEAL	
80	PADDLE	
81	occupied	inhabited
82	select	choose
83	dish	bowl
84	frost	ice
85	melody	tune
86	V	Y
87	H16	K19
88	T	J
89	V	X
90	15K	16O
91	TABLE	
92	PEACE	
93	SPLICE	
94	REPLY	
95	CREATE	
96	animal	
97	colour	
98	profession	
99	container	
100	insect	

*spellings must be correct

Progress Paper 5

1	water	blood*
2	sunny	cloud*
3	sweet	round*
4	rough	stone*
5	paint	brush*
6	IT	
7	GH	
8	NE	
9	AD	
10	CE	
11	hand	
12	night	
13	pluck	
14	see	
15	quadruple	
16	drag	pull
17	begin	commence
18	relative	relation
19	below	under
20	attempt	try
21	r	fail	horse
22	i	bran	paint
23	u	case	gauze
24	l	idea	flair
25	h	same	thank
26	SCORE*	
27	BUILDER*	
28	DIFFICULT*	
29	COLLECT*	
30	PHRASE*	
31	break	fast
32	tar	get
33	day	light
34	lamp	shade
35	pot	hole
36	skin	
37	tilt	
38	over	
39	tile	
40	read	

Paper 5 – continued

41	flower		
42	tool		
43	weapon		
44	fabric		
45	timber		
46	C		
47	A		
48	C		
49	B		
50	B		
51	6	9	
52	5	10	
53	3	7	
54	1	8	
55	2	4	
56	37	49	
57	32	42	
58	43	57	
59	31	34	
60	17	3	
61	D		
62	B		
63	C		
64	D		
65	A		
66	solution	answer	
67	unknown	obscure	
68	silence	calm	
69	slender	slim	
70	restricted	limited	
71	sheriff	outlaw	gaol
72	cereal	breakfast	school
73	aunt	mother's	sister
74	pool	water	swimming
75	leap	year	four
76	nation		
77	reseed		
78	misted		
79	noted		
80	circled		

Paper 5 – continued

81	5 4 2 3 1	
82	4 3 5 1 2	
83	3 5 2 4 1	
84	3 4 1 5 2	
85	2 1 3 5 4	
86	ART	
87	BIT	
88	AND	
89	ALL	
90	RID	
91	field	present
92	medium	hill
93	test	queen
94	slice	greener
95	duet	hungry
96	TRAIN	STOPPING*
97	DOCTOR	UNWELL*
98	WAYS	ROAD*
99	FIRST	TEST*
100	FORWARD	HOLIDAY*

*spellings must be correct

Progress Paper 6

1 52
2 67
3 29
4 72
5 17.5 *or* $17\frac{1}{2}$

6 serious
7 ancient
8 untrustworthy
9 beautiful
10 hidden

11 MALE   MOLE
    or DARE   MARE
12 BARE   CARE
13 PART   DART
    or DARK   DART
14 BARE   FARE
15 RIDE   RITE

Accept any accurate response to word chain questions.

16 melt   freeze
17 friend   foe
18 awake   asleep
19 lenient   strict
20 proud   humble

21 Lucy
22 Amy
23 first floor
24 Kim
25 Sophie

26 MANES
27 NAMES
28 NEAT
29 MEANS
30 STEAM

31 US   TR
32 TU   WX
33 SD   UB
34 ABD   FGI
35 YL   CJ

Paper 6 – *continued*

36 shun *or* mesh *or* ours
37 scar
38 land
39 full
40 chat

41 2012
42 2013
43 2010
44 2013
45 2014

46 brave   oven
47 shine   into
48 steps   spar
49 trail   pill
50 cakes   meal

51 so   raining
52 mend   broken
53 me   Mum
54 down   up
55 looked   stood

56 kid   calf
57 sprout   leek
58 peach   pear
59 canary   eagle
60 reins   bridle

61 (died) dyed*
62 (parasol) parachute*
63 (chum) charm*
64 (manger) manager*
65 (suet) suit *or* suite*

66 sling
67 fine
68 port
69 last
70 mustard

71 35   43
72 19   30
73 57   71
74 12   10
75 34   68

Paper 6 – *continued*

76 five
77 burrow
78 computer
79 wire
80 hand

81 owlet*
82 prince*
83 Earth*
84 cheese *or* butter*
85 canal*

86 servant
87 mention
88 singed
89 idled
90 terminal

91 SCENT
92 TOOTH
93 BOUGHT
94 COURT
95 PALACE

96 e   star   tear
97 m   cries   seams
98 b   tale   bright
99 f   rat   flint
100 r   tough   grave

*spellings must be correct

MARK
✓ OR ✗

Q. 6–10

jumbled words in grids

The letters in each grid make **two** four-letter words. The letters must stay in the same columns. Work out where each letter goes.

Example

w	a	l	k
s	w	i	m
s	a	i	k
w	w	l	m

6

w	e	n	f
h	o	l	s

7

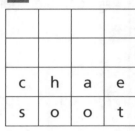

c	h	a	e
s	o	o	t

8

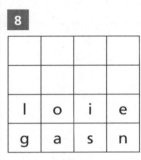

l	o	i	e
g	a	s	n

9

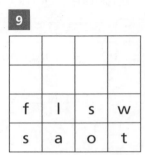

f	l	s	w
s	a	o	t

10

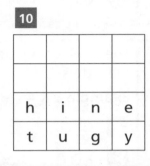

h	i	n	e
t	u	g	y

6 ☐
7 ☐
8 ☐
9 ☐
10 ☐

Q. 11–15

match the codes

The words below have been written in code. Which code belongs to which word? Write the answers on the lines.

GREAT	GRATE	TEARS	GATES	RAGES
VWYZX	WYVXU	VYZXU	VWXYZ	ZXYWU

11 The code for GREAT is _____.

12 The code for GRATE is _____.

13 The code for TEARS is _____.

14 The code for GATES is _____.

15 The code for RAGES is _____.

11 ☐
12 ☐
13 ☐
14 ☐
15 ☐

Q. 16–20

make a word

Look at how the second word is made from the first word in each pair. Complete the third pair in the same way. Write the answers on the lines.

Example (rat rates) (mop mopes) (fin __fines__)

16 (old bold)   (ark bark)   (utter _____)

17 (tile stile)   (mile smile)   (car _____)

18 (pans snap)   (mood doom)   (step _____)

19 (upper utter)   (pray tray)   (sipping _____)

20 (bate beat)   (hate heat)   (mate _____)

16 ☐
17 ☐
18 ☐
19 ☐
20 ☐

MARK ☐

MARK
✓ OR ✗

Q. 21–25
antonyms

Underline the **two** words in each question that have the **opposite** meaning.

Example <u>happy</u>   kind   grin   <u>sad</u>   face   cheerful

21	gamble	gain	dollar	loss	save	bank	invest	21 ☐
22	manly	lady	feminine	female	person	masculine	opposite	22 ☐
23	gently	severe	fine	course	coarse	jagged	plane	23 ☐
24	add	spread	attack	divide	maths	conquer	multiply	24 ☐
25	go	wait	departure	journey	train	station	arrival	25 ☐

Q. 26–30
missing
letters

The same **two** letters end the first word and begin the next word. Write the letters.

Example T R A <u>I</u> <u>L</u>   <u>I</u> <u>L</u> L N E S S

26	G R E __ __ __ __ T I C	26 ☐
27	F O __ __ __ __ H E R	27 ☐
28	T R I __ __ __ __ F O R E	28 ☐
29	B I __ __ __ __ E T H	29 ☐
30	L I V __ __ __ __ C L O S E	30 ☐

Q. 31–35
word chains

Turn the word at the top of each grid into the word at the bottom. You can only change one letter at a time. Each change must result in a real word.

Example

T	A	L	E
T	A	K	E
L	A	K	E
L	I	K	E

31

F	I	V	E
M	I	L	D

32

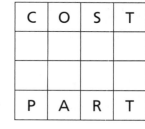

C	O	S	T
P	A	R	T

31 ☐
32 ☐

33

F	A	R	M
P	A	L	E

34

B	O	L	D
C	O	R	E

35

T	I	L	E
S	O	L	E

33 ☐
34 ☐
35 ☐

MARK ☐

MARK
✓ OR ✗

Q. 36–40 number sequences	Write the next two numbers in each sequence.	
	Example 2 4 6 8 __10__ __12__	
36	60 30 15 ____ ____	36 ☐
37	9 17 25 ____ ____	37 ☐
38	96 84 72 ____ ____	38 ☐
39	50.0 25.0 12.5 ____ ____	39 ☐
40	2 6 14 30 ____ ____	40 ☐

Q. 41–45 spot the word	A four-letter word is hidden in each of these sentences. You will find the hidden word at the end of one word and the beginning of the next. Underline the hidden word and then write it on the line.	
	Example Daniel _end_ed his speech with a joke. __lend__	
41	Joel's concerned wife elbowed her way through the crowd of tourists. _____	41 ☐
42	"That explanation is not clear enough," repeated the head teacher. _____	42 ☐
43	You should put only cold ashes in your dustbin. _____	43 ☐
44	The company made nylon kites to send to lots of countries. _____	44 ☐
45	We could not deny our enjoyment of the practical joke. _____	45 ☐

Q. 46–50 analogies	Underline **one** word in the brackets to complete these analogies.	
	Example Arrive is to depart as come is to (run hurry <u>go</u> hide).	
46	Happy is to smile as unhappy is to (yell shout miserable weep anger).	46 ☐
47	Wide is to narrow as tiny is to (small huge minute scarce little).	47 ☐
48	Chef is to cookery as professor is to (sewing frying chemistry teaching).	48 ☐
49	Is is to was as hold is to (grab throw held bowled carry).	49 ☐
50	Part is to trap as live is to (vile dead snare evil victim).	50 ☐

MARK ☐

MARK
✓ OR ✗

Q. 51–55

crosswords

Look at the clues. Write in the answers.

		e		
	■	m	■	
		b		
	■	e	■	
		r		

(grid with 1, 2 in top row cells; 3 in left cell of middle row; 4 in bottom-left cell)

51	**1 across** to pay out money	51 ☐
52	**3 across** a mechanical human	52 ☐
53	**4 across** sewing or knitting threads	53 ☐
54	**1 down** to wander away	54 ☐
55	**2 down** times of historical events	55 ☐

Q. 56–60

complete the sentence

Underline **one** word in the brackets to make the sentence sensible.

Example The yacht sailed into the (shop hospital <u>harbour</u> cinema matchbox).

56	Firefighters use (water drills engines) to put out fires.	56 ☐
57	The mechanic could not start the car's (driver engine windscreen tyre).	57 ☐
58	Flour is used by (florists bakers penguins) to make bread.	58 ☐
59	I am (my their her) parents' only child.	59 ☐
60	The driver was bitten by the (tenor terrier terror terrain tepid).	60 ☐

Q. 61–65

always has

Look at the word in **bold**. Underline **one** option in the brackets. It must describe what the word in bold **always has**.

Example A **lake** always has (boats <u>water</u> ducks swimmers fish).

61	A **pond** always has (frogs birds rushes pebbles waves depth).	61 ☐
62	A **bird** always has (eggs a nest a tree wings flight seed).	62 ☐
63	A **table** always has (food a tablecloth cutlery chairs a top diners).	63 ☐
64	A **book** always has (a title pages a story writing an author a reader).	64 ☐
65	A **planet** always has (water air people an orbit heat).	65 ☐

MARK ☐

MARK
✓ OR ✗

Q. 66–70

sorting information

Read the information below carefully. Tick (✓) true, false or unknown for each statement. Tick **one** only.

My name is Lucas. My brother is Jack. My sister is Grace. Our parents have never separated. My friend is Freddie. Our mother is Jo and our father is Michael. My aunt and uncle are Gill and Peter. Katy is our next door neighbour.

		true	false	unknown	
66	Freddie is Katy's son.	☐	☐	☐	66 ☐
67	Gill is my mother's sister.	☐	☐	☐	67 ☐
68	Freddie is my father.	☐	☐	☐	68 ☐
69	Jack is Michael's son.	☐	☐	☐	69 ☐
70	Lucas is my father.	☐	☐	☐	70 ☐

Q. 71–75

mixed-up sentences

Two words must swap places for each sentence to make sense. Underline these **two** words in each sentence.

Example The <u>bone</u> growled softly as he approached the <u>dog</u>.

71 We could not use the car because the puncture had a tyre.   71 ☐

72 In the angel where the two walls met stood the statue of an angle.   72 ☐

73 Him asked I for a packet of chocolate biscuits.   73 ☐

74 The doctor said she could not describe any medication unless I could prescribe my symptoms.   74 ☐

75 Unlike a submarine, a trawler can travel under water.   75 ☐

Q. 76–80

symbol codes

The word **PEDAL** is written as ◄ ■ ▲ ► ♦ in code. Use the same code to work out the hidden words.

76 ♦ ■ ► ◄   _____   76 ☐

77 ◄ ♦ ■ ► ▲   _____   77 ☐

78 ◄ ■ ► ♦ ■ ▲   _____   78 ☐

79 ▲ ■ ► ♦   _____   79 ☐

80 ◄ ► ▲ ▲ ♦ ■   _____   80 ☐

MARK ☐

MARK
✓ OR ✗

Q. 81–85
synonyms

Underline two words, **one** from **each** set of brackets, that are **similar** in meaning.

Example (large great <u>tiny</u> huge) (box <u>small</u> hungry crate)

81 (occupied home empty address)   (away garden inhabited full) | 81 ☐
82 (shop buy discard select)   (sell deal choose bargain) | 82 ☐
83 (dish plate cup mug)   (knife fork bowl crockery) | 83 ☐
84 (season frost weather heat)   (cold ice month spring) | 84 ☐
85 (music melody pianist composer)   (song symphony sing tune) | 85 ☐

Q. 86–90
letter
sequences

Write the next two items in each sequence. Use the alphabet to help you.

Example AB CD EF GH <u>IJ</u> <u>KL</u>

A B C D E F G H I J K L M N O P Q R S T U V W X Y Z

86 G J M P S _____ _____ | 86 ☐
87 S1 V4 Y7 B10 E13 _____ _____ | 87 ☐
88 A Z D W G _____ _____ | 88 ☐
89 G I L N Q S _____ _____ | 89 ☐
90 7Q 9U 10Y 12C 13G _____ _____ | 90 ☐

Q. 91–95
add a letter

Read the clue in brackets. Add **one** letter to the word in CAPITALS to make a new word that matches the clue. Write the new word on the line.

Example CANE (lifts heavy objects) <u>CRANE</u>

91 TALE (an article of furniture) _____ | 91 ☐
92 PACE (the opposite of war) _____ | 92 ☐
93 SPICE (to unite or join together) _____ | 93 ☐
94 RELY (an answer or acknowledgement) _____ | 94 ☐
95 CRATE (to invent, make or produce) _____ | 95 ☐

MARK ☐

Q. 96–100 word categories	Underline the **general** word in each row, which is the word that includes all the others.						
	Example banana apple <u>fruit</u> raspberry pear kiwi						
	96 goat	dog	rabbit	animal	cow	sheep	96 ☐
	97 red	colour	yellow	brown	vermillion	pink	97 ☐
	98 music	law	teaching	profession	architecture	medicine	98 ☐
	99 jug	bucket	bowl	can	bottle	container	99 ☐
	100 fly	insect	ant	wasp	mosquito	beetle	100 ☐

MARK ☐

END OF TEST

PROGRESS PAPER 4 TOTAL ☐

MARK
✓ OR ✗

...in each grid make **two** five-letter words. The letters must stay in ...columns. Work out where each letter goes.

	o	w	n
f	r	u	i	t
c	r	o	w	t
f	l	u	i	n

1

b	l	t	o	r
w	a	o	e	d

2

c	u	o	u	y
s	l	n	n	d

1 ☐
2 ☐

3

s	o	e	n	t
r	w	u	e	d

4

r	t	u	g	h
s	o	o	n	e

5

p	r	u	n	h
b	a	i	s	t

3 ☐
4 ☐
5 ☐

Q. 6–10

missing letters

The same **two** letters end the first word and begin the next word. Write the letters.

Example T R A <u>I L</u>   <u>I L</u> L N E S S

6   F R U <u>I T</u>   <u>I T</u> E M

7   H I <u>D E</u>   <u>D E</u> O S T

8   F I ___ ___   ___ ___ A T

9   R E ___ ___   ___ ___ J E C T I V E

10   J U I ___ ___   ___ ___ L E R Y

6 ☐
7 ☐
8 ☐
9 ☐
10 ☐

Q. 11–15

analogies

Underline **one** word in the brackets to complete these analogies.

Example Arrive is to depart as come is to (run hurry <u>go</u> hide).

11   Toe is to foot as finger is to (wrist elbow arm knuckle hand).

12   Sun is to day as moon is to (dusk <u>night</u> evening darkness stars).

13   Horn is to blow as harp is to (scrape fiddle bow music pluck).

14   Nose is to smell as eye is to (site hear sense <u>see</u> touch).

15   Two is to double as four is to (triple treble <u>quadruple</u> fourth quarter).

11 ☐
12 ☐
13 ☐
14 ☐
15 ☐

MARK ☐

MARK
✓ OR ✗

Q. 16–20
synonyms

Underline two words, **one** from **each** set of brackets, that are **similar** in meaning.

Example (large great <u>tiny</u> huge)   (box <u>small</u> hungry crate)

16 (hop drag catch down)   (throw press many pull) | 16 ☐
17 (begin finish under serious)   (depart commence arrive slide) | 17 ☐
18 (smart between relative friend)   (uncle relation dull below) | 18 ☐
19 (loose shred below tight)   (under behind before begin) | 19 ☐
20 (attempt descend forget stale)   (ascend fresh try conclude) | 20 ☐

Q. 21–25
move a letter

Take **one** letter from the first word and put it in the second word to make two new words. Write the letter you have moved and the two new words in the table below.

	First word	Second word	Letter moved	New first word	New second word	
Example	slope	feat	s	lope	feast	
21	frail	hose				21 ☐
22	brain	pant				22 ☐
23	cause	gaze				23 ☐
24	ideal	fair				24 ☐
25	shame	tank				25 ☐

Q. 26–30
jumbled words with clues

Each question has a word in CAPITALS. The letters in this word have been mixed up. Use the clue to work out what the word is. Write it on the line.

Example NIBOR   (a bird)   <u>ROBIN</u>

26 CEROS   (a football result)   _____ | 26 ☐
27 DRIBULE   (puts up houses)   _____ | 27 ☐
28 CUFFILDIT   (not easy)   _____ | 28 ☐
29 ELCLOCT   (to gather together)   _____ | 29 ☐
30 HEARSP   (a group of words)   _____ | 30 ☐

MARK ☐

MARK
✓ OR ✗

Q. 31–35

join two words to make one

Circle **one** word from **each** group which together will make a longer word.

Example (pond (dam) river)   (era down (age))

31	(mend break cure)	(ding ring fast)	31 ☐
32	(grit road tar)	(street get repairs)	32 ☐
33	(day evening morning)	(light bright early)	33 ☐
34	(traffic lamp stars)	(sign shine shade)	34 ☐
35	(pot jug cup)	(tea hole glare)	35 ☐

Q. 36–40

spot the word

A four-letter word is hidden in each of these sentences. You will find the hidden word at the end of one word and the beginning of the next. Underline the hidden word and then write it on the line.

Example Daniel <u>ended</u> his speech with a joke.   <u>lend</u>

36 Go and ask in the post office where Derwent Road is. _____   36 ☐

37 We waited until the rain stopped before we began our journey.

_____   37 ☐

38 I love reading stories about cowboys in the wild west. _____   38 ☐

39 You cannot play until everything in your room has been put away.

_____   39 ☐

40 Mr Scott gave the pupils more advice on their career choices.

_____   40 ☐

Q. 41–45

word categories

Underline the **general** word in each row, which is the word that includes all the others.

Example banana apple <u>fruit</u> raspberry pear kiwi

41	hyacinth flower tulip geranium rose marigold carnation	41 ☐
42	chisel hammer spanner saw tool pliers wrench mallet	42 ☐
43	weapon axe dagger sword pike lance spear	43 ☐
44	cotton nylon polyester fabric silk linen velvet	44 ☐
45	ebony mahogany pine walnut timber willow oak beech	45 ☐

MARK ☐

MARK
✓ OR ✗

Q. 46–50

true statements

Read the information in each question. Circle the **only** statement (A, B, C, D or E) that has to be true, based on this information.

46 Manchester is north of Birmingham, which is north of Swindon. Swindon is north of Bournemouth, which overlooks the English Channel.
A Swindon is north of Birmingham.
B Manchester overlooks the English Channel.
C Birmingham is south of Manchester.
D Bournemouth is north of Swindon.
E Swindon is south of Bournemouth.

46 ☐

47 Letters make up words. Words make up sentences. Sentences make up paragraphs. Words must be spelled correctly.
A Words are made from letters.
B Letters are made from paragraphs.
C You need to be good at spelling.
D Sentences are made from paper.
E Paragraphs are made from books.

47 ☐

48 Eagles are birds. Eagles have wings and feathers. Eagles are predators. Baby eagles are called eaglets.
A All eagles are eaglets.
B Baby eagles lay eggs.
C Eagles hunt.
D All birds are eagles.
E Eaglets are not eagles.

48 ☐

49 Grandpa is 80 years old. He has a daughter aged 50, who is my mother's sister.
A My mother's sister is older than grandpa.
B My mother's sister is my aunt.
C Grandpa is younger than my mother.
D Grandma is Grandpa's wife
E My uncle is Grandpa's son.

49 ☐

50 Seven-year-old John is older than his sister Jen, who is three years younger. Jacob is three years older than his brother John and six years older than his sister.
A Jen is the eldest child.
B Jacob is ten years old.
C Jen is eight years old.
D John is older than Jacob.
E John has two sisters.

50 ☐

MARK ☐

MARK
✓ OR ✗

Q. 51–55
word meanings

Each of these words can have **two** meanings. Write the numbers of the two meanings in the table below.

Example		51		52		53		54		55	
organ		stable		rent		break		dart		shade	
11	12										

Meanings 1 to move quickly   **2** to colour in   **3** to damage something
4 out of the sun   **5** money paid to live somewhere
6 a building for horses   **7** a short rest from work
8 something sharp thrown at a board   **9** steady and firm
10 ripped or torn   **11** part of the body   **12** a musical instrument

51 ☐
52 ☐
53 ☐
54 ☐
55 ☐

Q. 56–60
number sequences

Write the next two numbers in each sequence.

Example 2   4   6   8   _10_   _12_

56   7   9   13   19   27   ____   ____   56 ☐

57   14   11   21   18   28   25   35   ____   ____   57 ☐

58   3   7   13   21   31   ____   ____   58 ☐

59   31   29   32   30   33   ____   ____   59 ☐

60   87   73   59   45   31   ____   ____   60 ☐

Q. 61–65
letters for numbers

Find the answers to these calculations. Write each answer as a letter.

Example If C is 2, D is 8 and E is 10, answer this calculation. C + D = ■ _E_

61   If A is 4, B is 6, C is 8, D is 26 and E is 12, answer this calculation.
B × E ÷ A + C = ■   _____   61 ☐

62   If A is 3, B is 15, C is 25, D is 75 and E is 5, answer this calculation.
C ÷ E × A = ■   _____   62 ☐

63   If A is 8, B is 4, C is 2, D is 32 and E is 8, answer this calculation.
A × B ÷ C ÷ E = ■   _____   63 ☐

64   If A is 5, B is 6, C is 9, and D is 8, answer this calculation.
A + C – B = ■   _____   64 ☐

65   If A is 4, B is 8, C is 10, D is 12 and E is 20, answer this calculation.
D + E ÷ B = ■   _____   65 ☐

MARK ☐

Q. 66–70

odd ones out

Two words in each question do **not** belong with the rest. Underline these **two** words.

Example horrid   nasty   <u>kind</u>   mean   unfriendly   <u>helpful</u>

66	mystery	solution	puzzle	riddle	answer	66
67	famous	unknown	renowned	notable	obscure	67
68	uproar	silence	calm	noise	hullabaloo	68
69	fat	slender	obese	slim	stout	69
70	boundless	limitless	infinite	restricted	limited	70

Q. 71–75

complete the sentence

Underline **one** word in **each** set of brackets to make the sentence sensible.

Example The (plumber <u>electrician</u> baker) repaired the (<u>light</u> loaf sink) so that we could (lamp hear <u>see</u>) again.

71   The (dentist hedgehog sheriff) set out to arrest the (outlaw pigeon baker) and put him in (goal gaol custard).   71

72   We always eat (cereal lollipops coffee) for our (burger birthday breakfast) before we go to (hospital school mushroom).   72

73   My (aunt hamster uncle) is my (mother's son's grandfather's) (goldfish sister alien).   73

74   The (pool pull swim) has (café water coffee) for (drinking washing swimming).   74

75   A (hop leap skip) (day month year) happens every (two four ten) years.   75

Q. 76–80

which word

One word in each question **can** be made from the word in CAPITALS. Underline this word. You may only use each letter once.

Example SPEEDBOAT   toast   debated   poems   <u>beast</u>   poser

76	PRESENTATION	sentence	nation	resented	spread	feather	76
77	DESERVED	servant	drive	swerve	reseed	verdant	77
78	EPITOMISED	miser	misted	promise	polished	mister	78
79	DEFINITION	define	notion	noted	finish	tender	79
80	CHRONICLED	cornet	leader	rounded	deliver	circled	80

MARK

MARK
✓ OR ✗

Q. 81–85

alphabetical order

Number the words in each line in alphabetical order. Use the alphabet to help you.

Example HIGH LOUD TAKE FAIL MEAL

2   3   5   1   4

A B C D E F G H I J K L M N O P Q R S T U V W X Y Z

81   TREE   MARBLE   COMB   DISTANCE   AMATEUR   81 ☐

82   ORANGE   LEMON   PINEAPPLE   BANANA   FRUIT   82 ☐

83   ONE   TWO   FOUR   SIX   EIGHT   83 ☐

84   STICK   STOOL   STALE   STUPID   STEER   84 ☐

85   GREEN   GREAT   GREMLIN   GREY   GRENADE   85 ☐

Q. 86–90

missing three-letter words

In each of these sentences, the word in CAPITALS has three letters missing. These three letters make a real three-letter word. Write the three-letter word on the line.

Example My father SED me a photo of my mother.   HOW

86   My father's PNER is my mother.   _____   86 ☐

87   Our teacher took us to see and EXHIION of Dutch paintings.

      _____   87 ☐

88   The HLE on the front door was broken.   _____   88 ☐

89   In autumn Ava loved to walk through the FEN leaves.

      _____   89 ☐

90   The woman and her BEGROOM looked very happy.

      _____   90 ☐

MARK ☐

Q. 91–95
mixed-up groups

Two groups of three words have been mixed up in each question. Work out which would be the **middle** word in each group if they were in the correct order. Underline these **two** words.

Example city <u>adolescent</u> village <u>town</u> infant adult

91	past	garden	field	future	moor	present	91 ☐
92	tall	mound	mountain	short	medium	hill	92 ☐
93	jack	exam	king	test	quiz	queen	93 ☐
94	slice	greener	green	crumb	loaf	greenest	94 ☐
95	duet	peckish	solo	starving	hungry	trio	95 ☐

Q. 96–100
jumbled words in sentences

The letters of the words in CAPITALS have been mixed up. Write the **two** correct words on the lines.

Example The TERWA was too cold to WSIM in. <u> WATER </u> and <u> SWIM </u>

96 The RINAT passed through the station without PINGPOTS.

_____ and _____   96 ☐

97 Our CODROT came to see Mum when she felt LUENWL.

_____ and _____   97 ☐

98 Look both SWAY before crossing the DORA.

_____ and _____   98 ☐

99 Jasmine came STRIF in the maths STET.

_____ and _____   99 ☐

100 I am looking WARFORD to my summer LIDOHAY.

_____ and _____   100 ☐

MARK ☐

END OF TEST

PROGRESS PAPER 5 TOTAL ☐

Q. 1–5

algebra

Work out these number problems. Write the answers on the lines.

1   If S = 5x + 2 and x = 10, what is S?   _____   1 ☐

2   If B = 3y − 8 and y = 25, what is B?   _____   2 ☐

3   If X = 3b + 5 and b = 8, what is X?   _____   3 ☐

4   If Z = 4a × 3 and a = 6, what is Z?   _____   4 ☐

5   If P = 7q ÷ 2 and q = 5, what is P?   _____   5 ☐

Q. 6–10

odd ones out

One word in each question does **not** belong with the rest. Underline this word.

Example horrid   nasty   <u>kind</u>   mean   unfriendly

6	ridiculous	amusing	funny	serious	hilarious	comical	6 ☐
7	fresh	new	modern	recent	up-to-date	ancient	7 ☐
8	reliable	faithful	dependable	true	devoted	untrustworthy	8 ☐
9	ghastly	horrible	beautiful	awful	dreadful	hideous	9 ☐
10	clear	obvious	plain	evident	hidden	apparent	10 ☐

Q. 11–15

word chains

Turn the word at the top of each grid into the word at the bottom. You can only change one letter at a time. Each change must result in a real word.

Example

T	A	L	E
T	A	K	E
L	A	K	E
L	I	K	E

11

D	A	L	E
M	O	R	E

12

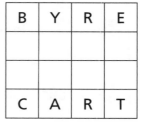

B	Y	R	E
C	A	R	T

11 ☐

12 ☐

13

P	A	R	K
D	I	R	T

14

B	A	R	N
F	I	R	E

15

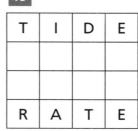

T	I	D	E
R	A	T	E

13 ☐

14 ☐

15 ☐

MARK ☐

Q. 16–20

antonyms

Underline two words, **one** from **each** set of brackets, that have the **opposite** meaning.

Example (<u>happy</u> kind grin) (<u>sad</u> face cheerful)

16	(melt water frozen)	(warm hot freeze)
17	(mate enemy friend)	(pal foe acquaintance)
18	(awake aware away)	(asphalt assert asleep)
19	(stern lenient leaning)	(strict cross punishment)
20	(pride prude proud)	(hurtful harmful humble)

16 ☐
17 ☐
18 ☐
19 ☐
20 ☐

Q. 21–25

position problems

Read the information carefully. Answer the questions.

21 Mark, Lucy, Majid, Thomas and Yasmin are 9, 10, 11, 12 and 13 years old, but not in that order. Two are older than Yasmin. Majid is the oldest. There are three younger than Thomas. Mark is not the youngest.

Who is the youngest in the group? _____   21 ☐

22 Danek is taller than Preeti but not as tall as Maya, who is shorter than Amy.

Who is the tallest? _____   22 ☐

23 A, B, C, D and E are people who live on the five floors of a block of flats. B can't climb stairs and can't use the lift. D presses floor 4 in the lift when going home. C lives midway between D and B. A has one flight of steps to climb. E does not like his neighbour upstairs.

What floor does A live on? Circle the correct answer.

ground floor   first floor   second floor   third floor   fourth floor   23 ☐

24 Joseph runs faster than Lily and Jai who are slower than Kim. Kim is not as fast as Joseph.

Who is the second fastest? _____   24 ☐

25 In a group of five children, Chris is the tallest. Siraj is shorter than Chris but taller than Aaron and Jamie. Sophie is the only girl in the group and taller than three of the boys.

Who is the second tallest? _____   25 ☐

MARK
✓ OR ✗

Q. 26–30
symbol codes

The word **STAMEN** is written as ╬ ╠ ╙ ┐ ║ ╡ in code. Use the same code to work out the hidden words.

26 ┐ ╙ ╡ ║ ╬   _____ 26 ☐

27 ╡ ╙ ┐ ║ ╬   _____ 27 ☐

28 ╡ ║ ╙ ╠   _____ 28 ☐

29 ┐ ║ ╙ ╡ ╬   _____ 29 ☐

30 ╬ ╠ ║ ╙ ┐   _____ 30 ☐

Q. 31–35
letter
sequences

Write the next two items in each sequence. Use the alphabet to help you.

Example AB   CD   EF   GH   _IJ_   _KL_

A B C D E F G H I J K L M N O P Q R S T U V W X Y Z

31 AY   ZX   YW   XV   WU   VT   _____ _____   31 ☐

32 BC   EF   HI   KL   NO   QR   _____ _____   32 ☐

33 ER   GP   IN   KL   MJ   OH   QF   _____ _____   33 ☐

34 BCE   GHJ   LMO   QRT   VWY   _____ _____   34 ☐

35 AX   EV   IT   MR   QP   UN   _____ _____   35 ☐

Q. 36–40
spot the
word

A four-letter word is hidden in each of these sentences. You will find the hidden word at the end of one word and the beginning of the next. Underline the hidden word and then write it on the line.

Example Daniel _ended_ his speech with a joke.   _lend_

36 Sometimes hunger can make your stomach rumble.   _____ 36 ☐

37 Seth parked his car in the garage.   _____ 37 ☐

38 Abbie fell and severely hurt herself.   _____ 38 ☐

39 The beautiful lady posed for a photograph.   _____ 39 ☐

40 The pupils went to learn French at lunchtime.   _____ 40 ☐

MARK ☐

MARK
✓ OR ✗

Q. 41–45

interpreting graphs

This graph shows the percentage of boys and girls who passed a maths test over a period of six years.

Study the graph. Then answer the questions.

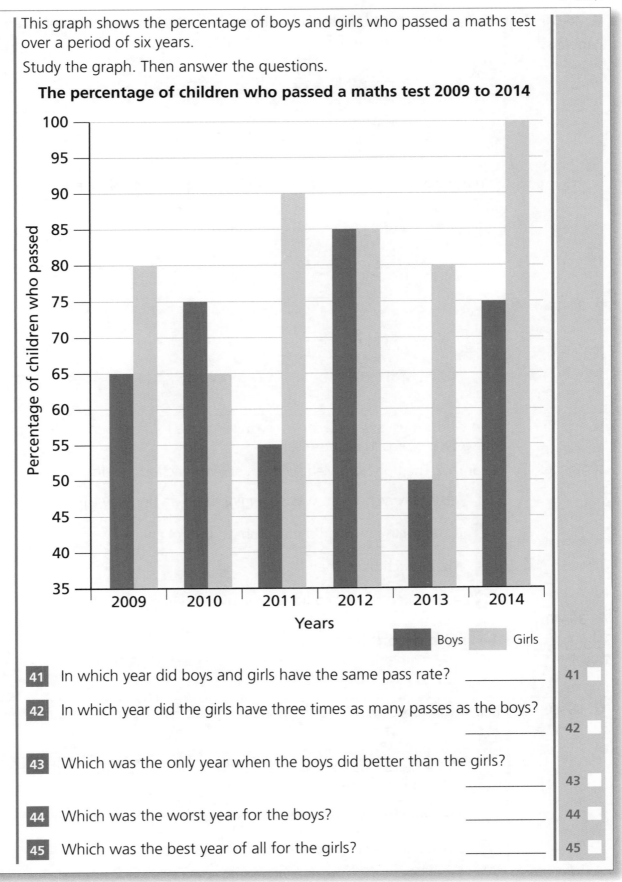

The percentage of children who passed a maths test 2009 to 2014

41 In which year did boys and girls have the same pass rate? _____ 41 ☐

42 In which year did the girls have three times as many passes as the boys?

_____ 42 ☐

43 Which was the only year when the boys did better than the girls?

_____ 43 ☐

44 Which was the worst year for the boys? _____ 44 ☐

45 Which was the best year of all for the girls? _____ 45 ☐

MARK ☐

MARK
✓ OR ✗

Q. 46–50

jumbled words in grids

The letters at the bottom of each grid fit into the boxes above them to make **two** words. Work out where each letter goes.

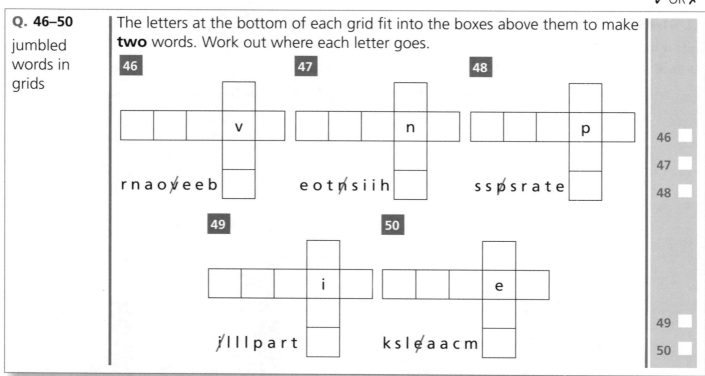

46
47
48

49
50

Q. 51–55

mixed-up sentences

Two words must swap places for each sentence to make sense. Underline these **two** words in each sentence.

Example The <u>bone</u> growled softly as he approached the <u>dog</u>.

51 Yesterday morning it was so raining hard on our way to school.

52 If something is mend then you have to broken it.

53 Me is much older than Mum.

54 As I looked down I could see the river flowing up the hill.

55 He looked on the chair and stood through the window.

51
52
53
54
55

Q. 56–60

word categories

Below this table are 10 words. Write each word in the correct column.

56 young	57 vegetables	58 fruit	59 birds	60 harness

canary   reins   kid   peach   eagle   pear
sprout   bridle   leek   calf

56
57
58
59
60

MARK

MARK
✓ OR ✗

Q. 61–65

change a word

One word is incorrect in each sentence. Underline this word. Write the correct word on the line.

Example Climbing over that wall is not <u>aloud</u>.   <u>allowed</u>

61   Last week my sister Louise died her hair a different colour.

_____ 61 ☐

62   The woman jumped from the plane and her parasol opened.

_____ 62 ☐

63   My Aunt Rachel gave me a chum bracelet for my birthday.

_____ 63 ☐

64   Dad asked the bank manger for a loan to buy the new car.

_____ 64 ☐

65   This weekend James is going out to buy a new three piece suet.

_____ 65 ☐

Q. 66–70

word connections

Underline the **one** word that fits with **both** pairs of words in brackets.

Example (heart club) (ruby emerald)   jewel brain <u>diamond</u> card brooch

66   (bandage strap) (throw hurl)   missile stone medicine sling plaster   66 ☐

67   (great good) (crushed ground)   excellent fine marvellous right   67 ☐

68   (dock harbour) (wine sherry)   seaside coffee lifeboat port drink   68 ☐

69   (final end) (persist stay)   result finish stop go last   69 ☐

70   (crimson green) (salt vinegar)   paint mustard condiment striped   70 ☐

Q. 71–75

number sequences

Write the next two numbers in each sequence.

Example 2   4   6   8   <u>10</u>   <u>12</u>

71   7   8   10   13   17   22   28   _____   _____   71 ☐

72   1   9   7   16   13   23   _____   _____   72 ☐

73   15   17   21   27   35   45   _____   _____   73 ☐

74   2   6   4   8   6   10   8   _____   _____   74 ☐

75   13   26   16   32   22   44   _____   _____   75 ☐

MARK ☐

MARK
✓ OR ✗

Q. 76–80

analogies

Underline **one** word in the brackets to complete these analogies.

Example Arrive is to depart as come is to (run hurry <u>go</u> hide).

76 Triangle is to three as pentagon is to (four five six seven eight). | 76 ☐

77 Bird is to nest as rabbit is to (field burrow stable house river). | 77 ☐

78 Mobile is to telephone as tablet is to (pill computer handset medicine). | 78 ☐

79 Water is to pipe as electricity is to (string box envelope wire shock). | 79 ☐

80 Sole is to foot as palm is to (tree head arm wrist hand). | 80 ☐

Q. 81–85

mixed-up
questions

The words are jumbled up in these questions. Work out what each question is. Then write the **answer** to that question. Put one letter in each box.

Example toes foot? are many How each on | f i v e

81 is owl What a baby called? | ☐☐☐☐☐ | 81 ☐

82 called? brother What the a is of princess | ☐☐☐☐☐☐ | 82 ☐

83 is the on What we planet live called? | ☐☐☐☐☐ | 83 ☐

84 can we cow's What food milk? make from | ☐☐☐☐☐ | 84 ☐

85 barge a What sail does on? | ☐☐☐☐☐ | 85 ☐

Q. 86–90

which word

One word in each question **can** be made from the word in CAPITALS. Underline this word. You may only use each letter once.

Example SPEEDBOAT toast debated poems <u>beast</u> poser

86 OBSERVATION invite observe restore vacation servant | 86 ☐

87 CONDIMENTS dimension comment stones mention count | 87 ☐

88 DISENGAGED encourage greed singed gender danger | 88 ☐

89 DELIGHTED lighten idled glittered tinge enlighten | 89 ☐

90 PARLIAMENT means pleated entrails terminal trailer | 90 ☐

MARK ☐

MARK
✓ OR ✗

Q. 91–95
add a letter

Read the clue in brackets. Add **one** letter to the word in CAPITALS to make a new word that matches the clue. Write the new word on the line.

Example CANE   (lifts heavy objects)   <u>CRANE</u>

91 SENT   (a pleasant smell) _____ 91 ☐

92 TOOT   (used to bite and chew) _____ 92 ☐

93 OUGHT   (purchased with money) _____ 93 ☐

94 CURT   (a place where people face criminal charges) _____ 94 ☐

95 PLACE   (the home of a king or queen) _____ 95 ☐

Q. 96–100
move a letter

Take **one** letter from the first word and put it in the second word to make two new words. Write the letter you have moved and the two new words in the table below.

	First word	Second word	Letter moved	New first word	New second word
Example	slope	feat	s	lope	feast
96	stare	tar			
97	crimes	seas			
98	table	right			
99	raft	lint			
100	trough	gave			

96 ☐
97 ☐
98 ☐
99 ☐
100 ☐

MARK ☐

END OF TEST

PROGRESS PAPER 6 TOTAL ☐

Topics chart

TOPICS COVERED	Paper	Book 1						Book 2						Book 3					
		1	2	3	4	5	6	7	8	9	10	11	12	13	14	15	16	17	18
vocabulary	analogies	•	•		•	•	•	•	•	•	•	•	•	•	•	•			•
	antonyms	•	•	•	•		•			•	•	•	•	•	•		•	•	•
	complete the sentence	•		•	•	•			•	•		•		•	•	•	•	•	
	compound words				•			•	•								•		•
	crosswords																		
	mixed-up groups	•		•		•				•			•		•			•	•
	odd ones out	•	•	•	•	•	•	•		•	•	•	•	•	•	•	•	•	
	rhyming words								•		•			•	•		•		•
	synonyms				•	•		•	•										•
	word categories	•	•	•		•		•	•		•	•	•	•	•		•	•	•
	word connections	•	•	•			•	•	•			•	•	•			•	•	
	word meanings	•	•	•		•	•	•		•	•		•	•		•			•
	add a letter			•	•		•		•			•			•		•	•	•
	change a letter														•		•		
	change a word			•			•								•			•	
	join two words to make one	•	•	•		•					•		•		•				
spelling	jumbled words in grids		•		•	•	•		•	•	•	•	•	•			•		•
	jumbled words in sentences		•	•	•	•		•		•				•		•	•	•	•
	jumbled words with clues	•	•			•				•								•	
	leftover letters				•		•		•									•	
	missing four-letter words													•				•	
	missing letters			•	•	•	•	•	•	•	•	•	•	•	•	•	•	•	•
	missing three-letter words	•														•	•	•	
	move a letter			•	•	•	•	•	•	•	•	•	•						•

Schofield & Sims • Progress Papers • Verbal Reasoning 1

TOPICS COVERED

	Paper	1	2	3	4	5	6	7	8	9	10	11	12	13	14	15	16	17	18
spelling (continued)	spot the word	•	•	•	•	•	•	•	•	•	•	•	•	•	•	•		•	•
	take a letter										•								
	which word	•	•	•		•		•	•	•	•	•				•	•	•	•
	word chains		•	•	•		•	•	•	•	•	•		•		•	•	•	•
logical reasoning	always has	•	•	•	•		•	•		•		•		•		•		•	•
	mixed-up sentences	•	•	•	•			•		•	•			•			•	•	•
	mixed-up questions						•								•	•			
	position problems	•					•		•							•		•	•
	sorting information		•		•					•		•		•			•		
	time problems		•	•						•	•	•	•	•	•		•	•	•
	true statements	•				•							•					•	•
	word grids	•	•					•	•						•				
codes, sequences and patterns	alphabetical order	•		•		•	•		•				•	•	•				
	letter codes	•																	
	letter sequences		•		•		•	•	•	•	•		•	•		•	•		
	make a word		•	•	•	•		•		•			•	•	•				•
	match the codes		•		•						•								
	number sequences				•		•	•		•		•			•			•	
	symbol codes				•			•	•	•					•	•			
	word codes	•		•									•		•		•		•
numerical reasoning	algebra						•												
	interpreting graphs		•		•				•			•	•	•	•	•	•		
	interpreting tables	•							•							•			
	letters for numbers	•		•		•		•	•	•		•	•	•	•	•	•	•	•
	number connections	•										•							

Progress chart

Write the score (out of 100) for each paper in the box provided at the bottom of the chart. Then colour in the column above the box to the appropriate height to represent this score.

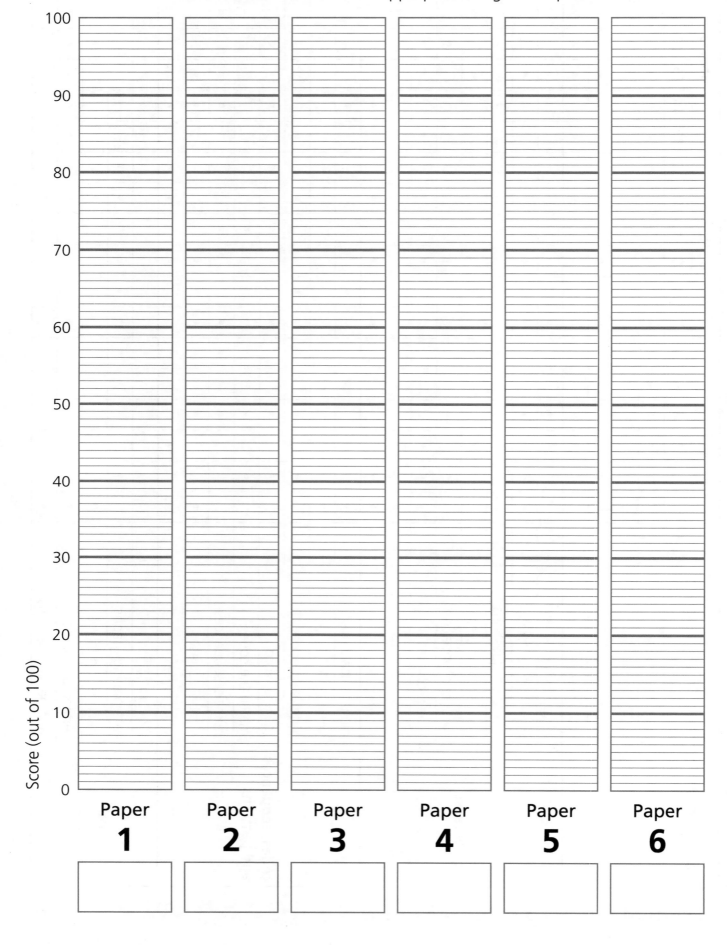

THE INFINITY OF LISTS

Published in Great Britain in 2009 by

MacLehose Press
an imprint of Quercus
21 Bloomsbury Square
London
WC1A 2NS

First published with the title *La Vertigine della Lista*
in 2009 by Bompiani, Milan

A CIP catalogue reference for this book is available
from the British Library

ISBN 978 1 906694 82 1

10 9 8 7 6 5 4 3 2 1

Printed and bound in Italy by Errestampa S.r.L. –
Orio al Serio (BG)

Editorial Director – Elisabetta Sgarbi
Editorial Coordination – Anna Maria Lorusso
Editing – Federica Matteoli and Alta Price
Picture Research – Ilaria Fabrizio
Graphic Design – Polystudio
Production – Sergio Daniotti

UMBERTO ECO
THE INFINITY
OF LISTS
FROM HOMER
TO JOYCE

Translation from the Italian by Alastair McEwen

MACLEHOSE PRESS
AN IMPRINT OF QUERCUS

CONTENTS

The names in **bold** in the text refer to the extracts reproduced
in the anthology at the end of each chapter.

When the Louvre invited me to organize for the whole of November 2009 a series of conferences, exhibitions, public readings, concerts, film projections and the like on the subject of my choice, I did not hesitate for a second and proposed the list (and as we shall see we shall also be talking about catalogues and enumeration). Why did this idea come to mind?

If anyone were to read my novels he would see that they abound with lists, and the origins of this predilection are two, both of which derive from my studies as a young man: certain medieval texts and many works by James Joyce (and we should not overlook the influence of medieval rituals and texts on the young Joyce). But between litanies and the list of things contained in the drawer of Leopold Bloom's kitchen in the penultimate chapter of Ulysses *there stand a good number of centuries, and many more centuries again stand between medieval lists and the model list par excellence: the catalogue of ships in Homer's* Iliad, *from which this book takes its cue. It is also in Homer that we find the celebration of another descriptive model: the one ordered and inspired by the criteria of harmonious completion and closure represented by Achilles' shield. In other words, already in Homer it seems that there is a swing between a poetics of "everything included" and a poetics of the "etcetera".*

While this was already clear to me, I had never set myself the task of making a meticulous record of the infinite cases in which the history of literature (from Homer to Joyce to the present day) offers examples of lists, even though names such as Perec, Prévert, Whitman and Borges all came to mind right away. The result of this hunt was prodigious, enough to make your head spin, and I already know that a great number of people will write to me asking why this or that author is not mentioned in this book. The fact is that not only am I not omniscient and do not know a multitude of texts in which lists appear, but even had I wished to include in the anthology all the lists I gradually encountered in the course of my exploration, this book would be at least one thousand pages long, and maybe even more.

Then there is the problem of deciding what a figurative list may be. The few books on the poetics of lists prudently limit themselves to verbal lists, because it is very hard to say in what way a picture can present things and yet suggest an "etcetera", as if to admit that the limits of the frame oblige it to say nothing about an immense number of other things. In addition, my research also had to serve to show things, *both in the Louvre and in a book like this one, which follows in the wake of the two previous volumes* On Beauty *and* On Ugliness. *Hence a search that is a little less obvious than that carried out on beauty and ugliness, namely the search for* visual etceteras, *in which I was greatly aided by Anna Maria Lorusso and Mario Andreose.*

In conclusion, the search for lists was a most exciting experience not so much for what we managed to include in this volume as for all those things that had to be left out. What I mean to say, in other words, is that this is a book that cannot but end with an etcetera.

Missorium (*Shield of Achilles*)
4th-5th century A.D.,
Paris, Bibliothèque Nationale de France

1.   THE SHIELD AND ITS FORM

While Achilles is sulking in his tent, a prey to his grim wrath, Patroclus takes his weapons, fights Hector, is killed by him, and his arms (those of Achilles, that is) go the victor.

But when Achilles decides to return to the fray, his mother Thetis asks Hephaestus to forge new arms for her son. Hephaestus gets to work and Homer devotes part of Book XVIII of the *Iliad* to a description of the shield he is preparing.

Hephaestus, or Vulcan, divided this immense shield into five zones, in which appear the earth, the sea, the sky, the sun, the moon, the stars, the Pleiades, Orion and the Great Bear. Then he modelled two populous cities on it. In the first he portrays a wedding feast, with the couple parading around by torchlight, and young men playing on pipes and kitharas. There is also a crowded forum where a kind of trial is going on, with plaintiffs, witnesses, advocates, gawking crowd, and the elders sitting in a circle who at a certain point grasp the sceptre and stand to pronounce the verdict. The second scene shows a beleaguered castle: on the walls, as in Troy, wives, maidens, and old men watch the battle. Led by Minerva, the enemy advances and, as they come to a river where they used to water the herds, they prepare an ambush. As soon as two unwitting shepherds come along playing on their pipes, the enemy attack them, steal their herds, and kill them. Warriors on horseback sally forth from the besieged city to pursue the enemy, and along the riverbank the battle begins. Among the combatants we see Strife, Riot, and Fate, covered in blood, clawing and seizing the living and the dead alike as the fighters try to save the bodies of their own dead.

Then Hephaestus sculpts a fertile, well-ploughed field of grain

with ploughmen and their oxen crossing it from side to side, and he who comes to the end of his furrow makes a toast with a glass of wine before making his way back again. Elsewhere we see the field already full of crops with reapers at work as others bind the sheaves. In their midst sits the king, while his servitors lay out a meal beneath an oak tree, with the flesh of a newly sacrificed ox, as the women knead the flour to make loaves.

We also see a vineyard laden with ripe grapes, with golden shoots and vines trained on silver poles. Around this, a hedge wrought of tin, while youths and maidens bring fruits as one of them plays the cithara, whose sound the others follow singing rhythmically. Then Hephaestus adds a herd of cattle sculpted in gold and tin that race to the pasture, along the banks of a river whose waters flow among the reeds. Four herdsmen, all in gold, follow them, accompanied by nine white mastiffs. But suddenly two lions appear and pounce on the heifers and a bull, wounding it and dragging it along as it bellows pitifully. The herdsmen come running with the dogs, but by now the wild beasts are devouring the disembowelled bull as the mastiffs bark, powerless to intervene.

Finally, Hephaestus, the lord of fire, sculpts more flocks in a pleasant valley dotted with huts and pens for the sheep, and dancing youths and virgins, the latter in robes of light stuff, the former in doublets, the girls wearing garlands, the boys with golden daggers at their sides, whirling round and round like a potter's wheel. Many people watch the dance, after which appear three tumblers who sing as they perform their acrobatics.

The mighty river Oceanus surrounds, limits, and ends every scene and separates the shield from the rest of the universe.

The shield has so many scenes that, unless we presume infinitesimally minute goldsmithery, it is difficult to imagine the object in all its wealth of detail; what is more, the portrayal does not concern space alone, but also time, in the sense that various events follow one another, as if the shield were a cinema screen or a long strip cartoon.

Thetis and Hephaestus
fresco from Pompeii, first century A.D.,
Naples, Museo Archeologico Nazionale

page 13: Quatremère de Quincy
The Shield of Achilles from *Le Jupiter olympien
ou l'Art de la sculpture antique*
Paris, de Bure frères, 1815,
Bibliothèque Nationale de France

True, the art of the past was capable of portraying a sequence of successive scenes, using techniques similar to those of the strip cartoon, with the same characters reappearing several times in different times and places (see for example Piero della Francesca's *True Cross* cycle in Arezzo), but this is precisely why the shield should have more scenes than it could materially contain. And in fact various artists have tried to reproduce Hephaestus' work visually, but all they managed to do was make fairly cursory approximations.

Even if we grant that the shield has a realistically reproducible structure, its perfect circular nature does not permit us to presume that there is anything else beyond its bounds: it is a *finite* form. Everything that Hephaestus wanted to say is inside the shield, it has no outside: it is a closed world.

Achilles' shield is therefore the epiphany of Form, of the way in which art manages to construct harmonious representations that establish an order, a hierarchy, and a figure-to-background relationship between the things portrayed.

Note that we are not talking about an "aesthetic" point of view: aesthetics tells us that a form can be infinitely interpreted, finding new aspects and new relationships every time, and this can happen both with the Sistine Chapel and with a monochromatic painting by Klein or Rothko. But a figurative work of art (like a poem or a narrative for that matter) nonetheless possesses a *referential* function: a narrative told either in words or images tells us that in the real world, or in a possible one such as the world of fairy tales or the poetic imagination, there are objects and situations of this or that kind. And this is also the "narrative" function of Achilles' shield.

From the referential standpoint, a *mise-en-forme* does not encourage us to see things other than those that it represents. Achilles' shield tells us about *that* urban and rural district and not about another, and it tells us nothing about what may lie beyond the circle of Oceanus. This does not mean that we cannot interpret that district as the universal model of the city and its countryside, or see those images as an allegory of good government, or war and peace, or the state of nature. But form limits the universe of what is "said".

This holds for all the arts: while behind the Mona Lisa there is a landscape that we may suppose continues beyond the frame, the viewer does not wonder what lies outside the painting, because the seal of form that the artist has imparted on the picture makes it focussed, as if it were round like Achilles' shield and its figurative nucleus were at the centre. In literature, if on reading *The Red and the Black*, we learn that Julien Sorel shoots at Madame de Rênal in the church of Verrière and the first shot misses, we can also fantasize (as some have done) about where that first shot ended up, but in reality the question is irrelevant: from the standpoint of Stendhal's narrative strategy that detail is insignificant. Those who wonder about the first shot are wasting their time and giving up on understanding and enjoying the novel.

2. THE LIST AND THE CATALOGUE

Homer was able to construct (imagine) a closed form because he had a clear idea of the agricultural and warrior culture of his own day. He knew the world he talked about, he knew its laws, causes and effects, and this is why he was able to *give it a form*.

There is, however, another mode of artistic representation, i.e., when we do not know the boundaries of what we wish to portray, when we do not know how many things we are talking about and presume their number to be, if not infinite, then at least astronomically large. Or when we cannot provide a definition by essence for something and so, to be able to talk about it, to make it comprehensible or in some way perceivable, we list its properties—and as we shall see the accidental properties of something, from the Greeks to modern times, are thought to be infinite.

It is not that form cannot suggest infinity, and the entire history of aesthetics reiterates this, but we must not play with terms. The infinity of aesthetics is the *subjective* feeling of something greater than us, it is an emotional condition; instead, the infinity we are talking about now is an *actual* infinity, made up of objects that can perhaps be numbered but that we cannot number—and we fear that their numeration (and enumeration) may never stop. When Kant had a sense of the sublime on gazing at the starry sky above him he had the (subjective) feeling that what he was seeing went beyond his sensibilities, and so he postulated an infinity that not only our senses fail to grasp but one that not even our imagination can embrace in a

Étienne Léopold Trouvelot
Part of the Milky Way Visible in Winter, 1874-1875,
Paris, Observatoire de Paris

ALEXANDER·M·DARIVM·VLT·SVPERAT
CÆSIS·IN·ACIE·PERSAR·PEDIT·CM·EQVT̄
VERO·X·M·IN·PERFECTIS·MATRE·QVOQVE
CONIVGE·LIBERIS·DARII·REGIS·CVM·M·HAVD
AMPLIVS·EQVITIB·FVGA·DILAPSI·CAPTIS.

single perception. Hence an uneasy pleasure, which makes us feel the greatness of our subjectivity, capable of wishing for something we cannot have. The infinity of the feeling Kant experienced has a highly emotional charge (and it could be aesthetically portrayed even by painting or writing a poetic description of a *single* star); instead the innumerability of the stars is an infinity that we should call objective (there would be billions of stars even if we did not exist). The artist who attempts only a partial list of all the stars in the universe, in some way wishes to make us think of this objective infinity.

The infinity of aesthetics is a sensation that follows from the finite and perfect completeness of the thing we admire, while the other form of representation we are talking about suggests infinity almost *physically*, because in fact *it does not end*, nor does it conclude in form.

We shall call this representative mode the *list*, or *catalogue*.

Let us return to the *Iliad*. There is a point in which **Homer** wants to give a sense of the immensity of the Greek army (in Book II of the poem, in order to give an idea of the mass of men who in that moment the terrified Trojans see spreading out along the sea shore).

At first he attempts a comparison: that mass of men, whose arms reflect the sunlight, is like a fire raging through a forest, it is like a flock of geese or cranes that seem to cross the sky like a thunderclap—but no metaphor comes to his aid, and he calls on the Muses for help: "Tell me, O Muses who dwell on Olympus, you who know all … you who were the leaders and the guides of the Danae; I shall not call the host by name, not even had I ten tongues and ten mouths", and so he prepares to name only the captains and the ships.

It looks like a shortcut, but this shortcut takes him three hundred and fifty verses of the poem. Apparently the list is finite (there should not be other captains and other ships), but since he cannot say how many men there are for every leader, the number he alludes to is still indefinite.

Albrecht Altdorfer
The Battle of Issus (*The Battle of Alexander*), 1529,
Munich, Alte Pinakothek

At first sight we might think that form is characteristic of mature cultures, which know the world around them, whose order they have recognized and defined; on the contrary the list would seem to be typical of primitive cultures that still have an imprecise image of the universe and limit themselves to listing as many of its properties as they can name without trying to establish a hierarchical relationship among them. For example, we might interpret **Hesiod**'s *Theogony* in this sense: it is an inexhausted list of divine creatures that certainly refer to a genealogical tree that a philologically patient reading could reconstruct, but this is definitely not the way in which the reader (even the original reader) reads or listens to the text, which presents itself rather as an intolerable swarm of monstrous and prodigious beings, a universe overpopulated with invisible individuals that runs parallel to that of our experience, and whose roots are sunk in the mists of time.

Yet the list turns up again in the Middle Ages (when the great theological *Summae* and the encyclopaedias claimed to provide a definitive form for the material and spiritual universe), in the Renaissance and in the Baroque period, where the form of the world is that of a new astronomy, and especially in the modern and post-modern world. A sign that we are subject to the infinity of lists for many diverse reasons.

HESIOD (VIII-VII CENT. B.C.)
THEOGONY, VV. 126-452

And Earth first bare starry Heaven, equal to herself, to cover her on every side, and to be an ever-sure abiding-place for the blessed gods. And she brought forth long Hills, graceful haunts of the goddess-Nymphs who dwell amongst the glens of the hills. She bare also the fruitless deep with his raging swell, Pontus, without sweet union of love. But afterwards she lay with Heaven and bare deep-swirling Oceanus, Coeus and Crius and Hyperion and Iapetus, Theia and Rhea, Themis and Mnemosyne and gold-crowned Phoebe and lovely Tethys. After them was born Cronos the wily, youngest and most terrible of her children, and he hated his lusty sire.
And again, she bare the Cyclopes, overbearing in spirit, Brontes, and Steropes and stubborn-hearted Arges, who gave Zeus the thunder and made the thunderbolt: in all else they were like the gods, but one eye only was set in the midst of their fore-heads. And they were surnamed Cyclopes (Orb-eyed) because one orbed eye was set in their foreheads. Strength and might and craft were in their works.
And again, three other sons were born of Earth and Heaven, great and doughty beyond telling, Cottus and Briareos and Gyes, presumptuous children. From their shoulders sprang an hundred arms, not to be approached, and each had fifty heads upon his shoulders on their strong limbs, and irresistible was the stubborn strength that was in their great forms. For of all the children that were born of Earth and Heaven, these were the most terrible, and they were hated by their own father from the first. And he used to hide them all away in a secret place of Earth so soon as each was born, and would not suffer them to come up into the light: and Heaven rejoiced in his evil doing. But vast Earth groaned within, being straitened, and she made the element of grey flint and shaped a great sickle, and told her

plan to her dear sons. And she spoke, cheering them, while she was vexed in her dear heart:
"My children, gotten of a sinful father, if you will obey me, we should punish the vile outrage of your father; for he first thought of doing shameful things."
So she said; but fear seized them all, and none of them uttered a word. But great Cronos the wily took courage and answered his dear mother:
"Mother, I will undertake to do this deed, for I reverence not our father of evil name, for he first thought of doing shameful things."
So he said: and vast Earth rejoiced greatly in spirit, and set and hid him in an ambush, and put in his hands a jagged sickle, and revealed to him the whole plot.
And Heaven came, bringing on night and longing for love, and he lay about Earth spreading himself full upon her.

Then the son from his ambush stretched forth his left hand and in his right took the great long sickle with jagged teeth, and swiftly lopped off his own father's members and cast them away to fall behind him. And not vainly did they fall from his hand; for all the bloody drops that gushed forth Earth received, and as the seasons moved round she bare the strong Erinyes and the great Giants with gleaming armour, holding long spears in their hands and the Nymphs whom they call Meliae all over the boundless earth. And so soon as he had cut off the members with flint and cast them from the land into the surging sea, they were swept away over the main a long time: and a white foam spread around them from the immortal flesh, and in it there grew a maiden. First she drew near holy Cythera, and from there, afterwards, she came to sea-girt Cyprus, and came forth an awful and lovely goddess, and grass grew up about her beneath her shapely feet. Her gods and men call Aphrodite, and the foam-born goddess and rich-crowned Cytherea, because she grew amid the foam, and

Cytherea because she reached Cythera, and Cyprogenes because she was born in billowy Cyprus, and Philommedes because she sprang from the members. And with her went Eros, and comely Desire followed her at her birth at the first and as she went into the assembly of the gods. This honour she has from the beginning, and this is the portion allotted to her amongst men and undying gods—the whisperings of maidens and smiles and deceits with sweet delight and love and graciousness.

But these sons whom be begot himself great Heaven used to call Titans (Strainers) in reproach, for he said that they strained and did presumptuously a fearful deed, and that vengeance for it would come afterwards. And Night bare hateful Doom and black Fate and Death, and she bare Sleep and the tribe of Dreams. And again the goddess murky Night, though she lay with none, bare Blame and painful Woe, and the Hesperides who guard the rich, golden apples and the trees bearing fruit beyond glorious Ocean. Also she bare the Destinies and ruthless avenging Fates, Clotho and Lachesis and Atropos, who give men at their birth both evil and good to have, and they pursue the transgressions of men and of gods: and these goddesses never cease from their dread anger until they punish the sinner with a sore penalty. Also deadly Night bare Nemesis (Indignation) to afflict mortal men, and after her, Deceit and Friendship and hateful Age and hard-hearted Strife.

But abhorred Strife bare painful Toil and Forgetfulness and Famine and tearful Sorrows, Fightings also, Battles, Murders, Manslaughters, Quarrels, Lying Words, Disputes, Lawlessness and Ruin, all of one

Hendrick de Clerck
The Wedding of Peleus and Thetis (*Festival of the Gods*),
c. 1606-1609, Paris, Musée du Louvre

nature, and Oath who most troubles men upon earth when anyone wilfully swears a false oath.

And Sea begat Nereus, the eldest of his children, who is true and lies not: and men call him the Old Man because he is trusty and gentle and does not forget the laws of righteousness, but thinks just and kindly thoughts. And yet again he got great Thaumas and proud Phoreys, being mated with Earth, and fair-cheeked Ceto and Eurybia who has a heart of flint within her. And of Nereus and rich-haired Doris, daughter of Ocean the perfect river, were born children, passing lovely amongst goddesses, Ploto, Eucrante, Sao, and Amphitrite, and Eudora, and Thetis, Galene and Glauce, Cymothoe, Speo, Thoe and lovely Halie, and Pasithea, and Erato, and rosy-armed Eunice, and gracious Melite, and Eulimene, and Agaue, Doto, Proto, Pherusa, and Dynamene, and Nisaea, and Actaea, and Protomedea, Doris, Panopea, and comely Galatea, and lovely Hippothoe, and rosy-armed Hipponoe, and Cymodoce who with Cymatolege and Amphitrite easily calms the waves upon the misty sea and the blasts of raging winds, and Cymo, and Eione, and rich-crowned Alimede, and Glauconome, fond of laughter, and Pontoporea, Leagore, Euagore, and Laomedea, and Polynoe, and Autonoe, and Lysianassa, and Euarne, lovely of shape and without blemish of form, and Psamathe of charming figure and divine Menippe, Neso, Eupompe, Themisto, Pronoe, and Nemertes who has the nature of her deathless father. These fifty daughters sprang from blameless Nereus, skilled in excellent crafts.

And Thaumas wedded Electra the daughter of deep-flowing Ocean, and she bare him swift Iris and the long-haired Harpies, Aello (Storm-swift) and Ocypetes (Swift-flier) who on their swift wings keep pace with the blasts of the winds and the birds; for quick as time they dart along.

And again, Ceto bare to Phoreys the fair-cheeked Graiae, sisters grey from their birth: and both deathless gods and men who walk on earth call them Graiae, Pemphredo well-clad, and saffron-robed Enyo, and the Gorgons who dwell beyond glorious Ocean in the frontier land towards Night where are the clear-voiced Hesperides, Sthenno, and Euryale, and Medusa who suffered a woeful fate: she was mortal, but the two were undying and grew not old. With her lay the Dark-haired One in a soft meadow amid spring flowers. And when Perseus cut off her head, there sprang forth great Chrysaor and the horse Pegasus who is so called because he was born near the springs (pegae) of Ocean; and that other, because he held a golden blade (aor) in his hands. Now Pegasus flew away and left the earth, the mother of flocks, and came to the deathless gods: and he dwells in the house of Zeus and brings to wise Zeus the thunder and lightning. But Chrysaor was joined in love to Callirrhoe, the daughter of glorious Ocean, and begot three-headed Geryones. Him mighty Heracles slew in sea-girt Erythea by his shambling oxen on that day when he drove the wide-browed oxen to holy Tiryns, and had crossed the ford of Ocean and killed Orthus and Eurytion the herdsman in the dim stead out beyond glorious Ocean.

And in a hollow cave she bare another monster, irresistible, in no wise like either to mortal men or to the undying gods, even the goddess fierce Echidna who is half a nymph with glancing eyes and fair cheeks, and half again a huge snake, great and awful, with speckled skin, eating raw flesh beneath the secret parts of the holy earth. And there she has a cave deep down under a hollow rock far from the deathless gods and mortal men. There, then, did the gods appoint her a glorious house to dwell in: and she keeps guard in Arima beneath the earth, grim Echidna, a nymph who dies not nor grows old all her days.

Men say that Typhaon the terrible, outrageous and lawless, was joined in love to her, the maid with glancing eyes. So she conceived and brought forth fierce offspring; first she bare Orthus the hound of Geryones, and then again she bare a second, a monster not to be overcome and that may not be described, Cerberus who eats raw flesh, the brazen-voiced hound of Hades, fifty-headed, relentless and strong. And again she bore a third, the evil-minded Hydra of Lerna, whom the goddess, white-armed Hera nourished, being angry beyond measure with the mighty Heracles. And her Heracles, the son of Zeus, of the house of Amphitryon, together with warlike Iolaus, destroyed with the unpitying sword through the plans of Athene the spoil-driver. She was the mother of Chimaera who breathed raging fire, a creature fearful, great, swift-footed and strong, who had three heads, one of a grim-eyed lion; in her hinderpart, a dragon; and in her middle, a goat, breathing forth a fearful blast of blazing fire. Her did Pegasus and noble Bellerophon slay; but Echidna was subject in love to Orthus and brought forth the deadly Sphinx which destroyed the Cadmeans, and the Nemean lion, which Hera, the good wife of Zeus, brought up and made to haunt the hills of Nemea, a plague to men. There he preyed upon the tribes of her own people and had power over Tretus of Nemea and Apesas: yet the strength of stout Heracles overcame him. And Ceto was joined in love to Phorcys and bare her youngest, the awful snake who guards the apples all of gold in the secret places of the dark earth at its great bounds. This is the offspring of Ceto and Phoreys. And Tethys bare to Ocean eddying rivers, Nilus, and Alpheus, and deep-swirling Eridanus, Strymon, and Meander, and the fair stream of Ister, and Phasis, and Rhesus, and the silver eddies of Achelous, Nessus, and Rhodius, Haliacmon, and Heptaporus, Granicus, and Aesepus, and holy Simois, and Peneus, and Hermus, and Caicus fair stream, and great Sangarius, Ladon, Parthenius, Euenus, Ardescus, and divine Scamander. Also she brought forth a holy company of daughters who with the lord Apollo and the

Rivers have youths in their keeping—to this charge Zeus appointed them—Peitho, and Admete, and Ianthe, and Electra, and Doris, and Prymno, and Urania divine in form, Hippo, Clymene, Rhodea, and Callirrhoe, Zeuxo and Clytie, and Idyia, and Pasithoe, Plexaura, and Galaxaura, and lovely Dione, Melobosis and Thoe and handsome Polydora, Cerceis lovely of form, and soft eyed Pluto, Perseis, Ianeira, Acaste, Xanthe, Petraea the fair, Menestho, and Europa, Metis, and Eurynome, and Telesto saffron-clad, Chryseis and Asia and charming Calypso, Eudora, and Tyche, Amphirho, and Ocyrrhoe, and Styx who is the chiefest of them all. These are the eldest daughters that sprang from Ocean and Tethys; but there are many besides. For there are three thousand neat-ankled daughters of Ocean who are dispersed far and wide, and in every place alike serve the earth and the deep waters, children who are glorious among goddesses. And as many other rivers are there, babbling as they flow, sons of Ocean, whom queenly Tethys bare, but their names it is hard for a mortal man to tell, but people know those by which they severally dwell.

And Theia was subject in love to Hyperion and bare great Helius (Sun) and clear Selene (Moon) and Eos (Dawn) who shines upon all that are on earth and upon the deathless Gods who live in the wide heaven.

And Eurybia, bright goddess, was joined in love to Crius and bare great Astraeus, and Pallas, and Perses who also was eminent among all men in wisdom.

And Eos bare to Astraeus the strong-hearted winds, brightening Zephyrus, and Boreas, headlong in his course, and Notus—a goddess mating in love with a god. And after these Erigenia bare the star Eosphorus (Dawn-bringer), and the gleaming stars with which heaven is crowned.

And Styx the daughter of Ocean was joined to Pallas and bare Zelus (Emulation) and trim-ankled Nike (Victory) in the house. Also she brought forth Cratos (Strength) and Bia

(Force), wonderful children. These have no house apart from Zeus, nor any dwelling nor path except that wherein God leads them, but they dwell always with Zeus the loud-thunderer. For so did Styx the deathless daughter of Ocean plan on that day when the Olympian Lightener called all the deathless gods to great Olympus, and said that whosoever of the gods would fight with him against the Titans, he would not cast him out from his rights, but each should have the office which he had before amongst the deathless gods. And he declared that he who was without office and rights as is just. So deathless Styx came first to Olympus with her children through the wit of her dear father. And Zeus honoured her, and gave her very great gifts, for her he appointed to be the great oath of the gods, and her children to live with him always. And as he promised, so he performed fully unto them all. But he himself mightily reigns and rules.
Again, Phoebe came to the desired embrace of Coeus.
Then the goddess through the love of the god conceived and brought forth dark-gowned Leto, always mild, kind to men and to the deathless gods, mild from the beginning, gentlest in all Olympus. Also she bare Asteria of happy name, whom Perses once led to his great house to be called his dear wife. And she conceived and bare Hecate whom Zeus the son of Cronos honoured above all. He gave her splendid gifts, to have a share of the earth and the unfruitful sea. She received honour also in starry heaven, and is honoured exceedingly by the deathless gods. For to this day, whenever any one of men on earth offers rich sacrifices and prays for favour according to custom, he calls upon Hecate. Great honour comes full easily to him whose prayers the goddess receives favourably, and she bestows wealth upon him; for the power surely is with her. For as many as were born of Earth and Ocean amongst all these she has her due portion. The son of Cronos did her no wrong nor took anything away of all

that was her portion among the former Titan gods: but she holds, as the division was at the first from the beginning, privilege both in earth, and in heaven, and in sea. Also, because she is an only child, the goddess receives not less honour, but much more still, for Zeus honours her. Whom she will she greatly aids and advances: she sits by worshipful kings in judgment, and in the assembly whom she will is distinguished among the people. And when men arm themselves for the battle that destroys men, then the goddess is at hand to give victory and grant glory readily to whom she will. Good is she also when men contend at the games, for there too the goddess is with them and profits them: and he who by might and strength gets the victory wins the rich prize easily with joy, and brings glory to his parents. And she is good to stand by horsemen, whom she will: and to those whose business is in the grey discomfortable sea, and who pray to Hecate and the loud-crashing Earth-Shaker, easily the glorious goddess gives great catch, and easily she takes it away as soon as seen, if so she will. She is good in the byre with Hermes to increase the stock. The droves of kine and wide herds of goats and flocks of fleecy sheep, if she will, she increases from a few, or makes many to be less. So, then, albeit her mother's only child, she is honoured amongst all the deathless gods. And the son of Cronos made her a nurse of the young who after that day saw with their eyes the light of all-seeing Dawn. So from the beginning she is a nurse of the young, and these are her honours.

pages 24-25: Matthias Gerung
The Judgement of Paris and the Trojan War, 1540,
Paris, Musée du Louvre

CONSPICIS HAC FICTA VEL ZEVSIDIS ARTE TABELLA
CLECTOR, ILIARDANIDVM MOENIA QVASSA VIRVM,
FRAVDE VIRVS DANAIS QVA PRAECIPITATA, VEL IGNE,
FERRO, VEL VALIDIS MILITIS INSIDIIS.
IN CINERES CVLVERSA LEVES VRBS TANTA, LACENAE
TYNDARIS ILLICITVS PARERE FECIT AMOR.
EX HOC EVENTVS HOMINVM RESCIRE CADVCOS
IAM POTIS ES, MVNDI FALLIBILEMQVE STATVM
∞ M   I D XXXX   W S
           O W M O N

HOMER (IX CENT. B.C.)
THE ILIAD OF HOMER,
FROM BOOK II, VV. 595-1015

[...] As on some mountain, through the lofty grove,
The crackling flames ascend, and blaze above;
The fires expanding, as the winds arise,
Shoot their long beams, and kindle half the skies:
So from the polish'd arms, and brazen shields,
A gleamy splendour flash'd along the fields.
Not less their number than the embodied cranes,
Or milk-white swans in Asius' watery plains.
That, o'er the windings of Cayster's springs,
Stretch their long necks, and clap their rustling wings,
Now tower aloft, and course in airy rounds,
Now light with noise; with noise the field resounds.
Thus numerous and confused, extending wide,
The legions crowd Scamander's flowery side;
With rushing troops the plains are cover'd o'er,
And thundering footsteps shake the sounding shore.
Along the river's level meads they stand,
Thick as in spring the flowers adorn the land,
Or leaves the trees; or thick as insects play,
The wandering nation of a summer's day:
That, drawn by milky steams, at evening hours,
In gather'd swarms surround the rural bowers;
From pail to pail with busy murmur run
The gilded legions, glittering in the sun.
So throng'd, so close, the Grecian squadrons stood
In radiant arms, and thirst for Trojan blood.
Each leader now his scatter'd force conjoins
In close array, and forms the deepening lines.
Not with more ease the skilful shepherd-swain

Collects his flocks from thousands on the plain.
The king of kings, majestically tall,
Towers o'er his armies, and outshines them all;
Like some proud bull, that round the pastures leads
His subject herds, the monarch of the meads,
Great as the gods, the exalted chief was seen,
His strength like Neptune, and like Mars his mien;
Jove o'er his eyes celestial glories spread,
And dawning conquest played around his head.

Say, virgins, seated round the throne divine,
All-knowing goddesses! immortal nine!
Since earth's wide regions, heaven's umneasur'd height,
And hell's abyss, hide nothing from your sight,
(We, wretched mortals! lost in doubts below,
But guess by rumour, and but boast we know,)
O say what heroes, fired by thirst of fame,
Or urged by wrongs, to Troy's destruction came.
To count them all, demands a thousand tongues,
A throat of brass, and adamantine lungs.
Daughters of Jove, assist! inspired by you
The mighty labour dauntless I pursue;
What crowded armies, from what climes they bring,
Their names, their numbers, and their chiefs I sing.

The hardy warriors whom Boeotia bred,
Penelius, Leitus, Prothoenor, led:
With these Arcesilaus and Clonius stand,
Equal in arms, and equal in command.
These head the troops that rocky Aulis yields,
And Eteon's hills, and Hyrie's watery fields,

And Schoenos, Scholos, Graea near the main,
And Mycalessia's ample piny plain;
Those who in Peteon or Ilesion dwell,
Or Harma where Apollo's prophet fell;
Heleon and Hyle, which the springs o'erflow;
And Medeon lofty, and Ocalea low;
Or in the meads of Haliartus stray,
Or Thespia sacred to the god of day:
Onchestus, Neptune's celebrated groves;
Copae, and Thisbe, famed for silver doves;
For flocks Erythrae, Glissa for the vine;
Platea green, and Nysa the divine;
And they whom Thebe's well-built walls
    inclose,
Where Myde, Eutresis, Corone, rose;
And Arne rich, with purple harvests crown'd;
And Anthedon, Boeotia's utmost bound.
Full fifty ships they send, and each conveys
Twice sixty warriors through the foaming
    seas.

To these succeed Aspledon's martial train,
Who plough the spacious Orchomenian
    plain.
Two valiant brothers rule the undaunted
    throng,
Ialmen and Ascalaphus the strong:
Sons of Astyoche, the heavenly fair,
Whose virgin charms subdued the god
    of war:
(In Actor's court as she retired to rest,
The strength of Mars the blushing maid
    compress'd)
Their troops in thirty sable vessels sweep,
With equal oars, the hoarse-resounding
    deep.

The Phocians next in forty barks repair;
Epistrophus and Schedius head the war:
From those rich regions where Cephisus
    leads
His silver current through the flowery meads;
From Panopea, Chrysa the divine,
Where Anemoria's stately turrets shine,
Where Pytho, Daulis, Cyparissus stood,

And fair Lilaea views the rising flood.
These, ranged in order on the floating tide,
Close, on the left, the bold Boeotians' side.

Fierce Ajax led the Locrian squadrons on,
Ajax the less, Oileus' valiant son;
Skill'd to direct the flying dart aright;
Swift in pursuit, and active in the fight.
Him, as their chief, the chosen troops attend,
Which Bessa, Thronus, and rich Cynos send;
Opus, Calliarus, and Scarphe's bands;
And those who dwell where pleasing Augia
    stands,
And where Boagrius floats the lowly lands,
Or in fair Tarphe's sylvan seats reside:
In forty vessels cut the yielding tide.

Euboea next her martial sons prepares,
And sends the brave Abantes to the wars:
Breathing revenge, in arms they take their
    way
From Chalcis' walls, and strong Eretria;
The Istiean fields for generous vines
    renown'd,
The fair Caristos, and the Styrian ground;
Where Dios from her towers o'erlooks the
    plain,
And high Cerinthus views the neighbouring
    main.
Down their broad shoulders falls a length
    of hair;
Their hands dismiss not the long lance in air;
But with protended spears in fighting fields
Pierce the tough corslets and the brazen
    shields.
Twice twenty ships transport the warlike
    bands,
Which bold Elphenor, fierce in arms,
    commands.

Full fifty more from Athens stem the main,
Led by Menestheus through the liquid plain.
(Athens the fair, where great Erectheus sway'd,
That owed his nurture to the blue-eyed maid,
But from the teeming furrow took his birth,

Anonymous painter from the Veneto
Francesco Morosini following the Turkish Fleet as it Retreats,
April 1659, 1659-1730,
Venice, Museo Correr

The mighty offspring of the foodful earth.
Him Pallas placed amidst her wealthy fane,
Adored with sacrifice and oxen slain;
Where, as the years revolve, her altars blaze,
And all the tribes resound the goddess' praise.)
No chief like thee, Menestheus! Greece could
    yield,
To marshal armies in the dusty field,
The extended wings of battle to display,
Or close the embodied host in firm array.
Nestor alone, improved by length of days,
For martial conduct bore an equal praise.

With these appear the Salaminian bands,
Whom the gigantic Telamon commands;
In twelve black ships to Troy they steer their
    course,
And with the great Athenians join their force.

Next move to war the generous Argive train,
From high Troezene, and Maseta's plain,
And fair Ægina circled by the main:
Whom strong Tyrinthe's lofty walls surround,
And Epidaure with viny harvests crown'd:
And where fair Asinen and Hermoin show
Their cliffs above, and ample bay below.
These by the brave Euryalus were led,
Great Sthenelus, and greater Diomed;
But chief Tydides bore the sovereign sway:
In fourscore barks they plough the watery
    way.

The proud Mycene arms her martial powers,
Cleone, Corinth, with imperial towers,
Fair Araethyrea, Ornia's fruitful plain,
And Ægion, and Adrastus' ancient reign;
And those who dwell along the sandy shore,
And where Pellene yields her fleecy store,
Where Helice and Hyperesia lie,
And Gonoessa's spires salute the sky.
Great Agamemnon rules the numerous band,
A hundred vessels in long order stand,
And crowded nations wait his dread
    command.

High on the deck the king of men appears,
And his refulgent arms in triumph wears;
Proud of his host, unrivall'd in his reign,
In silent pomp he moves along the main.

His brother follows, and to vengeance warms
The hardy Spartans, exercised in arms:
Phares and Brysia's valiant troops, and those
Whom Lacedaemon's lofty hills inclose;
Or Messe's towers for silver doves renown'd,
Amyclae, Laas, Augia's happy ground,
And those whom Œtylos' low walls contain,
And Helos, on the margin of the main:
These, o'er the bending ocean, Helen's cause,
In sixty ships with Menelaus draws:
Eager and loud from man to man he flies,
Revenge and fury flaming in his eyes;
While vainly fond, in fancy oft he hears
The fair one's grief, and sees her falling tears.

In ninety sail, from Pylos' sandy coast,
Nestor the sage conducts his chosen host:
From Amphigenia's ever-fruitful land,
Where Æpy high, and little Pteleon stand;
Where beauteous Arene her structures
    shows,
And Thryon's walls Alpheus' streams inclose:
And Dorion, famed for Thamyris' disgrace,
Superior once of all the tuneful race,
Till, vain of mortals' empty praise, he strove
To match the seed of cloud-compelling Jove!
Too daring bard! whose unsuccessful pride
The immortal Muses in their art defied.
The avenging Muses of the light of day
Deprived his eyes, and snatch'd his voice
    away;
No more his heavenly voice was heard to
    sing,
His hand no more awaked the silver string.

Where under high Cyllene, crown'd with
    wood,
The shaded tomb of old Æpytus stood;
From Ripe, Stratie, Tegea's bordering towns,

The Phenean fields, and Orchomenian downs,
Where the fat herds in plenteous pasture
  rove;
And Stymphelus with her surrounding grove;
Parrhasia, on her snowy cliffs reclined,
And high Enispe shook by wintry wind,
And fair Mantinea's ever-pleasing site;
In sixty sail the Arcadian bands unite.
Bold Agapenor, glorious at their head,
(Ancaeus' son) the mighty squadron led.
Their ships, supplied by Agamemnon's care,
Through roaring seas the wondering warriors
  bear;
The first to battle on the appointed plain,
But new to all the dangers of the main.

Those, where fair Elis and Buprasium join;
Whom Hyrmin, here, and Myrsinus confine,
And bounded there, where o'er the valleys
  rose
The Olenian rock; and where Alisium flows;
Beneath four chiefs (a numerous army)
  came:

The strength and glory of the Epean name.
In separate squadrons these their train
  divide,
Each leads ten vessels through the yielding
  tide.
One was Amphimachus, and Thalpius one;
(Eurytus' this, and that Teatus' son;)
Diores sprung from Amarynceus' line;
And great Polyxenus, of force divine.

But those who view fair Elis o'er the seas
From the blest islands of the Echinades,
In forty vessels under Meges move,
Begot by Phyleus, the beloved of Jove:
To strong Dulichium from his sire he fled,
And thence to Troy his hardy warriors led.

The Portonaccio Sarcophagus
**180-190 A.D.,
Rome, Museo Nazionale Romano, Palazzo Massimo**

Ulysses follow'd through the watery road,
A chief, in wisdom equal to a god.
With those whom Cephalenia's line inclosed,
Or till their fields along the coast opposed;
Or where fair Ithaca o'erlooks the floods,
Where high Neritos shakes his waving woods,
Where Ægilipa's rugged sides are seen,
Crocylia rocky, and Zacynthus green.
These in twelve galleys with vermilion prores,
Beneath his conduct sought the Phrygian
    shores.

Thoas came next, Andraemon's valiant son,
From Pleuron's walls, and chalky Calydon,
And rough Pylene, and the Olenian steep,
And Chalcis, beaten by the rolling deep.
He led the warriors from the Ætolian shore,
For now the sons of Œneus were no more!
The glories of the mighty race were fled!
Œneus himself, and Meleager dead!
To Thoas' care now trust the martial train,
His forty vessels follow through the main. [...]

Alexander Fights a Pack of Unicorns
illustration from *Le livre des conquestes et faits d'Alexandre*,
fol. 260*r*, 15th century,
Paris, Musée du Petit-Palais

Andrea Vicentino (Andrea Michieli)
The Battle of Lepanto, 1595-1605,
Venice, Palazzo Ducale

3. THE VISUAL LIST

It is no accident if Homer, to talk to us about a form, chose the example of a visual work of art (albeit one recounted in words with the rhetorical technique known as hypotyposis), whereas when he had recourse to the list he did this with words and it did not cross his mind to recount a visual list verbally.

This is no small problem, especially if we think that we are talking—as we are in this book—about *verbal* lists and commenting on them through *images*. The fact is that an image in sculpture is defined in space (it is hard to imagine a statue that conveys an "etcetera", i.e., one that suggests it may continue beyond its own physical limits), while in paintings the image is limited by the frame.

As we have said, even the Mona Lisa is portrayed against the background of a landscape that could obviously continue beyond the frame, but no one wonders about how far the wood or forest behind her may extend, and no one thinks that Leonardo wished to suggest that it extended to infinity. Nonetheless, there are other figurative works that make us think that what we see within the frame is not all, but only an example of a totality whose number is hard to calculate, at least as much as Homer's warriors were.

page 36: Hieronymus Bosch
The Garden of Earthly Delights,
detail of right-hand panel, c. 1500,
Madrid, Museo del Prado

page 37: Hieronymus Bosch
The Garden of Earthly Delights,
detail of middle panel, c. 1500,
Madrid, Museo del Prado

Leonardo da Vinci
Portrait of the Mona Lisa
(*La Gioconda*), 1503-1506,
Paris, Musée du Louvre

page 39: Giovanni Paolo Pannini
Picture Gallery with Views of Ancient Rome, 1759,
Paris, Musée du Louvre

Think of Pannini's "picture galleries": they are not intended to represent merely what is shown but also the rest of the (indefinitely large) collection of which they are only an example. Think of Bosch's "The Garden of Earthly Delights": it suggests that the marvels it hints at should continue beyond the limits of the picture. The same holds for Carpaccio's "The Crucifixion and the Apotheosis of the Ten Thousand Martyrs on Mount Ararat" or Pontormo's "Eleven Thousand Martyrs". Evidently, the crucified portrayed are not ten thousand and the torturers are many more than those shown, but it is clear that the paintings are intended to describe a series of dying bodies that continues beyond the boundaries of the canvas, and it seems as if the pictures are intended to express their own incapacity to name them (or in other words to show them) all.

The same thing happens with many pictorial representations of battles and armies lined up, still according to the Homeric model, or with other disturbing quotations of measureless hosts.

Vittore Carpaccio
Crucifixion and the Apotheosis of the Ten Thousand
Martyrs on Mount Ararat, 1515,
Venice, Gallerie dell'Accademia

Albrecht Dürer
The Martyrdom of the Ten Thousand Christians, 1508,
Vienna, Kunsthistorisches Museum,
Gemäldegalerie

Palma il Giovane (Jacopo Negretti)
The Taking of Constantinople, c. 1587,
Venice, Palazzo Ducale

Vincenzo Campi
Still Life with Fruit, c. 1590,
Milan, Pinacoteca di Brera

Frans Snyders (school of)
The Fish Market, 1616-1621,
Paris, Musée du Louvre

Many Dutch still lifes that portray fruits, meats or fish are apparently composed as a form per se, not only because of the fact that they are delimited by a frame but because they are usually piled up in the centre; but so clear is the intention to attain an effect of abundance, of the ineffability of variety suggested, that we can number them among examples of visual lists. And there is an allusion to lists, albeit well composed, in the Dutch still lifes known as "Vanities", which mix up objects apparently devoid of any reciprocal relationship, but which stand for all that is perishable, and invite us to think of the transience of worldly goods.

Other examples of characters swarming beyond the boundaries of the canvas or the fresco can be said to include the "Last Judgement" in the Sistine Chapel or in Cousin's "Judgement".

Pieter Aertsen
Vanitas (Still Life), 1552,
Vienna, Kunsthistorisches Museum, Gemäldegalerie

Vincent Laurensz van de Vinne
Vanitas with a Royal Crown, after 1649,
Paris, Musée du Louvre

DENCKT
OP T'ENT

Chan Verkoven

In principle the list can be found in other art forms: Ravel's "Bolero" with its obsessive rhythms suggests that it could continue infinitely and it is no accident that an artist such as Rybczynski drew inspiration from it for a film in which certain characters (which he chose from the leading figures of the Russian Revolution, but from a formal standpoint nothing would change were they angels ascending to the seventh heaven) move up a stairway that is potentially endless.

Jean Cousin the Younger
The Last Judgment, c. 1585,
Paris, Musée du Louvre

Zbig Rybczynski
The Orchestra, 1990

4.   THE INEFFABLE[1]

With his catalogue of ships Homer does not merely give us a splendid example of the list, all the more effective the more it is contrasted with the form of the shield: he also brings on what has been called the "topos of ineffability". Faced with something that is immensely large, or unknown, of which we still do not know enough or of which we shall never know, the author tells us he is unable to say, and so he proposes a list very often as a specimen, example, or indication, leaving the reader to imagine the rest.

The topos of ineffability recurs several times in Homer (for example in Book IV of the *Odyssey*, 273 ff: "I certainly cannot tell, one by one, of all the deeds of the tenacious Ulysses …", not to mention the list of the dead that Ulysses meets in Hades in Book XI of the *Odyssey*, a model also used by **Virgil** for Aeneas' journey to the underworld (*Aeneid* VI, 264 ff.)

We might continue almost ad infinitum (and it would be a fine list) citing occurrences of the topos of ineffability in the history of literature, from Hesiod to Pindar or Thyrteus, before moving on to Latin literature and Virgil, who in his *Georgics* (II, 157), in order to talk of the impossibility of listing all grapes and wines, says: "But lo! how many kinds, and what their names / There is no telling, nor doth it boot to tell;/ Who lists to know it, he too would list to learn/ How many sand-grains are by Zephyr tossed / On Libya's plain (…) / Or how many waves / Come rolling shoreward from the Ionian sea", only to end with Saint John of the Apocalypse: "After this I saw a great multitude, which no man could number, of all nations, and tribes, and peoples, and tongues" (*Apocalypse* 7.9).

Correggio (Antonio Allegri)
Assumption of the Virgin (detail), 1526-1530,
Parma, Cupola del Duomo

In his *Ars Amandi* (I, 435) Ovid warns, with regard to the sacrilegious arts of women: "I could not name all those sacrilegious and meretricious arts, even had I ten mouths and as many tongues", and in Book II 149-152 he says that citing all women's outfits would be like counting the acorns on the oak tree or the wild beasts on the Alps. And in *Metamorphosis* (XV, 419-421) he complains about the impossibility of mentioning all the metamorphoses—but after all what else did he do for fifteen books and twelve thousand verses but list 246 metamorphoses?

Just as Homer was unable to name all the Argive warriors, in the same way, and indeed even more so, **Dante** was unable to name all the angels in the heavens because he did not know so much the names but the number. And so in Canto XXIX of *Paradise* we find another example of the topos of ineffability, because the number of angels exceeds the possibilities of the human mind.[2]

But Dante, faced with the ineffable, does not fall back on the list insofar as he tries to express the ecstasy of it; and still on the subject of the number of angels, when he yields to the dizzying fascination of geometrical progression, he alludes to the legend according to which the inventor of chess had asked the King of Persia, by way of a reward for his invention, for one grain of wheat for the first square on the board, two for the second, four for the third and so on until the sixty-fourth, thus reaching an astronomical number of grains: "In number did outmillion the account / Reduplicate upon the chequer'd board." (*Paradise* XXVIII. 91-93).

Yet there is a difference between complaining about not having enough tongues and mouths with which to say something (and then refrain from saying it, while trying variations on the topos of ineffability, even in the sublimely original way Dante does this), and attempting a list in some way, albeit incomplete and by way of a sample, as Homer and Virgil did, or as **Ausonius** did with his list of fishes in *La Mosella*.

Some have observed how the topos of lacking tongues or mouths is typical of oral poetry, and so the Homeric bard needed a lot of puff to recite at a steady rhythm the list of ships (as well as a good memory to recall all the names of Hesiod's mythological characters), but this topos is also found in periods where texts circulated in written form

(just for example, see Cecco Angiolieri's sonnet 103 "If I had a thousand tongues in my mouth") and at a certain point it was perceived as so threadbare that it was employed ironically by Boiardo and later by Ariosto who, in *Orlando Furioso*, mentions lovers who took great pleasure from the fact that "they often had more than one tongue in their mouths".

1. Cf. on this topic Giuseppe Ledda and his still unpublished essay "Elenchi impossibili: cataloghi e topos dell'indicibilità". The author had already dealt with this argument in published works such as *La Guerra della lingua. Ineffabilità, retorica e narrativa nella Commedia di Dante* (Ravenna, Longo, 2002) especially pp. 42–45; 195–200; 297–298, and in the article "Dante e la tradizione delle visioni medievali", in *Letture Classensi*, 37 (2007), pp. 119–142.

2. The list of the names of angels, both benevolent and malevolent, which appears in the anthology, is taken from the Scriptures, the apocryphal Gospels, the cabalistic tradition, the Muslim tradition, the Books of Enoch, the texts of the Sabians of Harran, and from the *Steganographia* of Trithemius (1621). The list of the devils is taken from the *Legemeton Clavicula Salomonis* (1641), from *Pseudomonarchia daemonum* by Johann Weyer (1515–1588), which appeared in the appendices of various editions of his *De Praestigiis daemonum* (1563), from Collin de Plancy's *Dictionnaire infernal* (1812) and from other texts on demonology.

VIRGIL (70-19 B.C.)
THE ÆNEID OF VIRGIL,
FROM BOOK VI, VV. 264-301

[...] Ye gods! who rule the spirits of the dead!
Ye voiceless shades and silent lands of night!
O Phlegethon! O Chaos! Let my song,
If it be lawful, in fit words declare
What I have heard; and by your help divine
Unfold what hidden things enshrouded lie
In that dark underworld of sightless gloom.

They walked exploring the unpeopled night,
Through Pluto's vacuous realms, and regions
    void,
As when one's path in dreary woodlands
    winds
Beneath a misty moon's deceiving ray,
When Jove has mantled all his heaven in
    shade,
And night seals up the beauty of the world.
In the first courts and entrances of Hell
Sorrows and vengeful Cares on couches lie:
There sad Old Age abides, Diseases pale,
And Fear, and Hunger, temptress to all crime;
Want, base and vile, and, two dread shapes
    to see,
Bondage and Death: then Sleep, Death's next
    of kin;
And dreams of guilty joy. Death-dealing War
Is ever at the doors, and hard thereby

The Furies' beds of steel, where wild-eyed
    Strife
Her snaky hair with blood-stained fillet binds.
There in the middle court a shadowy elm
Its ancient branches spreads, and in its
    leaves
Deluding visions ever haunt and cling.
Then come strange prodigies of bestial kind:
Centaurs are stabled there, and double
    shapes
Like Scylla, or the dragon Lerna bred,
With hideous scream; Briareus clutching far
His hundred hands, Chimaera girt with flame,
A crowd of Gorgons, Harpies of foul wing,
And giant Geryon's triple-monstered shade.
Æneas, shuddering with sudden fear,
Drew sword and fronted them with naked
    steel;
And, save his sage conductress bade him
    know
These were but shapes and shadows
    sweeping by,
His stroke had cloven in vain the vacant air.
Hence the way leads to that Tartarean stream
Of Acheron, whose torrent fierce and foul
Disgorges in Cocytus all its sands.
A ferryman of gruesome guise keeps ward
Upon these waters—Charon, foully garbed,
With unkempt, thick gray beard upon his
    chin,
And staring eyes of flame [...]

page 51: Filippo Lippi
Coronation of the Virgin (detail), 1441-1447,
Florence, Galleria degli Uffizi

pages 52-53: Jan Bruegel the Elder
Aeneas and the Sibyl in the Underworld, 1600,
Vienna, Kunsthistorisches Museum
Gemäldegalerie

DANTE ALIGHIERI (1265-1321)
THE DIVINE COMEDY, FROM PARADISE, CANTO XXIX, VV. 126-145

But since we have digressed abundantly,
Turn back thine eyes forthwith to the right
  path,
So that the way be shortened with the time.

This nature doth so multiply itself
In numbers, that there never yet was speech
Nor mortal fancy that can go so far.

And if thou notest that which is revealed
By Daniel, thou wilt see that in his thousands
Number determinate is kept concealed.

The primal light, that all irradiates it,
By modes as many is received therein,
As are the splendours wherewith it is mated.

Hence, inasmuch as on the act conceptive
The affection followeth, of love the
  sweetness
Therein diversely fervid is or tepid.

The height behold now and the amplitude
Of the eternal power, since it hath made
Itself so many mirrors, where 'tis broken,

One in itself remaining as before.

DECIMUS MAGNUS AUSONIUS (310-395)
THE MOSELLA, VV. 75-151

The slippery shoals of fishes at play among themselves tire the attentive eyes with their continual maze. But how many species there are swimming in slanting paths, and what armies of them pass up the stream, their names, and the number of the children of this great race, I must not say: he to whom fell the care of the second lot and the guardianship of the sea-trident does not allow it.
O Naiad, dweller of the river-banks, describe to me the hosts of the scaly tribes, speak to me of these hordes of fishes swimming in the liquid bed of the blue river.
The scaly bullhead shines in the grass-covered sand; its flesh is very tender, and is closely set with bones; it will not keep for more than six hours for the table. Then there is the trout, whose back is starred with purple spots; the loach, which has no pointed spine to harm with, and the light grayling, baffling the eyes with its swift passage. And you, O barbel, after being tossed in the narrow mouths of the crooked Saravus (Saar), where its six branches chafe against the rocky piles of a bridge, when you slipped into the more famous river, you were freer and enjoyed a wide range for your wanderings. You taste better in your worst years; and it falls to you of all breathing creatures to be praised in age. Not must I pass you over, O salmon, whose flesh gleams scarlet: the sudden lashes of your broad tail are borne up in ripples from the bottom to the surface of the stream, and your hidden strokes are betrayed in the calm waters. Your breast is clad in an armour of scales; your head is smooth; and you are a fit dish for feasts where choice is difficult; you will bear a long wait without going bad; the spots on your head mark you out; and your prodigious belly shakes and quivers with the weight of your fat sides. And you who, in Illyria, in the waters of the double-named Hister (Danube), are caught

by your track of floating foam, O burbot, you visit our river, so that the wide Mosella may not be defrauded of such a far-famed guest. With what colours has nature painted you! Black spots cover the upper part of your back, each surrounded by a yellow half-circle; your slippery body is dyed a dark blue colour: up to the middle, you are fat; thence to the end of your tail, you have a dry, rough skin. Nor shall I be silent about you, O perch, delight of the table, fresh-water fish worthy of the sea-fish, alone fit to compare with the red mullet; for you are not insipid to the taste; the parts of your firm body are in united segments separated by bones. This fish, too, with the laughable Latin name, the *Lucius* (pike), the pond-dweller and violent enemy of the plaintive frogs, haunts the pools dark with sedge. Never chosen for table use, it is boiled in smoky cookshops that reek with its fetid steam. Who does not know the green tench, the comfort of the vulgar, and the bleak, the prey of children's hooks, and the shad, that hisses on the fire, a favourite dish of the people? And you who of two species are neither and both, who are not yet salmon and no longer trout, and who, holding the place between the two, O salmon-trout, are caught at an intermediate

age? You also must be mentioned among the river-armies, O gudgeon, who are no larger than two thumbless hands, but very fat and round, and bigger with your egg-laden belly. O gudgeon, you have counterfeited the hanging beard of the barbel. You, now, shall be celebrated, great silurus, sea animal: your body seems smeared with Attic oil; I think of you as the dolphin of the river: so grandly do you glide through the water, and, in the shallows or the river's weeds, you move with difficulty and weariness the curves of your long body. But when you urge your quiet way in the stream, the green banks, the blue crowd of fishes, the clear waters wonder at you: the surging waters swell in their bed, and the last waves lap at the river's edge. So in the deep Atlantic the whale is sometimes driven by the wind or its own motion towards the shore; the sea is thrust aside, great waves rise up, and the neighbouring hills fear to seem smaller because of them. But this gentle whale of our Mosella, far from bringing ruin, adds but the more honour to the river.

But we have looked long enough at the waterways and the gliding shoals of fishes; we have counted their many bands long enough.

Marine Fauna
mosaic from Pompeii, c. 40-62 A.D.,
Naples, Museo Archeologico Nazionale

Roelant Savery
Paradise, 1626,
Berlin, Staatliche Museen zu Berlin
Gemäldegalerie

Angels

Abdizuel, Abriel, Adan, Adnachiel, Adonael,
Adriel, Ahayah, Aihel, Akaiah, Akibeel, Aladiah,
Aleasy, Alheniel, Aliel, Almadiel, Almesiel,
Almoel, Alsuel, Althor, Ambriel, Amezarak,
Amixiel, Amutiel, Anani, Anauel, Aniel, Ansoel,
Arael, Arafos, Arayl, Arazeyal, Ardefiel, Arepach,
Aridiel, Ariel, Arioch, Arisiel, Armany, Armaros,
Armers, Arnibiel, Arseyaleyor, Artinc, Asael,
Asaliah, Asbibiel, Asmodel, Asoriel, Asphor,
Asradel, Asuriel, Aumel, Azariel, Azazel,
Azeruel, Aziel, Azimel, Azra'il, Baoxas,
Baradiel, Baraqal, Baraquel, Barbiel, Barchiel,
Barfos, Barinael, Basiel, Batraal, Bedarys,
Befranzij, Belsay, Benoham, Bethnael, Binael,
Bitael, Budarym, Bufiel, Bulis, Burfa, Burisiel,
Busiel, Cabarym, Cabron, Cahetel, Caliel,
Camael, Camor, Camory, Capriel, Carasiba,
Carba, Carman, Carniel, Carnol, Carsiel, Cartael,
Casbriel, Cassiel, Cazul, Cesael, Chairum,
Chalkatura, Chariel, Charuth, Chasor, Chavaquiah,
Chomiel, Choriel, Chubor, Churibal, Clyssan,
Cugiel, Culmar, Cumeriel, Cuphar, Cupriel,
Curiel, Curifas, Dabrynos, Damabiah, Danael,
Daniel, Darbori, Decaniel, Dirachiel, Diuiel,
Dorael, Doriel, Dromiel, Drubiel, Druchas,
Drusiel, Dubiel, Dubilon, Duth, Efiel, Egibiel,
Elamyz, Elemiah, Elitel, Emuel, Enediel,
Ergediel, Ervihel, Etymel, Eyael, Ezeqeel,
Fadahel, Fanuel, Fariel, Femol, Fubiel, Futiel,
Gabriel, Galgaliel, Gamsiel, Gariel, Garrubiel,
Geliel, Geniel, Geremiel, Geriel, Gerthiel,
Godiel, Grafathas, Gudiel, Haamiah, Habuhiah,
Hahasiah, Haheuiah, Haiayel, Hamabiel,
Hamael, Hamarytz, Hanael, Harael, Haraqiel,
Hardiel, Hariel, Harut, Hayuiah, Haziel,
Hehahel, Hekamiah, Herachiel, Hesediel,
Hobrazym, Iachoroz, Iahhel, Ianiel, Iaoth,
Iastrion, Iatroziel, Iax, Ieiazel, Iezalel, Imamiah,
Ingethel, Irmanotz, Isbal, Israfil, Jabamiah,
Jazeriel, Jehudiel, Jeliel, Jibril, Jophiel,

Kamael, Karael, Kerkutha, Kjriel, Kobabel,
Kokbiel, Ladiel, Ladrotz, Lamael, Lamas,
Lamersy, Laphor, Larfos, Larmol, Lauviah,
Laylahel, Lazaba, Lecabel, Lehachiah, Lelahel,
Lomor, Luziel, Mador, Mafayr, Mahasiah,
Malchidael, Malik, Manakel, Manediel, Maniel,
Marae, Maras, Marianu, Marioch, Maruth,
Matariel, Mebahel, Mebahiah, Mechiel, Medar,
Melahel, Melanas, Melioth, Menadel, Menador,
Merach, Mermeoth, Merosiel, Metatron,
Michael, Mitzrael, Molael, Monael, Moniel,
Morael, Morias, Mugael, Mumiah, Munkar,
Murahe, Muriel, Musiriel, Myresyn, Nachiel,
Nakir, Nalael, Nanael, Narzael, Nastros,
Nathaniel, Nautha, Neciel, Nedriel, Nefonos,
Nefrias, Nelchael, Nemamiah, Nithael,
Nithaiah, Oeniel, Oertha, Ofaniel, Ofisiel,
Omael, Onomataht, Orouel, Orym, Ossidiel,
Otiel, Pafiel, Pandiel, Pandor, Paniel, Paras,
Parius, Pathyr, Peniel, Pharol, Phounebiel,
Poyel, Quibda, Raamiel, Raaziel, Raguel,
Rahel, Raiouoth, Ramuel, Rapsiel,
Rarideris, Rasuil, Rathiel, Rehael, Reiyel,
Remiel, Remihel, Requiel, Reuel, Richel,
Ridwan, Rizoel, Rochel, Rouiel, Rufiyael,
Ruthiel, Sabael, Sachiel, Saddiel, Sahaiah,
Salgiel, Samael, Sams, Samsaweel, Samziel,
Sandalphon, Sarach, Saraguel, Sardiel, Sariel,
Sartael, Saruiel, Satanael, Satifiel, Scaltiel,
Sebach, Sehaliah, Seheliel, Semeil,
Semeyaza, Sitael, Sobiel, Soriel, Souiel,
Suraquyal, Suriel, Syliael, Tagriel, Takiel,
Tamiel, Taros, Temel, Thalbos, Thariel,
Themaz, Thurcal, Turel, Tzaphkiel,
Umabel, Urakibaramel, Uriel, Ursiel,
Vadriel, Vadros, Vasariah, Vauliah, Vehuel,
Vehuiah, Verchiel, Vereveil, Veuliah, Xanoryz,
Xanthir, Yecabel, Yehuiah, Yeialel, Yeiayel,
Yelahiah, Yeratel, Yomyael, Zaafiel, Zaameel,
Zadkiel, Zamael, Zaphkiel, Zaqebe, Zawael,
Zerael, Zeruel, Zetachiel, Ziquiel, Zoeniel,
Zuriel, Zutiel, Zymeloz.

Gustave Doré
The Angels in the Planet Mercury:
Beatrice Ascends with Dante to the Planet Mercury, c. 1868,
from Dante Alighieri, *Divine Comédie, Paradis,* Paris 1868

Deumus.

Demons

Aamon, Abigor, Abracace, Adramelech,
Agares, Aguare, Aivion, Alastorr, Alloces,
Amduscias, Amon, Amy, Aarazel, Andras,
Andras, Arioch, Andrealphus, Andromalius,
Asmoday, Astaroth, Aubras, Azazel,
Baalzefon, Bael, Baelbalan, Balam, Barbato,
Bathym, Beleth, Belfagor, Belial, Belzebú,
Beret, Berith, Biemot, Bifrons, Bitru, Botis,
Buer, Bune, Byleth, Caacrinolaas,
Caassimolar, Calì, Carabia, Caym, Cerberos,
Chax, Cimeries, Dantalion, Decarabia,
Eyrevr, Flauros, Focalor, Foraii, Forcas,
Forneus, Furfur, Furinomius, Gaap, Gamygyn,
Gemory, Glasya, Gusoyn, Haagenti,
Haborym, Halphas, Ipes, Ipos, Labolas,
Leonardo, Leraye, Lucifer, Malaphar,
Malèhas, Malfa, Malphas, Marbas, Marchocias,
Marcocia, Melchom, Micales, Moloch,
Morax, Murmur, Naberius, Nibba, Nicliar,
Orias, Orobas, Ose, Otis, Paimon, Phoenix,
Picollus, Procel, Prufla, Purson, Rahouart,
Raum, Ronove, Ronwe, Sabnach, Saleos,
Satanas, Scox, Seere, Separ, Shax, Sitri,
Stola, Svcax, Tap, Ukobach, Valac,
Vapula, Vassago, Vepar, Vine, Volac, Vual,
Wall, Xafan, Zagam, Zaleos, Zebos, Zepar.

Diabolical Figures
from J. Collin de Plancy,
Dictionnaire Infernal,
Paris, Plon, 1863

Gustave Doré
The Fall of the Rebel Angels,
from John Milton's, *Paradise Lost,*
Paris 1867

Tintoretto (Jacopo Robusti)
The Assumption of the Virgin (Paradise), c. 1580,
Paris, Musée du Louvre

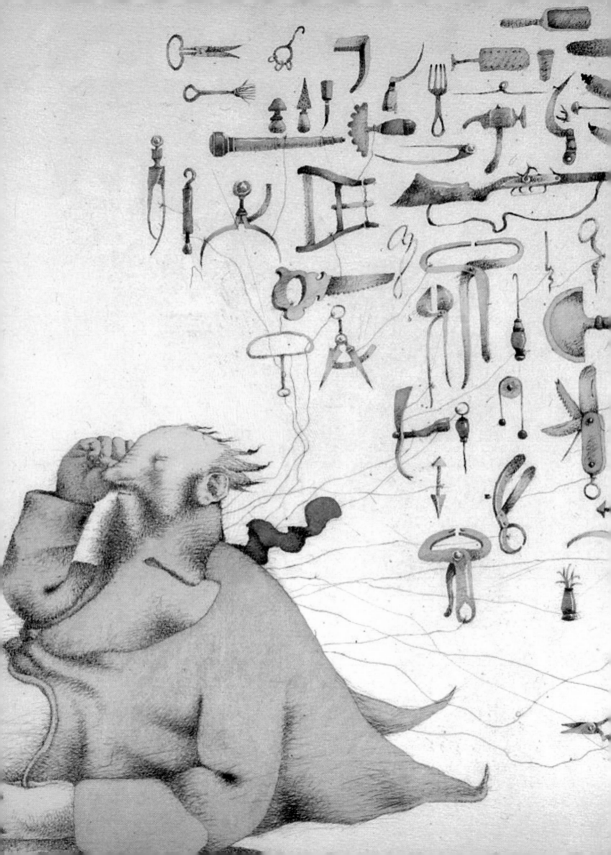

5.   LISTS OF THINGS

The fear of being unable to say everything seizes us not only when we are faced with an infinity of names but also with an infinity of things. The history of literature is full of obsessive collections of objects. Sometimes these are fantastic, such as the things (as **Ariosto** tells us) found on the moon by Astolfo, who had gone there to get back Orlando's brain; sometimes they are disturbing, such as the list of malign substances used by the witches in **Shakespeare**'s *Macbeth*; sometimes they are ecstasies of perfumes, such as the collection of flowers that **Marino** describes in his *Adonis*; sometimes they are poor and essential, such as the collection of flotsam that enables Robinson Crusoe to survive on his island, or the poor little treasure that **Mark Twain** tells us Tom Sawyer put together; sometimes they are dizzyingly normal, such as the huge collection of insignificant objects in the drawer of Leopold Bloom's kitchen table in **Joyce**'s *Ulysses* (which for various reasons will be found in the anthology in the chapter on *chaotic enumeration*), sometimes they are poignant, despite a museal, almost funereal immobility, such as the collection of musical instruments described by **Mann** in *Doctor Faustus*.

Sometimes things are simply smells, or stinks, as in the city described by **Süskind**.

Tullio Pericoli
Robinson e gli attrezzi ("Robinson and the Tools", detail), 1984

LUDOVICO ARIOSTO
ORLANDO FURIOSO
FROM CANTO XXXIV, VERSES 72-86
(1532)

Here other river, lake, and rich champaign
Are seen, than those which are below
    descried;
Here other valley, other hill and plain,
With towns and cities of their own supplied;
Which mansions of such mighty size contain,
Such never he before of after spied.
Here spacious hold and lonely forest lay,
Where nymphs for ever chased the panting
    prey.

He, that with other scope had thither soared,
Pauses not all these wonder to peruse:
But led by the disciple of our Lord,
His way towards a spacious vale pursues;
A place wherein is wonderfully stored
Whatever on our earth below we lose.
Collected there are all things whatsoe'er,
Lost through time, chance, or our own folly,
    here.

Nor here alone of realm and wealthy dower,
O'er which aye turns the restless wheel, I say:
I speak of what it is not in the power
Of Fortune to bestow, or take away.
Much fame is here, whereon Time and the Hour,
Like wasting moth, in this our planet prey.
Here countless vows, here prayers
    unnumbered lie,
Made by us sinful men to God on high:

The lover's tears and sighs; what time in
    pleasure
And play we here unprofitably spend;
To this, of ignorant men the eternal leisure,
And vain designs, aye frustrate of their end.
Empty desires so far exceed all measure,
They o'er that valley's better part extend.
There wilt thou find, if thou wilt thither post,
Whatever thou on earth beneath hast lost.
He, passing by those heaps, on either hand,
Of this and now of that the meaning sought;
Formed of swollen bladders here a hill did
    stand,

Whence he heard cries and tumults, as he
    thought.
These were old crowns of the Assyrian land
And Lydian—as that paladin was taught—
Grecian and Persian, all of ancient fame;
And now, alas! well-nigh without a name.

Golden and silver hooks to sight succeed,
Heaped in a mass, the gifts which courtiers
    bear,
—Hoping thereby to purchase future meed—
To greedy prince and patron; many a snare,
Concealed in garlands, did the warrior heed,
Who heard, these signs of adulation were;
And in cicalas, which their lungs had burst,
Saw fulsome lays by venal poets versed.

Loves of unhappy end in imagery
Of gold or jewelled bands he saw exprest;
Then eagles' talons, the authority
With which great lords their delegates invest:
Bellows filled every nook, the fume and fee
Wherein the favourites of kings are blest:
Given to those Ganymedes that have their hour,
And reft, when faded is their vernal flower.

O'erturned, here ruined town and castle lies,
With all their wealth: "The symbols" (said his
    guide)
"Of treaties and of those conspiracies,
Which their conductors seemed so ill to hide."
Serpents with female faces, felonies
Of coiners and of robbers, he descried;
Next broken bottles saw of many sorts,
The types of servitude in sorry courts.

He marks mighty pool of porridge spilled,
And asks what in that symbol should be read,
And hears 'twas charity, by sick men willed
For distribution, after they were dead.
He passed a heap of flowers, that erst distilled
Sweet savours, and now noisome odours shed;
The gift (if it may lawfully be said)
Which Constantine to good Sylvester made.

A large provision, next, of twigs and lime
—Your witcheries, O women!—he explored.
The things he witnessed, to recount in rhyme
Too tedious were; were myriads on record,

To sum the remnant ill should I have time.
'Tis here that all infirmities are stored,
Save only Madness, seen not here at all,
Which dwells below, nor leaves this earthly ball.

He turns him back, upon some days and deeds
To look again, which he had lost of yore;
But, save the interpreter the lesson reads,
Would know them not, such different form
    they wore.
He next saw that which man so little needs,
—As it appears—none pray to Heaven for more;
I speak of sense, whereof a lofty mount
Alone surpast all else which I recount.

Max Ernst
The Eye of Silence, 1943-1944,
St. Louis, Mildred Lane Kemper Art Museum, Washington
University

It was as 'twere a liquor soft and thin,
Which, save well corked, would from the
    vase have drained;
Laid up, and treasured various flasks within,
Larger or lesser, to that use ordained.
That largest was which of the paladin,
Anglantes' lord, the mighty sense contained;
And from those others was discerned, since
    writ
Upon the vessel was ORLANDO'S WIT.

The names of those whose wits therein were
    pent
He thus on all those other flasks espied.
Much of his own, but with more wonderment,
The sense of many others he descried,
Who, he believed, no dram of theirs had
    spent;

But here, by tokens clear was satisfied,
That scantily therewith were they purveyed;
So large the quantity he here surveyed.

Some waste on love, some seeking honour, lose
Their wits, some, scowering seas, for merchandise,
Some, that on wealthy lords their hope repose,
And some, befooled by silly sorceries;
These upon pictures, upon jewels those;
These on whatever else they highest prize.
Astrologers' and sophists' wits mid these,
And many a poet's too, Astolpho sees.

Since his consent the apostle signified
Who wrote the obscure Apocalypse, his own
He took, and only to his nose applied,
When (it appeared) it to its place was gone;
And henceforth, has Sir Turpin certified,
That long time sagely lived king Otho's son;
Till other error (as he says) again
Deprived the gentle baron of his brain.

WILLIAM SHAKESPEARE
MACBETH, ACT IV, SCENE 1 (1606)

Enter the three Witches.

First Witch. Thrice the brinded cat hath mew'd.

Second Witch. Thrice and once the hedge-pig
    whined.

Third Witch. Harpier cries, —'Tis time, 'tis time.

First Witch. Round about the cauldron go:
In the poison'd entrails throw.
Toad, that under cold stone
Days and nights has thirty one
Swelter'd venom sleeping got,
Boil thou first i' the charmed pot.

All. Double, double, toil and trouble;
Fire burn and cauldron bubble.

Second Witch. Fillet of a fenny snake,
In the cauldron boil and bake;
Eye of newt and toe of frog,
Wool of bat and tongue of dog,

Adder's fork and blind-worm's sting,
Lizard's leg and howlet's wing,
For a charm of powerful trouble,
Like a hell-broth boil and bubble.

All. Double, double, toil and trouble;
Fire burn and cauldron bubble.

Third Witch. Scale of dragon, tooth of wolf,
Witch's mummy, maw and gulf
Of the ravin'd salt-sea shark,
Root of hemlock digg'd i' the dark,
Liver of blaspheming Jew,
Gall of goat and slips of yew
Sliver'd in the moon's eclipse,
Nose of Turk and Tartar's lips,
Finger of birth-strangled babe
Ditch-deliver'd by a drab,
Make the gruel thick and slab:
Add thereto a tiger's chaudron,
For the ingredients of our cauldron.

All. Double, double, toil and trouble;
Fire burn and cauldron bubble.

Alberto Savinio
La città delle promesse ("The City of Promises"), 1928,
Paris, Galerie Daniel Malingue

GIAMBATTISTA MARINO, L'ADONE, CANTO VI, "THE GARDEN OF PLEASURE," VV. 121-129, 131-135, 145-150 (1623)

Long stretches of flower-lined lanes
look out over shaded promenades
whose straight margins are a veritable
ruby mine of blossoming roses.
The panorama is dotted with flowers
gracefully and ingeniously painted,
in different forms and various colors,
with a thousand scents to dazzle the senses.
Braided wicker, latticework, and jalousies
weave about the hillsides,
dividing lawns from lanes;
their measured, well composed lines are
made in accordance with the excellent and
    skillful
direction the goddess of this ground gave
    to its fine keeper,
her footsteps treading upon that soil,
a mosaic of shining stones.
Love, with the most unusual wonders,
keeps his beloved here,
such that she may imbue these enamored plants
with absolute, impeccable perfection:
thicker leaves, and more scented petals;
when the rose unveils its beautiful conception,
white or purple or damascene,
only the flower is born, not the thorn.
The quintessence of the mellow Sabians'
    softness,
of the Indians' fruitfulness and of the Arabs'
    happiness,
the riches that come from the Hyblean Hills,
the Œbalian beaches and the foothills of Attica,
all that fosters growth in Panchean gardens,
Mount Hymettos's meadows and Mount
    Corycus's fields,
under a benign, favorable star,
Ciprigna gathered it all in these gardens.
Therein an Abyssinian cat toils, and, secluded,
leaves traces of her scent on the breeze,
and all about is a mixed odor
of perfumer's Spanish Paste and mixed berries.
Cassia, sweet marjoram, cardamom, dill,
    spiral gingers,

citronella grass, and thyme cure all heavy hearts;
habrothamnus, wild thyme, helichrysum,
Common broom shrub, watercress, and
    bluebottle.
There are red berries on the open slopes
created to send one's limbs into a panic;
there are acacias and spikenards,
that, high up, have more bunched-up
    branches;
Ethiopian Bagana plants burgeon here,
Syrian kola nut trees flourish in this ground;
the cinnamon-tree shoots up elsewhere
and the nuts of the hazel tree rain down at
    its base.
The panacea plant is among the most worthy
    sprouts
its healthy leaves can be mixed and drunk
and terebinth goes well with dittany,
from which a medicinal distillate is obtained;
Libyan rush, used by the Nabataeans,
and white calamus from India all grow here.
Who can include in this series the many
odd barbarian plants unknown to us and our
    lands?
Here the sacred, smoking incense erupts
in a pilgrim's breath of pleasant vapors;
dissolving her lazy balm in brooks of sweetwater
and precious, noble perspirations;
dripping into soft rubbers and living plants
with her viscous fluids and unwavering humours,
Myrrh, handsome Adonis's mother,
redoubles her tears now that he draws near.
[...]
In flowers—at the flower's heart—that's
    where Love is found,
they love fine privet and amaranth,
narcissus and hyacinth, crocus and Ajax,
the beautiful clivia and the broad acanthus.
The rose is afire in a vermilion glow,
its scent is a sigh, its dewdrops are the tears
    of its cry.
The buttercup laughs, and the wan, pale,
listless violet is tinged its vivid hue by love.
Even you, oh handsome Adonis, were not yet
    extinct,
had not yet changed into a new blossom.
Alas, who ever would have said that, shortly
    thence,

the lawn would be painted red, drenched in
    your very own blood?
There had been an omen, albeit confused
    and defeated,
that fate had writ such an honor in your destiny;
all your companions honored you and yielded,
bowing in homage at your feet.
There was the graceful tulip, wherein it seemed
Nature almost wanted to compete with Art;
she rimmed the leaf with a splendid gilt curl,
it was the pride of Persian brocades;
she tinged its bud a deep purple,
so intense it obscures the starry heavens of
    Arabia;
spangled by needlepoint or spun by shuttle,
there is no cloth that can compare to this.
But the lily is the most ambitious of all,
sublime king majestically rising and,
to the shame of both white and vermilion,
propelling his stem high above all others.
[...]
All this, upon Adonis's arrival, seemed to smile
and the beautiful garden was cloaked in new
    colors;
humble and reverent, all around
the treetops bowed their branches, the
    flowers rose up;
the breezes were charming, the winds flattering,
and both applauded him with adulatory
    whispers;
all were ready, all eager to greet him,
the birds were singing, the springs' waters
    murmuring.
With their deepest hearts opened up wide
every coarse sprout grew civil,
devoting to him affectionate offerings
of all their most valuable, most gentle aspects;
everywhere he turned, everywhere he set foot,
April was there to court him;
oranges and cedars and myrtles and jasmines
all emanated their noble and characteristic
    scents.
Here the noble peacock's magnificent image

Jan van Huysum
Vase of Flowers in a Niche, c. 1720-1740,
Paris, Musée du Louvre

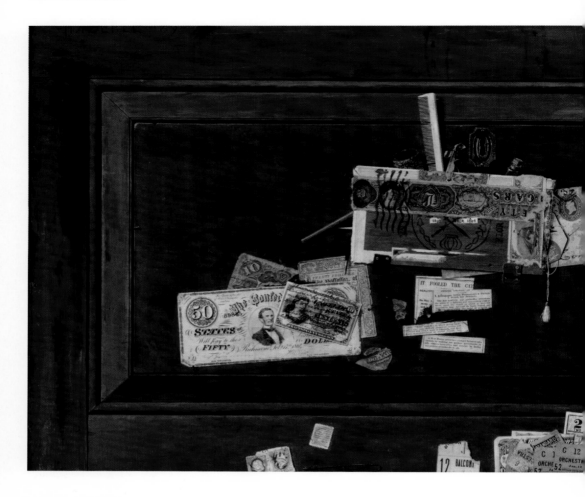

wove about through the thick, broad
    boxwoods,
and in his proud, pretty, circling tail
various flowers opened up in place of
    patterned eyes.
There the mastic shrub became the effigy
of a true, living, awe-inspiring dragon,
and the breeze, ringing 'round the myrtle,
became a whistle and inspired his spirit.
There the branching ivy, artfully made out,
ably feigned the shape of natural cup,
wherein the fallen dewdrops' liquor
carried out the office of divine nectar;
with green veils and sails here, and green
    tailors there,
it fabricated ships' rudders and galleys,

and on the stern beauteous birds sang out,
performing the explorers' exercises.
Sweet Joy and Rich Delight—
the former caresses, the latter welcomes.
Diligence raises the flowers to stand out
    upon the lawn,
Industry cradles the most graceful in her lap;
Fragrance distills the medicinal herbs,
and Kindness spreads all leaves wide;
Idolatry holds the censers in her hands,
from which Pride then exhales her vain smoke.
Then came languid, lascivious Tenderness,
delicate, manicured Decorum,
Nobility, steering shy of any stench,
Vanity, so abundantly scented,
affable, festive Gentility,

MARK TWAIN
TOM SAWYER, CHAPTER II (1876)

[Ben speaking] "Oh, shucks, I'll be just as careful. Now lemme try. Say—I'll give you the core of my apple."
[Tom Speaking] "Well, here—No, Ben, now don't. I'm afeard—"
"I'll give you *all* of it!"
Tom gave up the brush with reluctance in his face, but alacrity in his heart. And while the late steamer *Big Missouri* worked and sweated in the sun, the retired artist sat on a barrel in the shade close by, dangled his legs, munched his apple, and planned the slaughter of more innocents. There was no lack of material; boys happened along every little while; they came to jeer, but remained to whitewash. By the time Ben was fagged out, Tom had traded the next chance to Billy Fisher for a kite, in good repair; and when *he* played out, Johnny Miller bought in for a dead rat and a string to swing it with—and so on, and so on, hour after hour. And when the middle of the afternoon came, from being a poor poverty-stricken boy in the morning, Tom was literally rolling in wealth. He had besides the things before mentioned, twelve marbles, part of a jews-harp, a piece of blue bottle-glass to look through, a spool cannon, a key that wouldn't unlock anything, a fragment of chalk, a glass stopper of a decanter, a tin soldier, a couple of tadpoles, six fire-crackers, a kitten with only one eye, a brass door-knob, a dog-collar—but no dog— the handle of a knife, four pieces of orange-peel, and a dilapidated old window sash.
He had had a nice, good, idle time all the while—plenty of company—and the fence had three coats of whitewash on it! If he hadn't run out of whitewash he would have bankrupted every boy in the village.

pleasant, playful Beauty,
Ambition, swollen as a sail by the wind,
soft Luxury, and barbaric Ornament.
All these phantasms came, and, their hands
    brimming with riches,
showered Adonis's handsome visage
in splendidly scented liquids, and infused his
    veins
with vigorous lifeblood and subtle sparks.
Then, with tenacious yet tender chains,
which thousands upon thousands of flowers
    had formed,
the young man and divine diva were bound
    together
in the place where Love peacefully sleeps in
    Dignified Leisure's lap.

John Haberle
A Bachelor's Drawer, 1890-1894,
New York, Metropolitan Museum of Art

THE INFINITY OF LISTS

THOMAS MANN
DOCTOR FAUSTUS
FROM CHAPTER VII (1947)

The warerooms in the mezzanine often resounded with such rehearsals, the voices running through the octaves in the most varied colours. The whole place afforded a splendid, I might say a culturally enchanting and alluring sight, stimulating the aural imagination till it effervesced. Excepting the piano, which Adrien's foster-father gave over to that special industry, everything was here spread out: all that sounds and sings, that twangs and crashes, hums and rumbles and roars—even the keyboard instruments, in the form of the celesta, the lovely *Glockenklavier*, were always represented. There hung behind glass, or lay bedded in receptacles which like mummy cases were made in the shape

of their occupants, the charming violins, varnished some yellower and some browner, their slender bows with silver wire round the nut fixed into the lid of the case; Italian ones, the pure, beautiful shapes of which would tell the connoisseur that they came from Cremona; also Tirolese, Dutch, Saxon, Mittenwald fiddles, and some from Leverkühn's own workshop. The melodious cello, which owes its perfect form to Antonio Stradivari, was there in rows; likewise its predecessor, the six-stringed viola da gamba, in older works still honoured next to it; the viola and that other cousin of the fiddle, the viola alta, were always to be found, as well as my own viola d'amore, on whose seven strings I have all my life enjoyed performing. My instrument came from the Parochialstrasse, a present from my parents at my confirmation. There were several specimens of the violone,

76

the giant fiddle, the unwieldy double-bass, capable of majestic recitative, whose pizzicato is more sonorous than the stroke of the kettle-drum, and whose harmonics are a veiled magic of almost unbelievable quality. And there was also more than one of its opposite number among the wood-wind instruments, the contra-bassoon, sixteen-foot likewise—in other words, sounding an octave lower than the notes indicate—mightily strengthening the basses, built in twice the dimensions of its smaller brother the humorous bassoon, to which I give that name because it is a bass instrument without proper bass strength, oddly weak in sound, bleating, burlesque. How pretty it was, though, with its curved mouthpiece, shining in the decoration of its keys and levers! What a charming sight altogether, this host of shawms in their highly developed stage of technical perfection, challenging the passion of the virtuoso in all of their forms: as bucolic oboe, as *cor Anglais* well versed in tragic ways; the many-keyed clarinet, which can sound so ghostly in the deep chalumeau register but higher up can gleam in silvery blossoming harmony, as basset-horn and bass clarinet. All of these, in their velvet beds, offered themselves in Uncle Leverkühn's stock; also the transverse flute, in various systems and varied execution, made of beechwood, granadilla, or ebony, with ivory head-pieces, or else entirely of silver; next their shrill relative the piccolo, which in the orchestral tutti piercingly holds the treble, dancing in the music of the will-o'-the-wisp and the fire-magic. And now the shimmering chorus of the brasses, from the trim trumpet, visible symbol of the clear call, the sprightly song, the melting cantilena, through that darling of the romantics, the voluted valve-horn,

the slender and powerful trombone, and the cornet-à-pistons, to the weighty bass tuba. Rare museum pieces such as a pair of beautifully curved bronze lurer turned right and left, like steer-horns, were also to be found in Leverkühn's warehouse. But in a boy's eyes, as I see it again in retrospect, most gay and glorious of all was the comprehensive display of percussion instruments—just because the things that one had found under the Christmas tree, the toys and dream-possessions of childhood, now turned up in this dignified grown-up display. The side drum, how different it looked here from the ephemeral painted thing of wood, parchment, and twine we thumped on as six-year-olds! It was not meant to hang round your neck. The lower membrane was stretched with gut strings; it was screwed fast for orchestral use, in conveniently slanting position, on a metal trivet, and the wooden sticks, also much nicer than ours, stuck invitingly into rings at the sides. There was the glockenspiel; we had had a childhood version of it, on which we practised *Kommt ein Vogel geflogen*. Here, in an elegant locked case, lying in pairs on cross-bars and free to swing, were the metal plates, so meticulously tuned, with the delicate little steel hammers belonging to them and kept in the lined lid of the case. The xylophone, which seems made to conjure up a vision of a dance of skeletons—here it was with its numerous wooden bars, arranged in the chromatic scale. There was the giant studded cylinder of the bass drum, with a felt-covered stick to beat it; and the copper kettle-drum, sixteen of which Berlioz still included in his orchestra. He did not know the pedal drum as represented here, which the drummer can with his hand easily adapt to a change of key.

Jan Bruegel the Elder and Peter Paul Rubens
Allegory of Hearing (detail), 1617,
Madrid, Museo del Prado

PATRICK SÜSKIND
PERFUME, FROM CHAPTER I (1985)

In the period of which we speak, there reigned in the cities a stench barely conceivable to us modern men and women. The streets stank of manure, the courtyards of urine, the stairwells stank of moldering wood and rat droppings, the kitchens of spoiled cabbage and mutton fat; the unaired parlors stank of stale dust, the bedrooms of greasy sheets, damp featherbeds, and the pungently sweet aroma of chamber pots. The stench of sulfur rose from the chimneys, the stench of caustic lyes from the tanneries, and from the slaughterhouses came the stench of congealed blood. People stank of sweat and unwashed clothes; from their mouths came the stench of rotting teeth, from their bellies that of onions, and from their bodies, if they were no longer very young, came the stench of rancid cheese and sour milk and tumorous disease. The rivers stank, the marketplaces stank, the churches stank, it stank beneath the bridges and in the palaces. The peasant stank as did the priest, the apprentice as did his master's wife, the whole of the aristocracy stank, even the king himself stank, stank like a rank lion, and the queen like an old goat, summer and winter. For in the eighteenth century there was nothing to hinder bacteria busy at decomposition, and so there was no human activity, either constructive or destructive, no manifestation of germinating or decaying life that was not accompanied by stench.

Renato Guttuso
Study for *La Vucciria*, c. 1970-1974,
Milano, private collection

6. LISTS OF PLACES

Just as individuals and things are ineffable, the same holds also for places, and yet again the writer relies on the *etcetera* of the list. **Ezekiel** provides a list of properties to give an idea of the greatness of Tyre, **Sidonius Apollinaris** listed buildings and squares to give an idea of the beauty of Narbonne, **Dickens** took pains to show a London with places made invisible by the soot that dominated the city, **Poe** trained his visionary gaze on a series of different individuals that he perceived compactly as a "crowd", **Proust** called up the city of his childhood, **Calvino** those dreamed of by the Great Khan, **Cendrars** portrayed the panting of the train across the Siberian steppes through the memory of different places, **Whitman** (also celebrated as the poet who excelled the most—and was the most excessive—in infinitesimal lists)[1] piled places one on top of the other, starting from the island on which he was born...

Regarding the accumulation of places, in **Hugo**'s *Ninety-Three* there is a singular list of localities in the Vendée that the marquis of Lantenac communicates orally to the sailor Halmalo so he may pass through them all bearing the order for insurrection. It is obvious that poor Halmalo cannot ever remember that huge list, nor should we think that Hugo expected the reader to remember it either: the immensity of the spatial list is intended simply to suggest the immensity of the popular rebellion.

Another dizzying list of places is brought into play by **Joyce** in

Giorgio de Chirico, *Mephistopheles and the Cosmos*
set design for Arrigo Boito's opera *Mefistofele*,
Teatro alla Scala, 1952,
Milan, Museo Teatrale alla Scala

the chapter of *Finnegans Wake* called "Anna Livia Plurabelle" where, to give the sense of the flowing of the river Liffey, Joyce inserted hundreds of names of rivers in all countries, variously disguised in the form of puns or portmanteau words. It is not easy for the reader to recognize virtually unknown rivers such as the Chebb, Futt, Bann, Duck, Sabrainn, Till, Waag, Bomu, Boyana, Chu, Batha, Skollis, Shari, Sui, Tom, Chef, Syr Darya, or Ladder Burn, and so on. Since the translations are usually very free, often the reference to the river is not in the same place in which it appears in the original or, as was the case with the first attempt at an Italian translation made with the collaboration of Joyce[2] himself, there are references to Italian rivers such as the Serio, Po, Serchio, Piave, Conca, Aniene, Ombrone, Lambro, Taro, Toce, Belbo, Sillaro, Tagliamento, Lamone, Brembo, Trebbio, Mincio, Tidone and Panaro, which do not exist in the English text. The same thing happened with the first historic French translation.[2]

In the brief passage reproduced in the anthology the reader of goodwill might find, as well as the two banks of the Seine and the Kattegat, references to the rivers Tell, Cheb, Répce, Blackwater, Steeping, Heart, Sale, Dirty Devil, Battle, Dneipr, Moldau, Ganges, Sendai, King, Ilisso, Tom, Elde, Rat, Derry, Qu'appelle, Thames and Merrimack, not to mention others.

What makes this list potentially infinite does not depend only on the effort the reader must make to identify all the rivers, but by the dual suspicion that the critics have identified more rivers than those Joyce deliberately introduced or that, as a consequence of the combinatorial possibilities offered by the letters of the English alphabet, there are far more than either the critics or Joyce thought of.

It is difficult to classify this kind of list. It is a list born of voraciousness, of the topos of ineffability (it is impossible to say how many rivers there are in the world), and of a pure love of lists. It seems that Joyce toiled for years to seek out all the names of rivers, making use of the collaboration of many people, and his goal was certainly not geographical. Probably, Joyce simply did not want the list to have an end.

Jan van Kessel
Asia, panel from the series *The Four Continents*, 1664-1666,
Munich, Alte Pinakothek

pages 84-85: Hans Memling
The Passion of Christ, 1470-1471,
Turin, Galleria Sabauda

Finally, the place of places, the entire universe that Borges (in *The Aleph*) viewed only through a cavity, and saw as a list fated to be incomplete of places, people, and disquieting epiphanies.

1. See in particular the chapter devoted to him by Robert E. Belknap in *The List* (New Haven, Yale University Press, 2004).
2. *Anna Livia Plurabelle*, translated by James Joyce and Nino Frank, 1938, now in Joyce, *Scritti italiani* (Milan, Mondadori, 1979).
3. Translated by Samuel Beckett, Alfred Perron, Philippe Soupault, Paul-L. Léon, Eugène Jolas, Ivan Goll, and Adrienne Monnier, with the collaboration of Joyce.

EZEKIEL
THE KING JAMES BIBLE,
FROM EZEKIEL, 3-27

[3] [...] Thus saith the Lord GOD; O Tyrus, thou hast said, I am of perfect beauty.
[4] Thy borders are in the midst of the seas, thy builders have perfected thy beauty.
[5] They have made all thy ship boards of fir trees of Senir: they have taken cedars from Lebanon to make masts for thee.
[6] Of the oaks of Bashan have they made thine oars; the company of the Ashurites have made thy benches of ivory, brought out of the isles of Chittim.
[7] Fine linen with broidered work from Egypt was that which thou spreadest forth to be thy sail; blue and purple from the isles of Elishah was that which covered thee.
[8] The inhabitants of Zidon and Arvad were thy mariners: thy wise men, O Tyrus, that were in thee, were thy pilots.
[9] The ancients of Gebal and the wise men thereof were in thee thy calkers: all the ships of the sea with their mariners were in thee to occupy thy merchandise.
[10] They of Persia and of Lud and of Phut were in thine army, thy men of war: they hanged the shield and helmet in thee; they set forth thy comeliness.
[11] The men of Arvad with thine army were upon thy walls round about, and the Gammadims were in thy towers: they hanged their shields upon thy walls round about; they have made thy beauty perfect.
[12] Tarshish was thy merchant by reason of the multitude of all kind of riches; with silver, iron, tin, and lead, they traded in thy fairs.
[13] Javan, Tubal, and Meshech, they were thy merchants: they traded the persons of

The Fleet Sets Sail
detail of the Akrotiri fresco, Thera (Santorini),
c. 1650-1500 B.C.,
Athens, National Archeological Museum

men and vessels of brass in thy market.
[14] They of the house of Togarmah traded in thy fairs with horses and horsemen and mules.
[15] The men of Dedan were thy merchants; many isles were the merchandise of thine hand: they brought thee for a present horns of ivory and ebony.
[16] Syria was thy merchant by reason of the multitude of the wares of thy making: they occupied in thy fairs with emeralds, purple, and broidered work, and fine linen, and coral, and agate.
[17] Judah, and the land of Israel, they were thy merchants: they traded in thy market wheat of Minnith, and Pannag, and honey, and oil, and balm.
[18] Damascus was thy merchant in the multitude of the wares of thy making, for the multitude of all riches; in the wine of Helbon, and white wool.
[19] Dan also and Javan going to and fro occupied in thy fairs: bright iron, cassia, and calamus, were in thy market.
[20] Dedan was thy merchant in precious clothes for chariots.
[21] Arabia, and all the princes of Kedar, they occupied with thee in lambs, and rams, and goats: in these were they thy merchants.
[22] The merchants of Sheba and Raamah, they were thy merchants: they occupied in thy fairs with chief of all spices, and with all precious stones, and gold.
[23] Haran, and Canneh, and Eden, the merchants of Sheba, Asshur, and Chilmad, were thy merchants.
[24] These were thy merchants in all sorts of things, in blue clothes, and broidered work, and in chests of rich apparel, bound with cords, and made of cedar, among thy merchandise.
[25] The ships of Tarshish did sing of thee in thy market: and thou wast replenished, and made very glorious in the midst of the seas.
[26] Thy rowers have brought thee into great waters: the east wind hath broken thee in the midst of the seas.
[27] Thy riches, and thy fairs, thy merchandise, thy mariners, and thy pilots, thy calkers, and the occupiers of thy merchandise, and all thy men of war, that are in thee, and in all thy company which is in the midst of thee, shall fall into the midst of the seas in the day of thy ruin.

SIDONIUS APOLLINARIS
POEMS AND LETTERS
FROM POEM XXIII, "TO CONSENTIUS"
(C. 470)

Hail, Narbo, surpassing in thy healthiness, gladdening the eye with thy town and thy countryside alike, with thy walls, citizens, circuit, shops, gates, porticoes, forum, theatre, shrines, capitol, mint, baths, arches, granaries, markets, meadows, fountains, islands, salt-mines, ponds, river, merchandise, bridge and brine; thou who hast the best title of all to worship as thy gods Bacchus, Ceres, Pales and Minerva in virtue of thy corn, thy vines, thy pastures, and thine olive-mills! Thou hast put thy trust in thy men alone, and seeking no aid from Nature thou dost soar to heights that leave mountains far behind. No gaping fosse, no mound with its barrier of bristling stakes surrounds thee; no marble workmanship, no gilding or glass, no shining Indian tortoiseshell, no bars of ivory broken off from the mouths of Marmaric elephants dost thou fix upon thy walls; thou adornest no golden gates with mosaic; but proud among thy half-demolished strongholds thou dost display thy glory won in the old war, and though thy great stones have been battered down thou art prized more highly for those glorious ruins. Let other cities menace by their sites—cities built on high by lowly powers; let walls set on precipitous ridges boast that they have never been felled; as for thee, shattered as thou art thou dost win favour; the widespread fame of that assault hath made thy staunch loyalty renowned.

CHARLES DICKENS
BLEAK HOUSE, CHAPTER I,
"IN CHANCERY" (1852-1853)

LONDON. Michaelmas term lately over, and the Lord Chancellor sitting in Lincoln's Inn Hall. Implacable November weather. As much mud in the streets as if the waters had but newly retired from the face of the earth, and it would not be wonderful to meet a Megalosaurus, forty feet long or so, waddling like an elephantine lizard up Holborn Hill. Smoke lowering down from chimney-pots, making a soft black drizzle, with flakes of soot in it as big as full-grown snowflakes—gone into mourning, one might imagine, for the death of the sun. Dogs, undistinguishable in mire. Horses, scarcely better; splashed to their very blinkers. Foot passengers, jostling one another's umbrellas in a general infection of ill temper, and losing their foot-hold at street-corners, where tens of thousands of other foot passengers have been slipping and sliding since the day broke (if this day ever broke), adding new deposits to the crust upon crust of mud, sticking at those points tenaciously to the pavement, and accumulating at compound interest.

Fog everywhere. Fog up the river, where it flows among green aits and meadows; fog down the river, where it rolls defiled among the tiers of shipping and the waterside pollutions of a great (and dirty) city. Fog on the Essex marshes, fog on the Kentish heights. Fog creeping into the cabooses of collier-brigs; fog lying out on the yards and hovering in the rigging of great ships; fog drooping on the gunwales of barges and small boats. Fog in the eyes and throats of ancient Greenwich pensioners, wheezing by the firesides of their wards; fog in the stem and bowl of the afternoon pipe of the wrathful skipper, down in his close cabin; fog cruelly pinching the toes and fingers of his shivering little 'prentice boy on deck. Chance people on the bridges peeping over the parapets into a nether sky of fog, with fog all round them, as if they were up in a balloon and hanging in the misty clouds.

Gas looming through the fog in divers places in the streets, much as the sun may, from the spongey fields, be seen to loom by husbandman and ploughboy. Most of the shops lighted two hours before their time—as the gas seems to know, for it has a haggard and unwilling look.

The raw afternoon is rawest, and the dense fog is densest, and the muddy streets are muddiest near that leaden-headed old obstruction, appropriate ornament for the threshold of a leaden-headed old corporation, Temple Bar. And hard by Temple Bar, in Lincoln's Inn Hall, at the very heart of the fog, sits the Lord High Chancellor in his High Court of Chancery.

pages 90-91: William Henry Crome
View of London with Saint Paul's Cathedral in the Distance, c. 1826-1873,
private collection

EDGAR ALLAN POE
TALES AND SKETCHES
"THE MAN OF THE CROWD" (1841)

This latter [street] is one of the principal thoroughfares of the city, and had been very much crowded during the whole day. But, as the darkness came on, the throng momently increased; and, by the time the lamps were well lighted, two dense and continuous tides of population were rushing past the door. [...] I looked at the passengers in masses, and thought of them in their aggregate relations. Soon, however, I descended to details, and regarded with minute interest the innumerable varieties of figure, dress, air, gait, visage, and expression of countenance.
By far the greater number of those who went by had a satisfied business-like demeanor, and seemed to be thinking only of making their way through the press. Their brows were knit, and their eyes rolled quickly; when pushed against by fellow-wayfarers they evinced no symptom of impatience, but adjusted their clothes and hurried on. [...] Descending in the scale of what is termed gentility, I found darker and deeper themes for speculation. I saw Jew pedlars, with hawk eyes flashing from countenances whose every other feature wore only an expression of abject humility; sturdy professional street beggars scowling upon mendicants of a better stamp, whom despair alone had driven forth into the night for charity; feeble and ghastly invalids, upon whom death had placed a sure hand, and who sidled and tottered through the mob, looking every one beseechingly in the face, as if in search of some chance consolation, some lost hope; modest young girls returning from long and late labor to a cheerless home, and shrinking more tearfully than indignantly from the glances of ruffians, whose direct contact, even, could not be avoided; women of the town of all kinds and of all ages—the unequivocal beauty in the prime of her womanhood, putting one in mind of the statue in Lucian, with the

surface of Parian marble, and the interior filled with filth—the loathsome and utterly lost leper in rags—the wrinkled, bejewelled and paint-begrimed beldame, making a last effort at youth—the mere child of immature form, yet, from long association, an adept in the dreadful coquetries of her trade, and burning with a rabid ambition to be ranked the equal of her elders in vice; drunkards innumerable and indescribable—some in shreds and patches, reeling, inarticulate, with bruised visage and lack-lustre eyes—some in whole although filthy garments, with a slightly unsteady swagger, thick sensual lips, and hearty-looking rubicund faces—others clothed in materials which had once been good, and which even now were scrupulously well brushed—men who walked with a more than naturally firm and springy step, but whose countenances were fearfully pale, whose eyes hideously wild and red, and who clutched with quivering fingers, as they strode through the crowd, at every object which came within their reach; beside these, pie-men, porters, coal-heavers, sweeps; organ-grinders, monkey-exhibiters and ballad mongers, those who vended with those who sang; ragged artizans and exhausted laborers of every description, and all full of a noisy and inordinate vivacity which jarred discordantly upon the ear, and gave an aching sensation to the eye.

MARCEL PROUST
SWANN'S WAY
FROM "PLACE-NAMES: THE NAME" (1913)

Had my health definitely improved, had my parents allowed me, if not actually to go down to stay at Balbec, at least to take, just once, so as to become acquainted with the architecture and landscapes of Normandy or of Brittany, that one twenty-two train into which I had so often clambered in imagination, I should have preferred to stop, and to alight from it, at the most beautiful of its towns; but in vain might I compare and contrast them; how was one to choose, any more than between individual people, who are not interchangeable, between Bayeux, so lofty in its noble coronet of rusty lace, whose highest point caught the light of the old gold of its second syllable; Vitre, whose acute accent barred its ancient glass with wooden lozenges; gentle Lamballe, whose whiteness ranged from egg-shell yellow to a pearly grey; Coutances, a Norman Cathedral, which its final consonants, rich and yellowing, crowned with a tower of butter; Lannion with the rumble and buzz, in the silence of its village street, of the fly on the wheel of the coach; Questambert, Pontorson, ridiculously silly and simple, white feathers and yellow beaks strewn along the road to those well-watered and poetic spots; Benodet, a name scarcely moored that seemed to be striving to draw the river down into the tangle of its seaweeds; Pont-Aven, the snowy, rosy flight of the wing of a lightly poised coif, tremulously reflected in the greenish waters of a canal; Quimperle, more firmly attached, this, and since the Middle Ages, among the rivulets with which it babbled, threading their pearls upon a grey background, like the pattern made, through the cobwebs upon a window, by rays of sunlight changed into blunt points of tarnished silver?

ITALO CALVINO
INVISIBLE CITIES (1972)

The Great Kahn owns an atlas whose drawings depict the terrestrial globe all at once and continent by continent, the borders of the most distant realms, the ships' routes, the coastlines, the maps of the most illustrious metropolises and of the most opulent ports. He leafs through the maps before Marco Polo's eyes to put his knowledge to the test. The traveler recognizes Constantinople in the city which from three shores dominates a long strait, a narrow gulf, and an enclosed sea; he remembers that Jerusalem is set on two hills, of unequal height, facing each other; he has no hesitation in pointing to Samarkand and its gardens.

For other cities he falls back on descriptions handed down by word of mouth, or he guesses on the basis of scant indications: and so Granada, the streaked pearl of the Caliphs; Lübeck, the neat, boreal port; Timbuktu, black with ebony and white with ivory; Paris, where millions of men come home every day grasping a wand of bread. In colored miniatures the atlas depicts inhabited places of unusual form: an oasis hidden in a fold of the desert from which only palm crests peer out is surely Nefta; a castle amid quicksands and cows grazing in meadows salted by the

Raoul Dufy
The Bay of Sainte-Adresse, 1904,
**Paris, Musée National d'Art Moderne,
Centre Georges Pompidou**

Tetar van Elven

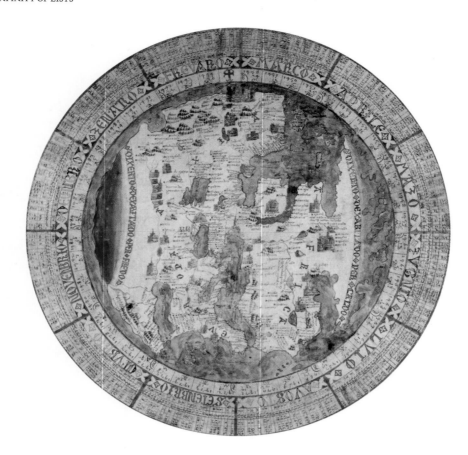

tides can only suggest Mont-Saint-Michel;
and a palace that instead of rising within
a city's walls contains within its own walls
a city that can only be Urbino.

The atlas depicts cities which neither Marco
nor the geographers know exist or where
they are, though they cannot be missing
among the forms of possible cities: a Cuzco
on a radial and multipartite plan which
reflects the perfect order of its trade, a
verdant Mexico on the lake dominated by
Montezuma's palace, a Novgorod with bulb-
shaped domes, a Lhassa whose white roofs
rise over the cloudy roof of the world. For
these, too, Marco says a name, no matter which,
and suggests a route to reach them. It is
known that names of places change as many
times as there are foreign languages; and

that every place can be reached from other
places, by the most various roads and routes,
by those who ride, or drive, or row, or fly. [...]
The Great Kahn owns an atlas in which are
gathered the maps of all the cities: those
whose walls rest on solid foundations, those
which fell in ruins and were swallowed up
by the sand, those that will exist one day and
in whose place now only hares' holes gape.
Marco Polo leafs through the pages; he
recognizes Jericho, Ur, Carthage, he points to
the landing at the mouth of the Scamander
where the Achaean ships waited for ten years
to take the besiegers back on board, until
the horse nailed together by Ulysses was
dragged by windlasses through the Scaean
gates. But speaking of Troy, he happened to
give the city the form of Constantinople and

foresee the siege which Mohammed would lay for long months until, astute as Ulysses, he had his ships drawn at night up the streams from the Bosporus to the Golden Horn, skirting Pera and Galata. And from the mixture of those two cities a third emerged, which might be called San Francisco and which spans the Golden Gate and the bay with long, light bridges and sends open trams climbing its steep streets, and which might blossom as capital of the Pacific a millennium hence, after the long siege of three hundred years that would lead the races of the yellow and the black and the red to fuse with the surviving descendants of the whites in an empire more vast than the Great Khan's.

The atlas has these qualities: it reveals the form of cities that do not yet have a form or a name. There is the city in the shape of Amsterdam, a semicircle facing north, with concentric circles—the princes', the emperors', the nobles'; there is the city in the shape of York, set among the high moors, walled, bristling with towers; there is the city in the shape of New Amsterdam known also as New York, crammed with towers of glass and steel on an oblong island between two rivers, with streets like deep canals, all of them straight, except Broadway.

The catalogue of forms is endless: until every shape has found its city, new cities will continue to be born. When the forms exhaust their variety and come apart, the end of cities begins. In the last pages of the atlas there is an outpouring of networks without beginning or end, cities in the shape of Los Angeles, in the shape of Kyoto-Osaka, without shape.

Giovanni Leardo
Mappa Mondi, 15th century,
Vicenza, Biblioteca Civica Bertoliana

BLAISE CENDRARS
LA PROSE DU TRANSSIBÉRIEN ET DE LA PETITE JEHANNE DE FRANCE (1913)

Jeanne, Jeannette, Ninette, nini, no-no, tit-ette
Mi-me my-love my dove-dew my Perú
Sleepy me, beddy-bye
Carrot my muck
Sweet li'l-heart
Tart
Be-lovèd li'l goat
My li'l sin sweet-tart
Half-wit
Coo-koo
She sleeps.

She sleeps
And in all the hours of the world, she's not
    swallowed a single one
All the faces glimpsed in the railway stations
All the clocks
The time in Paris in Berlin in Saint Petersburg
    and in all the stations
And in Ufa, the blood-stained face of the
    cannonier
And the ridiculously lit watch-dial in Grodno
And the perpetual advance of the train
Each morning we set our watches
The train is early and the sun is late
There's nothing doing, I listen to the bells
The large bell of Notre-Dame
The shrill bell of the Louvre on Saint
    Bartholomew's Day
The rusty carillons of Bruges-the-Dead
The electric ring of the New York library
The bells of Venice's countryside
And the bells of Moscow, the clock of the
    Red Gate that counted the hours as I sat
    in an office
And my memories
The train weighs on the revolving plates
The train rolls onward
A gramophone sounds a gypsy march
And the world, like the clock in Prague's
    Jewish quarter,
turns deliriously backward.

WALT WHITMAN
LEAVES OF GRASS
BOOK II: "STARTING FROM PAUMANOK" (1881)

Starting from fish-shape Paumanok where
  I was born,
Well-begotten, and rais'd by a perfect mother,
After roaming many lands, lover of populous
  pavements,
Dweller in Mannahatta my city, or on
  southern savannas,
Or a soldier camp'd or carrying my knapsack
  and gun, or a miner in California,
Or rude in my home in Dakota's woods,
  my diet meat, my drink from the spring,
Or withdrawn to muse and meditate in some
  deep recess,
Far from the clank of crowds intervals
  passing rapt and happy,
Aware of the fresh free giver the flowing
  Missouri, aware of mighty Niagara,
Aware of the buffalo herds grazing the plains,
  the hirsute and strong-breasted bull,
Of earth, rocks, Fifth-month flowers
  experienced, stars, rain, snow, my amaze,
Having studied the mocking-bird's tones
  and the flight of the mountain-hawk,
And heard at dawn the unrivall'd one, the
  hermit thrush from the swamp-cedars,
Solitary, singing in the West, I strike up for
  a New World.
[...]
Dead poets, philosophs, priests,
Martyrs, artists, inventors, governments
  long since,
Language-shapers on other shores,
Nations once powerful, now reduced,
  withdrawn, or desolate,
I dare not proceed till I respectfully credit
  what you have left wafted hither,
I have perused it, own it is admirable,
  (moving awhile among it,)
Think nothing can ever be greater, nothing
  can ever deserve more than it deserves,
Regarding it all intently a long while, then
  dismissing it,

I stand in my place with my own day here.
Here lands female and male,
Here the heir-ship and heiress-ship of the
  world, here the flame of materials,
Here spirituality the translatress, the openly-
  avow'd,
The ever-tending, the finale of visible forms,
The satisfier, after due long-waiting now
  advancing,
Yes here comes my mistress the soul.
[...]
The soul,
Forever and forever—longer than soil is
  brown and solid—longer than water ebbs
  and flows.
I will make the poems of materials, for I think
  they are to be the most spiritual poems,
And I will make the poems of my body and
  of mortality,
For I think I shall then supply myself with
  the poems of my soul and of immortality.
[...]
I will make a song for these States that no
  one State may under any circumstances
  be subjected to another State,
And I will make a song that there shall be
  comity by day and by night between all
  the States, and between any two of them,
And I will make a song for the ears of the
  President, full of weapons with menacing
  points,
And behind the weapons countless
  dissatisfied faces;
And a song make I of the One form'd out of all,
The fang'd and glittering One whose head is
  over all,
Resolute warlike One including and over all,
(However high the head of any else that head
  is over all.)
[...]
I will acknowledge contemporary lands,
I will trail the whole geography of the globe
  and salute courteously every city large
  and small,
And employments! I will put in my poems
  that with you is heroism upon land and
  sea,

And I will report all heroism from an
    American point of view.
[...]
I will sing the song of companionship,
I will show what alone must finally compact
    these,
I believe these are to found their own ideal
    of manly love, indicating it in me,
I will therefore let flame from me the burning
    fires that were threatening to consume me,
I will lift what has too long kept down those
    smouldering fires,
I will give them complete abandonment,
I will write the evangel-poem of comrades
    and of love,
For who but I should understand love with
    all its sorrow and joy?
And who but I should be the poet of
    comrades?
[...]
As I have walk'd in Alabama my morning
    walk,
I have seen where the she-bird the mocking-
    bird sat on her nest in the briers hatching
    her brood.
I have seen the he-bird also,
I have paus'd to hear him near at hand
    inflating his throat and
joyfully singing.
And while I paus'd it came to me that what
    he really sang for was
not there only,
Nor for his mate nor himself only, nor all sent
    back by the echoes,
But subtle, clandestine, away beyond,
A charge transmitted and gift occult for
    those being born.
[...]
Democracy! near at hand to you a throat is
    now inflating itself and
joyfully singing.
Ma femme! for the brood beyond us and of us,
For those who belong here and those to come,
I exultant to be ready for them will now
    shake out carols stronger and haughtier
    than have ever yet been heard upon earth.
    [...]

I will make the songs of passion to give them
    their way,
And your songs outlaw'd offenders, for I scan
    you with kindred eyes, and carry you with
    me the same as any.
[...]
I will make the true poem of riches,
To earn for the body and the mind whatever
    adheres and goes forward and is not dropt
    by death;
I will effuse egotism and show it underlying
    all, and I will be the bard of personality,
And I will show of male and female that
    either is but the equal of the other,
And sexual organs and acts! do you
    concentrate in me, for I am determin'd
    to tell you with courageous clear voice
    to prove you illustrious,
And I will show that there is no imperfection
    in the present, and can be none in the
    future,
And I will show that whatever happens to
    anybody it may be turn'd to beautiful
    results,
And I will show that nothing can happen
    more beautiful than death,
And I will thread a thread through my poems
    that time and events are compact,
And that all the things of the universe are
    perfect miracles, each as profound as any.
[...]
I will not make poems with reference to parts,
But I will make poems, songs, thoughts,
    with reference to ensemble,
And I will not sing with reference to a day,
    but with reference to all days,
And I will not make a poem nor the least part
    of a poem but has reference to the soul,
Because having look'd at the objects of the
    universe, I find there is no one nor any
    particle of one but has reference to the
    soul.
[...]
Whoever you are, to you endless
    announcements!
Daughter of the lands did you wait for your
    poet?

Johann Melchior Roos
The Animal Menagerie of Count Carl, 1728,
Kassel, Museumslandschaft Hessen,
Gemäldegalerie Alte Meister

Did you wait for one with a flowing mouth
    and indicative hand?
Toward the male of the States, and toward
    the female of the States,
Exulting words, words to Democracy's lands.

Interlink'd, food-yielding lands!
Land of coal and iron! land of gold! land of
    cotton, sugar, rice!
Land of wheat, beef, pork! land of wool and
    hemp! land of the apple and the grape!
Land of the pastoral plains, the grass-fields
    of the world! land of those sweet-air'd
    interminable plateaus!
Land of the herd, the garden, the healthy
    house of adobie!
Lands where the north-west Columbia winds,
    and where the south-west Colorado winds!
Land of the eastern Chesapeake! land of the
    Delaware!
Land of Ontario, Erie, Huron, Michigan!
Land of the Old Thirteen! Massachusetts
    land! land of Vermont and Connecticut!
Land of the ocean shores! land of sierras
    and peaks!
Land of boatmen and sailors! fishermen's
    land!
Inextricable lands! the clutch'd together!
    the passionate ones!
The side by side! the elder and younger
    brothers! the bony-limb'd!
The great women's land! the feminine! the
    experienced sisters and the inexperienced
    sisters!
Far breath'd land! Arctic braced! Mexican
    breez'd! the diverse! the compact!
The Pennsylvanian! the Virginian! the double
    Carolinian!
O all and each well-loved by me! my intrepid
    nations! O I at any rate include you all with
    perfect love!
I cannot be discharged from you! not from
    one any sooner than another!
O death! O for all that, I am yet of you
    unseen his hour with irrepressible love,
Walking New England, a friend, a traveler,
Splashing my bare feet in the edge of the

summer ripples on Paumanok's sands,
Crossing the prairies, dwelling again in
    Chicago, dwelling in every town,
Observing shows, births, improvements,
    structures, arts,
Listening to orators and oratresses in public
    halls,
Of and through the States as during life,
    each man and woman my neighbor,
The Louisianian, the Georgian, as near to me,
    and I as near to him and her,
The Mississippian and Arkansian yet with me,
    and I yet with any of them,
Yet upon the plains west of the spinal river,
    yet in my house of adobie,
Yet returning eastward, yet in the Seaside
    State or in Maryland,
Yet Kanadian cheerily braving the winter,
    the snow and ice welcome to me,
Yet a true son either of Maine or of the
    Granite State, or the Narragansett Bay
    State, or the Empire State,
Yet sailing to other shores to annex the same,
    yet welcoming every new brother,
Hereby applying these leaves to the new ones
    from the hour they unite with the old ones,
Coming among the new ones myself to be
    their companion and equal, coming
    personally to you now,
Enjoining you to acts, characters, spectacles,
    with me.
[...]
With me with firm holding, yet haste, haste on.
[...]
For your life adhere to me,
(I may have to be persuaded many times
    before I consent to give myself really to
    you, but what of that?
Must not Nature be persuaded many times?)
[...]
No dainty dolce affettuoso I,
Bearded, sun-burnt, gray-neck'd, forbidding,
    I have arrived,
To be wrestled with as I pass for the solid
    prizes of the universe,
For such I afford whoever can persevere to
    win them.

[...]
On my way a moment I pause,
Here for you! and here for America!
Still the present I raise aloft, still the future
    of the States I
harbinge glad and sublime,
And for the past I pronounce what the air
    holds of the red aborigines.
The red aborigines,
Leaving natural breaths, sounds of rain
    and winds, calls as of birds and animals
    in the woods, syllabled to us for names,
Okonee, Koosa, Ottawa, Monongahela, Sauk,
    Natchez, Chattahoochee, Kaqueta,
    Oronoco, Wabash, Miami, Saginaw,
    Chippewa, Oshkosh, Walla-Walla,
Leaving such to the States they melt, they
    depart, charging the water and the land
    with names.
[...]
Expanding and swift, henceforth,
Elements, breeds, adjustments, turbulent,
    quick and audacious,
A world primal again, vistas of glory
    incessant and branching,
A new race dominating previous ones and
    grander far, with new contests,
New politics, new literatures and religions,
    new inventions and arts.
These, my voice announcing—I will sleep no
    more but arise,
You oceans that have been calm within me!
    how I feel you, fathomless, stirring, preparing
    unprecedented waves and storms.
[...]
See, steamers steaming through my poems,
See, in my poems immigrants continually
    coming and landing,
See, in arriere, the wigwam, the trail, the
    hunter's hut, the flat-boat, the maize-leaf,
    the claim, the rude fence, and the
    backwoods village,
See, on the one side the Western Sea and
    on the other the Eastern Sea, how they
    advance and retreat upon my poems as
    upon their own shores,
See, pastures and forests in my poems—see,
    animals wild and tame—see, beyond the
    Kaw, countless herds of buffalo feeding
    on short curly grass,
See, in my poems, cities, solid, vast, inland,
    with paved streets, with iron and stone
    edifices, ceaseless vehicles, and
    commerce,
See, the many-cylinder'd steam printing-
    press—see, the electric telegraph
    stretching across the continent,
See, through Atlantica's depths pulses
    American Europe reaching, pulses of
    Europe duly return'd,
See, the strong and quick locomotive as it
    departs, panting, blowing the steam-
    whistle,
See, ploughmen ploughing farms—see,
    miners digging mines—see, the
    numberless factories,
See, mechanics busy at their benches with
    tools—see from among them superior
    judges, philosophs, Presidents, emerge,
    drest in working dresses,
See, lounging through the shops and fields
    of the States, me well-belov'd, close-held
    by day and night,
Hear the loud echoes of my songs there—
    read the hints come at last.
[...]

VICTOR HUGO
NINETY-THREE
PART I, BOOK III, CHAPTER II (1874)

"We are about to separate, Halmalo. Two men are of no use whatsoever. Unless they are a thousand, it is better for one man to be alone."

He stopped and pulled out of his pocket a knot of green silk resembling a cockade, with a fleur-de-lis embroidered in gold in the centre.

"Can you read?" he asked.

"No."

"That is fortunate. A man who knows how to read is embarrassing. Have you a good memory?"

"Yes."

"Very well. Listen, Halmalo. You will follow the road on the right, and I the one on the left. You are to turn in the direction of Bazouges, and I shall go towards Fougères. Keep your bag, because it makes you look like a peasant; hide your weapons; cut yourself a stick from the hedge; creep through the tall rye; glide behind the hedges; climb over fences and cross the fields: you will thus avoid the passers-by, as well as roads and bridges. Do not enter Pontorson. Ah! You will have to cross the Couesnon. How will you manage that?"

"I shall swim across."

"Excellent. Then you will come to a ford. Do you know where it is?"

"Between Nancy and Vieux-Viel."

"Correct. You are evidently familiar with the country."

"But night is coming on. Where will my lord sleep?"

"I can take care of myself. And where will you sleep?"

"There are plenty of *émousses*. I was a peasant before I was a sailor."

"Throw away your sailor hat; it would betray you. You can surely find some worsted head-covering."

"Oh, a cap is easily found. The first fisherman I meet will sell me his."

"Very well. Now listen. You are familiar with the woods?"

"All of them."

"Throughout this entire neighborhood?"

"From Noirmoutier to Laval."

"Do you know their names too?"

"I know the woods and their names; I know all about them."

"You will forget nothing?"

"Nothing."

"Good. Now mind. How many leagues can you walk in a day?"

"Ten, fifteen, eighteen, twenty if need be."

"It will have to be done. Do not miss a word of what I am about to tell you. You will go to the woods of Saint-Aubin."

"Near Lamballe?"

"Yes. On the edge of a ravine between Saint-Rieul and Plédéliac there is a large chestnut-tree. You will stop there. No one will be in sight."

"But a man will be there nevertheless. On that I can depend."

"You will give the call. Do you know it?"

Halmalo puffed out his cheeks, turned towards the sea, and there rand the "to-whit-to-hoo" of the owl. One would have supposed it came from the depths of a forest, so owl-like and sinister was the sound.

"Good!" said the old man. "You have it." He extended to Halmalo the green silk knot.

"This is my commander's badge. Take it. No one must know my name at present; but this knot is sufficient. The fleur-de-lis was embroidered by Madame Royale in the Temple prison."

Halmalo knelt. Trembling with awe he received the knot embroidered with the fleur-de-lis, and in the act of raising it to his lips, he paused as if in fear.

"May I?" he asked.

"Yes, since you kiss the crucifix."

Halmalo kissed the fleur-de-lis.

"Rise," said the old man.

Halmalo obeyed him, placing the knot in his bosom.

Théodore Rousseau
Forest of Fontainebleau, 19th century,
Hamburg, Hamburger Kunsthalle

"Listen carefully to what I am about to say. This is the order: 'Revolt! Give no quarter.' On the edge of the forest of Saint-Aubin you will give the call, repeating it three times. After the third time you will see a man rise from the ground."

"I know, from a hole under the trees."

"That man will be Planchenault, sometimes called Cœur-de-Roi. To him you will show this knot. He will know what it means. Then you are to go by ways that you must discover for yourself to the woods of Astillé, where you will see a cripple surnamed Mousqueton, a man who shows mercy to no human being. You are to tell him that I love him, and that he must stir up the parishes in his neighborhood. Thence you will go to the wood of Couesbon, which is one mile from Ploërmel. When you give the owl-cry, a man will come out of a hole; that will be M. Thuault, seneschal of Ploërmel, who formerly belonged to the Constitutional Assembly, but on the royalist side. You will direct him to fortify the castle of Couesbon, that belongs to the Marquis de Guer, a refugee. Ravines, woods of moderate extent, uneven soil, a good spot. M. Thuault is an able and upright man. From there you will go to Saint-Guen-les-Toits, and speak to Jean Chouan, whom I look upon as the actual leader, and then to the woods of Ville-Anglose, where you will see Guitter, called Saint-Martin; you will tell him to keep his eye on a certain Courmesnil, son-in-law of the old Jacobins of Argentan. Remember all this. I write nothing, because writing must be avoided. La Rouarie made out a list, which ruined everything. Thence you will go to the wood of Rougefeu, where Miélette lives, he who leaps across ravines by the help of a long pole."

"They call it a leaping-pole."

"Do you know how to use it?"

"Am I not a Breton peasant? The leaping-pole is our friend. It makes our arms bigger, our legs longer."

"Let us go on. Do you know the Tourgue?"

"Do I know it! I came from there."

"Let us go on. Listen. From Rougefeu you are to go into the wood of Montchevrier, where you will find Bénédicité, the leader of the Twelve. He is another good man. He recites his *Benedicité* while he has people shot. There is no room for sensibility in warfare. From Montchevrier you will go—"

He broke off.

"I had forgotten about the money."

He took from his pocket a purse and a pocket-book, which he put into Halmalo's hands.

"In this pocket-book you will find thirty thousand francs in paper money, which is worth about three livres and ten sous. The assignats are false, to be sure, but the real ones are no more valuable; and in this purse, mind, you will find one hundred louis d'ors. I give you all I have, because I have no need of anything here, and it is better that no money should be found on me. Now I will go on. From Montchevrier you are to go to Antrain, where you will meet M. de Frotté; from Antrain to Jupellière, where you will see M. de Rochecotte; from Jupellière to Noirieux, where you will find the Abbé Baudoin. Will you remember all this?"

"As I do my Pater Noster."

"You will see M. Dubois-Guy at Saint-Brice-en-Cogle, M. de Turpin at Morannes, which is a fortified town, and the Prince de Talmont at Château-Gonthier."

"Will a prince speak to me?"

"Am I not speaking to you?"

Halmalo took off his hat.

"You need but to show Madam's fleur-de-lis, and your welcome is assured. Remember that you will have to go to places where there are mountaineers and *patauds* [the Chouans' term for the republicans, a corruption of "patriot"]. You will disguise yourself. That is an easy matter, since the republicans are so stupid that with a blue coat, a three-cornered hat, and a cockade, you may go anywhere. The day of regiments and uniforms has gone by; the regiments are not even numbered, and every man is at liberty to wear whatever rag he fancies.

You will go to Saint-Mhervé. You will see Gaulier, called Grand-Pierre. You will go to the cantonment of Parné, where all the man have swarthy faces. They put gravel in their muskets and use a double charge of powder to make more noise. They do well; but be sure and tell them to kill, kill, and kill. You will go to the camp of the Vache-Noire, which is an elevation in the midst of the forest of La Charnie, from Vache-Noire to the camp of l'Avoine, then to the camp Vert, and afterwards to the camp of the Fourmis. You will go to Grand-Bordage, also called Haut-du-Pré, where lives the widow whose daughter married Treton the Englishman; that is in the parish of Quelaines. You will

visit Épineux-le-Chevreuil, Sillé-le-Guillaume, Parannes, and all the men in hiding throughout the woods. You will make friends and you will send them to the borders of upper and lower Maine; you will see Jean Treton in the parish of Vaisges, Saint-Regret in Bignon, Chambord in Bonchamps, the Courbin brothers at Maisoncelles, and Petit-Sans-Peur at Saint-Jean-sur-Evre. He is the one who is called Bourdoiseau. Having done this, and uttered the watchwords, 'Revolt!' 'No quarter!' in all these places, you will join the royal and catholic grand army, wherever it may be. You will see d'Elbée, de Lescure, de la Rochejaquelein, and such leaders as may still be living. You will show them my commander's knot. They will know what it means. "Do not forget anything."

"You may rest assured of that."

Charles Thévenin
The Storming of the Bastille, 18th century,
Paris, Musée Carnavalet

JAMES JOYCE
FINNEGANS WAKE
(1939)

O

tell me all about

Anna Livia! I want to hear all
about Anna Livia. Well, you know Anna Livia?
Yes, of course, we all know Anna Livia. Tell
me all. Tell me now. You'll die when you hear.
Well, you know, when the old cheb went futt
and did what you know. Yes, I know, go on.
Wash quit and don't be dabbling. Tuck up
your sleeves and loosen your talk-tapes.
And don't butt me—hike!—when you bend.
Or whatever it was they threed to make out
he thried to two in the Fiendish park. He's
an awful old reppe. Look at the shirt of him.
Look at the dirt of it! He has all my water
black on me. And it steeping and stuping
since this time last wik. How many goes is
it I wonder I washed it? I know by heart the
places he likes to saale, duddurty devil!
Scorching my hand and starving my famine
to make his private linen public. Wallop it well
with your battle and clean it. My wrists are
wrusty rubbing the mouldaw stains. And the
dneepers of wet and the gangres of sin in it!
What was it he did a tail at all on Animal
Sendai? And how long was he under loch and
neagh? It was put in the newses what he did,
nicies and priers, the King fierceas Humphrey,
with illysus distilling, exploits and all. But
toms will till. I know he well. Temp untamed
will hist for no man. As you spring so shall
you neap. O, the roughty old rappe! Minxing
marrage and making loof. Reeve Gootch was
right and Reeve Drughad was sinistrous!
And the cut of him! And the strut of him!
How he used to hold his head as high as
a howeth, the famous eld duke alien, with
a hump of grandeur on him like a walking
wiesel rat. And his derry's own drawl and his
corksown blather and his doubling stutter
and his gullaway swank. Ask Lictor Hackett
or Lector Reade of Garda Growley or the Boy
with the Billyclub. How elster is he a called
at all? Qu'appelle? Huges Caput Earlyfouler.
Or where was he born or how was he found?
Urgothland, Tvistown on the Kattekat? New
Hunshire, Concord on the Merrimake? Who
blocksmitt her-saft anvil or yelled lep to her
pail? Was her banns never loosened in Adam
and Eve's or were him and her but captain
spliced? For mine ether duck I thee drake.
And by my wildgaze I thee gander. Flowey
and Mount on the brink of time makes wishes
and fears for a happy isthmass. She can show
all her lines, with love, license to play. And if
they don't remarry that hook and eye may.

JORGE LUIS BORGES
THE ALEPH AND OTHER STORIES
FROM "THE ALEPH"

I arrive now at the ineffable core of my story. And here begins my despair as a writer. All language is a set of symbols whose use among its speakers assumes a shared past. How, then, can I translate into words the limitless Aleph, which my floundering mind can scarcely encompass? Mystics, faced with the same problem, fall back on symbols: to signify the godhead, one Persian speaks of a bird that somehow is all birds; Alanus de Insulis, of a sphere whose center is everywhere and circumference is nowhere; Ezekiel, of a four-faced angel who at one and the same time moves east and west, north and south. (Not in vain do I recall these inconceivable analogies; they bear some relation to the Aleph.) Perhaps the gods might grant me a similar metaphor, but then this account would become contaminated by literature, by fiction. Really, what I want to do is impossible, for any listing of an endless series is doomed to be infinitesimal. In that single gigantic instant I saw millions of acts both delightful and awful; not one of them amazed me more than the fact that all of them occupied the same point in space, without overlapping of transparency. What my eyes beheld was simultaneous, but what I shall now write down will be successive, because language is successive. Nonetheless, I'll try to recollect what I can.

On the back part of the step, toward the right, I saw a small iridescent sphere of almost unbearable brilliance. At first I thought it was revolting; then I realized that this movement was an illusion created by the dizzying world it bounded. The Aleph's diameter was probably little more than an inch, but all space was there, actual and undiminished. Each thing (a mirror's face, let us say) was infinite things, since I distinctly saw it from every angle of the universe. I saw the teeming sea; I saw daybreak and nightfall; I saw the multitudes of America; I saw a silvery cobweb in the center of a black pyramid; I saw a splintered labyrinth (it was London); I saw, close up, unending eyes watching themselves in me as in a mirror; I saw all the mirrors on earth and none of them reflected me; I saw in a backyard of Soler Street the same tiles that thirty years before I'd seen in the entrance of a house on Fray Bentos; I saw bunches of grapes, snow, tobacco, lodes of metal, steam; I saw convex equatorial deserts and each one of their grains of sand; I saw a woman in Inverness whom I shall never forget; I saw her tangled hair, her tall figure, I saw the cancer in her breast; I saw a ring of baked mud in a sidewalk, where before there had been a tree; I saw a summer house in Adrogué and a copy of the first English translation of Pliny— Philemon Holland's—and all at the same time saw each letter on each page (as a boy, I used to marvel that the letters in a closed book did not get scrambled and lost overnight); I saw a sunset in Querétaro that seemed to reflect the color of a rose in Bengal; I saw my empty bedroom; I saw in a closet in Alkmaar a terrestrial globe between two mirrors that multiplied it endlessly; I saw horses with flowing manes on a shore of the Caspian Sea at dawn; I saw the delicate bone structure of a hand; I saw the survivors of a battle sending out picture postcards; I saw in a showcase in Mirzapur a pack of Spanish playing cards; I saw the slanting shadows of ferns on a greenhouse floor; I saw tigers, pistons, bison, tides, and armies; I saw all the ants on the planet; I saw a Persian astrolabe; I saw in the drawer of a writing table (and the handwriting made me tremble) unbelievable, obscene, detailed letters, which Beatriz had written to Carlos Argentino; I saw a monument I worshiped in the Chacarita cemetery; I saw the rotted dust and bones that had once deliciously been Beatriz Viterbo; I saw the circulation of my own dark blood; I saw the coupling of love and the modification of death; I saw the Aleph from every point

and angle, and in the Aleph I saw the earth and in the earth the Aleph and in the Aleph the earth; I saw my own face and my own bowels; I saw your face, and I felt dizzy and wept, for my eyes had seen that secret and conjectured object whose name is common to all men but which no man has looked upon—the unimaginable universe.

Ebstorf Mappamundi
copy by Konrad Miller of the original 1239 parchment in the Cathedral of Hereford, Herefordshire

THERE ARE LISTS AND LISTS

In this regard, however, we must make an important distinction, and that is between practical or "pragmatic" and "poetic" lists (and by the latter term we mean any artistic end for which the list was proposed and whatever art form is used to express it).[1]

The practical list can be exemplified by a shopping list, the list of guests invited to a party, by a library catalogue, by the inventory of objects in any place (such as an office, an archive, or a museum), by the list of assets in a will, by an invoice for goods requiring payment, by a restaurant menu, by the list of sights to see in a tourist guide, and even by a dictionary that records all the words in the lexicon of a given language.

These lists have three characteristics: first they have a purely referential function, in other words they refer to objects in the outside world and have the purely practical purpose of naming and listing them (if these objects did not exist this list would not make any sense or we would already be in the presence of, as we shall see, a poetic list); second, since they record things that are really existent and known, such lists are finite, because they are intended to list all the objects to which they refer and no others—and these objects, if they are physically present somewhere, clearly have a defined number; third, they may not be altered, in the sense that it would be unethical as well as pointless to include in a museum catalogue a painting that is not kept there.

In their own way practical lists represent a form, because they confer unity on a set of objects that, no matter how dissimilar

Christian Boltanski
Les archives de C.B. 1965–1988, 1989,
Paris, Musée National d'Art Moderne,
Centre Georges Pompidou

114

among themselves, comply with a *contextual pressure*, in other words
they are related for their being or for their being expected to be found
all in the same place, or to constitute the goal of a certain project. In
this way an acceptable set is constituted by all the books in a certain
library, the guest list of a party, a list of things to buy at the supermarket,
and so on. A practical list is never incongruous, provided we can
identify the criterion of assembly that governs it. There would be
nothing incongruous even about a list that put together a broom, an
incomplete copy of a biography of Galen, a foetus preserved in alcohol
or (to quote Lautréamont) an umbrella and an anatomy table. It would
suffice to establish that this was an inventory of objects relegated to
the cellar of a medical school.

Belknap (cit., p. 31) thinks that "pragmatic" lists can be extended
to infinity (and in fact a telephone directory can become larger every
year, just as we may make a shopping list longer on our way to the
shops), while the lists he calls literary are in fact closed owing to the
formal constraints of the work that contains them (metre, rhyme,
sonnet form, and so on). It seems to me that the argument can easily
be turned on its head: insofar as practical lists designate a series of
things that, when the list is drawn up, are what they are and no
more, then such lists are finite (and the telephone directory of the
following year is simply a second list that differs from the first)
whereas, immaterial of the constraints involved in poetic techniques,
Homer could have extended his catalogue of ships to infinity and
Ezekiel could have added new attributes to the city of Tyre.

A fine model of the practical list, even though made in music and
verse, is that of Leporello in Mozart's *Don Giovanni*. Don Giovanni
has seduced a great number of countrywomen, maids, ladies of the
town, countesses, baronesses, marchionesses, princesses, and women
of all ranks, shapes and ages, but Leporello is a precise bookkeeper
and his catalogue is mathematically complete: "In Italy six hundred
and forty—in Germany two hundred and thirty-one—one hundred
in France, ninety-one in Turkey—but in Spain there are already one
thousand and three." That makes 2,065 in all, not one more and not
one less. If Don Giovanni were to seduce Donna Anna or Zerlina the
next day, then there would be a new list.

It is obvious why people make practical lists. But why do they make poetic ones?

In part we have already explained this: because we cannot manage to enumerate something that eludes our capacity for control and denomination, and this would be the case with Homer's catalogue of ships. But now let us try a mental experiment: Homer was not interested in knowing and telling us who the leaders of the

Stela of Princess Nefertiabet with the food placed in her tomb,
Old Kingdom, 4th dynasty, reign of Cheops (2590-2565 B.C.),
Paris, Musée du Louvre

Greeks really were; he, or the bards who came before him, were inventing. This would not make his list less referential except for the fact that, instead of referring to objects in the real world, it would refer to the objects of his epic world. Alternatively, in inventing or finding those names in the meanders of the mythological tradition, Homer might have been enamoured not by the form of his possible world, but by the sound of those names. In that case he would have passed from a list concerned with referents and in any event with the *signified*, to a list concerned with sounds, the phonic values of the list, in other words with *signifiers*.

Think of the genealogy of Jesus at the beginning of the Gospel according to **Matthew**. We are free to doubt the historic existence of many of those ancestors, but certainly Matthew (or someone in his stead) wanted to indicate "real" persons in the possible world of his beliefs, and so the list had practical value and a referential function. If we move on to the **Litanies of the Blessed Virgin**, we find that it is a list of properties, attributes and titles that regard the Virgin, many borrowed from passages of Scripture, others taken from the tradition or popular devotion (in this regard we talk of *panegyric* enumeration). But they must have been recited like a mantra, much like the Buddhists' *om mani padme hum*, it does not matter so much whether the *virgo* is *potens* or *clemens* (in any case until the Second Vatican Council litanies were recited in Latin by the faithful, the majority of whom did not understand that tongue): what matters is being seized by the dizzying sound of the list, just as in the **Litanies of the Saints** what matters is not so much which of them are present or absent, as the rhythmic enunciation of the names for a sufficiently long period of time.

1. On the difference between *pragmatic lists* and *literary lists* see Robert E. Belknap, *The List* (New Haven, Yale University Press, 2004). A valuable anthology of literary lists is also found in Francis Spufford, ed., *The Chatto Book of Cabbages and Kings: Lists in Literature* (London, Chatto & Windus, 1989).

The Angelic Ranks
The Mermengold Breviary, fol. 31v, 13th-14th century,
San Lorenzo de El Escorial,
Royal Monastery

li premiera gerarchia dels angels plus basta.

THE GOSPEL ACCORDING TO SAINT MATTHEW
THE KING JAMES BIBLE
FROM THE GOSPEL ACCORDING TO SAINT MATTHEW, BOOK 1, 1-16

[1] The book of the generation of Jesus Christ, the son of David, the son of Abraham. [2] Abraham begat Isaac; and Isaac begat Jacob; and Jacob begat Judas and his brethren; [3] And Judas begat Phares and Zara of Thamar; and Phares begat Esrom; and Esrom begat Aram; [4] And Aram begat Aminadab; and Aminadab begat Naasson; and Naasson begat Salmon; [5] And Salmon begat Booz of Rachab; and Booz begat Obed of Ruth; and Obed begat Jesse; [6] And Jesse begat David the king; and David the king begat Solomon of her that had been the wife of Urias; [7] And Solomon begat Roboam; and Roboam begat Abia; and Abia begat Asa; [8] And Asa begat Josaphat; and Josaphat begat Joram; and Joram begat Ozias; [9] And Ozias begat Joatham; and Joatham begat Achaz; and Achaz begat Ezekias; [10] And Ezekias begat Manasses; and Manasses begat Amon; and Amon begat Josias; [11] And Josias begat Jechonias and his brethren, about the time they were carried away to Babylon: [12] And after they were brought to Babylon, Jechonias begat Salathiel; and Salathiel begat Zorobabel; [13] And Zorobabel begat Abiud; and Abiud begat Eliakim; and Eliakim begat Azor; [14] And Azor begat Sadoc; and Sadoc begat Achim; and Achim begat Eliud; [15] And Eliud begat Eleazar; and Eleazar begat Matthan; and

Matthan begat Jacob; [16] And Jacob begat Joseph the husband of Mary, of whom was born Jesus, who is called Christ. [17] So all the generations from Abraham to David are fourteen generations; and from David until the carrying away into Babylon are fourteen generations; and from the carrying away into Babylon unto Christ are fourteen generations.

LITANIES
FROM THE LITANY OF MARY

Holy Mary, *pray for us.*
Holy Mother of God, *pray for us.*
Holy Virgin of virgins, *pray for us.*
Mother of Christ, *pray for us.*
Mother of divine grace, *pray for us.*
Mother most pure, *pray for us.*
Mother most chaste, *pray for us.*
Mother inviolate, *pray for us.*
Mother undefiled, *pray for us.*
Mother most amiable, *pray for us.*
Mother most admirable, *pray for us.*
Mother of good counsel, *pray for us.*
Mother of our Creator, *pray for us.*
Mother of our Savior, *pray for us.*
Virgin most prudent, *pray for us.*
Virgin most venerable, *pray for us.*
Virgin most renowned, *pray for us.*
Virgin most powerful, *pray for us.*
Virgin most merciful, *pray for us.*
Virgin most faithful, *pray for us.*
Mirror of justice, *pray for us.*
Seat of wisdom, *pray for us.*
Cause of our joy, *pray for us.*
Spiritual vessel, *pray for us.*
Vessel of honor, *pray for us.*
Singular vessel of devotion, *pray for us.*
Mystical rose, *pray for us.*
Tower of David, *pray for us.*
Tower of ivory, *pray for us.*
House of gold, *pray for us.*
Ark of the covenant, *pray for us.*
Gate of Heaven, *pray for us.*

Jesse's Tree
illustrated miniature from the *Ingeborg Psalter*, c. 1210, Chantilly, Musée Condé

page 120: *The Room of Miracles*
Church of Nosso Senhor do Bonfim
Salvador da Bahia, Brazil

page 121: *Shrine to Padre Pio*
San Giovanni Rotondo

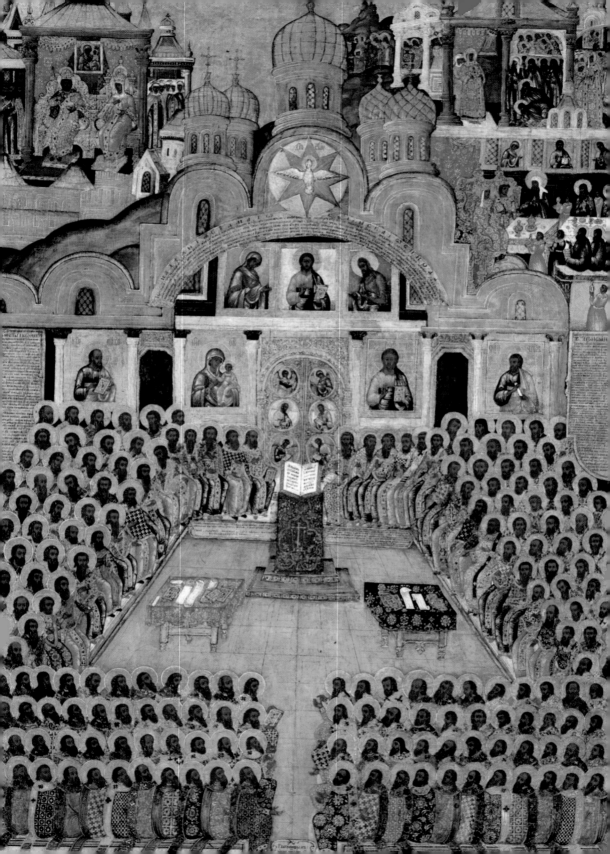

Morning star, *pray for us*.
Health of the sick, *pray for us*.
Refuge of sinners, *pray for us*.
Comforter of the afflicted, *pray for us*.
Help of Christians, *pray for us*.
Queen of Angels, *pray for us*.
Queen of Patriarchs, *pray for us*.
Queen of Prophets, *pray for us*.
Queen of Apostles, *pray for us*.
Queen of Martyrs, *pray for us*.
Queen of Confessors, *pray for us*.
Queen of Virgins, *pray for us*.
Queen of all Saints, *pray for us*.
Queen conceived without Original Sin, *pray for us*.
Queen assumed into Heaven, *pray for us*.

Queen of the most holy rosary, *pray for us*.
Lamb of God, who takest away the sins of the world, *spare us, O Lord*.
Lamb of God, who takest away the sins of the world, *graciously hear us, O Lord*.
Lamb of God, who takest away the sins of the world, *have mercy on us*.

Let us pray: Grant, we beseech Thee, O Lord God, unto us Thy servants, that we may rejoice in continual health of mind and body; and, by the glorious intercession of blessed Mary ever Virgin, may be delivered from present sadness, and enter into the joy of Thine eternal gladness. Through Christ our Lord. Amen.

Simon Ušakov, Gurij Nikitin and students
The Seventh Ecumenical Council, 1673,
Moscow, Monastery of Smolensk Cathedral

FROM THE LITANY OF LORETO AND THE LITANY OF SAINTS

Lord, *have mercy upon us.*
Christ, *have mercy upon us.*
Lord, *have mercy upon us.*
O Christ, *hear us.*
O Christ, *graciously hear us.*
O God the Father of heaven, *have mercy upon us.*
O God the Son, Redeemer of the world, *have mercy upon us.*
O God the Holy Spirit, *have mercy upon us.*
O Holy Trinity, one God, *have mercy upon us.*
Holy Mary, *pray for us.*
Holy Mother of God, *pray for us.*
Holy Virgin of virgins, *pray for us.*
Saint Michael, *pray for us.*
Saint Gabriel, *pray for us.*
Saint Raphael, *pray for us.*
All ye holy Angels and Archangels, *pray for us.*
All ye holy orders of blessed Spirits, *pray for us.*
Saint John the Baptist, *pray for us.*
Saint Joseph, *pray for us.*
All ye holy Patriarchs and Prophets, *pray for us.*
Saint Peter, *pray for us.*
Saint Paul, *pray for us.*
Saint Andrew, *pray for us.*
Saint James, *pray for us.*
Saint John, *pray for us.*
Saint Thomas, *pray for us.*
Saint James, *pray for us.*
Saint Philip, *pray for us.*
Saint Bartholomew, *pray for us.*
Saint Matthew, *pray for us.*
Saint Simon, *pray for us.*
Saint Jude, *pray for us.*
Saint Matthias, *pray for us.*
Saint Barnabas, *pray for us.*
Saint Luke, *pray for us.*
Saint Mark, *pray for us.*
All ye holy Apostles and Evangelists, *pray for us.*
All ye holy Disciples of the Lord, *pray for us.*
All ye Holy Innocents, *pray for us.*

Salvador Dalí
Palladio's Corridor of Thalia, 1937,
Mie, Japan, Prefectural Art Museum

Saint Stephen, *pray for us.*
Saint Lawrence, *pray for us.*
Saint Vincent, *pray for us.*
Saint Fabian and Saint Sebastian, *pray for us.*
Saint John and Saint Paul, *pray for us.*
Saint Cosmas and Saint Damian, *pray for us.*
Saint Gervasius and Saint Protasius, *pray for us.*
All ye holy Martyrs, *pray for us.*
Saint Sylvester, *pray for us.*
Saint Gregory, *pray for us.*
Saint Ambrose, *pray for us.*
Saint Augustine, *pray for us.*
Saint Jerome, *pray for us.*
Saint Martin, *pray for us.*
Saint Nicholas, *pray for us.*
All ye holy Bishops and Confessors, *pray for us.*
All ye holy Doctors, *pray for us.*
Saint Anthony, *pray for us.*
Saint Benedict, *pray for us.*
Saint Bernard, *pray for us.*
Saint Dominic, *pray for us.*
Saint Francis, *pray for us.*
All ye holy Priests and Levites, *pray for us.*
All ye holy Monks and Hermits, *pray for us.*
Saint Mary Magdalene, *pray for us.*
Saint Agatha, *pray for us.*
Saint Lucy, *pray for us.*
Saint Agnes, *pray for us.*
Saint Cecilia, *pray for us.*
Saint Catherine, *pray for us.*
Saint Anastasia, *pray for us.*
All ye holy Virgins and Widows, *pray for us.*
All ye Holy, Righteous, and Elect of God, *intercede for us.*
Be thou merciful, *spare us, Lord.*
Be thou merciful, *graciously hear us, Lord.*
From all evil, *good Lord, deliver us.*
From all deadly sin, *good Lord, deliver us.*
From thine anger, *good Lord, deliver us.*
From sudden and unrepentant death, *good Lord, deliver us.*
From the crafts and assaults of the devil, *good Lord, deliver us.*
From anger, and hatred, and all uncharitableness, *good Lord, deliver us.*
From the spirit of fornication, *good Lord, deliver us.*

From lightning and tempest, *good Lord, deliver us.*
From the peril of earthquake, fire, and flood, *good Lord, deliver us.*
From pestilence, famine, and battle, *good Lord, deliver us.*
From everlasting damnation, *good Lord, deliver us.*
By the mystery of thy Holy Incarnation, *good Lord, deliver us.*
By thine Advent, *good Lord, deliver us.*
By thy Nativity, *good Lord, deliver us.*
By thy Baptism and holy Fasting, *good Lord, deliver us.*
By thy Cross and Passion, *good Lord, deliver us.*
By thy precious Death and Burial, *good Lord, deliver us.*
By thy holy Resurrection, *good Lord, deliver us.*
By thy glorious Ascension, *good Lord, deliver us.*
By the coming of the Holy Spirit the Comforter, *good Lord, deliver us.*
In the day of judgement, *good Lord, deliver us.*
Even though we be sinners, *we beseech thee to hear us, Lord.*
That it may please thee to spare us, *we beseech thee to hear us, Lord.*
That it may please thee to pity and pardon us, *we beseech thee to hear us, Lord.*
That it may please thee to give us true repentance, *we beseech thee to hear us, Lord.*
That it may please thee to rule and govern thy holy Church, *we beseech thee to hear us, Lord.*
That it may please thee to preserve the Apostolic Lord, and to keep all orders of the Church in thy sacred religion, *we beseech thee to hear us, Lord.*
That it may please thee to overthrow the enemies of thy holy Church, *we beseech thee to hear us, Lord.*

That it may please thee to bestow on all Christian kings and princes true peace and concord, *we beseech thee to hear us, Lord.*
That it may please thee to give to all Christian nations both peace and unity, *we beseech thee to hear us, Lord.*
That it may please thee to restore unity to thy Church, and to lead all unbelievers into the light of thy holy Gospel, *we beseech thee to hear us, Lord.*
That it may please thee to strengthen and preserve us in true worshipping of thee, *we beseech thee to hear us, Lord.*
That it may please thee to endue our hearts with heavenly desires, *we beseech thee to hear us, Lord.*
That it may please thee to bestow on all our benefactors thine everlasting benefits, *we beseech thee to hear us, Lord.*
That it may please thee to deliver from eternal damnation our souls, and those of our brethren, kindred, and benefactors, *we beseech thee to hear us, Lord.*
That it may please thee to give and preserve to our use the kindly fruits of the earth, *we beseech thee to hear us, Lord.*
That it may please thee to bestow upon all thy faithful departed rest eternal, *we beseech thee to hear us, Lord.*
That it may please thee graciously to hear our prayer, *we beseech thee to hear us, Lord.*
O Son of God, *we beseech thee to hear us, Lord.*
O Lamb of God, that takest away the sins of the world, *spare us, Lord.*
O Lamb of God, that takest away the sins of the world, *graciously hear us, Lord.*
O Lamb of God, that takest away the sins of the world, *have mercy upon us.*
O Christ, *hear us.*
O Christ, *graciously hear us.*

8. EXCHANGES BETWEEN LIST AND FORM

In as much as a list characterizes even a dissimilar series of objects as things belonging to the same context or seen from the same point of view (for example, Jesus, Caesar, Cicero, Louis IX, Raymond Lully, Jeanne d'Arc, Gilles de Rais, Damiens, Lincoln, Hitler, Mussolini, Kennedy and Saddam Hussein constitute a homogeneous whole if we consider them as people who did not die in their beds), it confers order, and hence a hint of form, to an otherwise disordered set.

There are subtler ways of transforming a list into form, and the most typical example is Arcimboldo. He took the elements from a possible list (all the fruits or legumes in existence, or all those represented in the form of a list from many still lifes) and composed them into a form, but one that was neither expected nor due. In that certain Baroque way of his, he tells us that you can artfully pass from a list to a form. The form that emerges is different, deformed, and what prevails is the combination of diverse elements—which would have been considered licit on the plates of a table set for dinner and seem incongruous in a human face, but this was Baroque poetics ("the poet's aim is the wonder", as Marino said) and if four centuries were not too many we might find a kinship with the poetics of pre-Surrealism: to quote Lautréamont again, "like the fortuitous encounter on an anatomy table between a sewing machine and an umbrella".

Giuseppe Arcimboldo
Spring, 1573,
Paris, Musée du Louvre

9. THE RHETORIC OF ENUMERATION

Since antiquity, rhetoric has encompassed rhythmically enunciated and enunciable lists, in which it was less important to hint at inexhaustible quantities than to attribute properties to things in a redundant manner, often for pure love of iteration.

In general the various forms of lists would be covered by that figure of thought known as *accumulation*, in other words the sequence and juxtaposition of linguistic terms in some way belonging to the same conceptual sphere. In this sense, one form of accumulation is *enumeratio*, which regularly appears in medieval literature, even when the terms of the list do not seem coherent among themselves, because it was a question of defining the properties of God, which by definition cannot be said (according to Pseudo-Dionysus the Areopagite) unless through dissimilar images. Hence Ennodius (5th century) was to say that Christ is the "source, way, right, rock, lion, light-bearer, lamb—door, hope, virtue, word, wisdom, prophet—victim, scion, shepherd, mountain, nets, dove—flame, giant, eagle, spouse, patience, worm ..." and Notker the Stammerer (11th century) said God was "lamb, sheep, calf, serpent, ram, lion, worm—mouth, word, splendour, sun, glory, light, image—bread, flower, vine, mountain, door, rock, and stone", and not long after him Pierre de Corbeil was to describe the Trinity as "divinity, eternal unity—majesty, liberty, or superior compassion—sun, flame, will, peak, path—stone, mountain, rock, source, river, bridge and life—saviour, creator, lover, redeemer, sage, eternal light ... Summit, chasm, king of kings, law of laws, avenger, angelic light ... hero, most precious

Pietro Longhi (manner of)
The Banquet at Casa Nani, c. 1755,
Venice, Ca' Rezzonico

133

flower, living dew …". As we have already seen with the litanies of the Virgin, such lists are also *panegyric* or *encomiastic*.

Coherent forms of enumeration are those in Racine's *Phaedra* (2.2.: *Mon arc, mes javelots, mon char, tout m'importune*) and this prophetic list by Calvino in "The Moon as a Mushroom" (*The Memory of the World*): "He continued to describe life as it would have evolved on the emerged lands, the cities with the foundations of stone that would have arisen, the roads travelled by camels and horses and dogs and cats, and caravans, and the gold and silver mines, and the forests of sandalwood and Malacca, and the elephants, and the pyramids, and the towers and the clocks, and the lightning conductors, and the tramways, the cranes, the lifts, the skyscrapers, the festoons and the flags on national holidays, the lights of all colours on the façades of the theatres and the cinemas that would be reflected by the pearl necklaces on gala evenings."

Another form of accumulation is the *congeries*, a sequence of words or phrases that all mean the same thing, where the same thought is reproduced under different aspects. This corresponds to the principle of *oratorical amplification*, examples of which are metabola and *commoratio* (or delay, persistence) and paraphrasis itself. By way of example, let us take the first oration against Catiline: "When, O Catiline, will you stop abusing our patience? For how much longer will this madness of yours mock us? Is there no limit to your unbridled audacity? Are you left unaffected by the nightly guard on the Palatine, by the patrols that police the city, by the fears of the people, and all good citizens who come running [to help], by the use of this well fortified place for the Senate's assembly, or by the expressions on the faces of those present? Do you not realize that your plans have been unmasked?" And so on.

Slightly different forms are the *incrementum* or *climax* or *gradatio*: even though they still refer to the same conceptual field at every step they say something more, or with greater intensity (the converse procedure is *decrementum* or *anticlimax*). An example of this is to be found in another oration against Catiline: "You can do nothing, plot

Lucas Cranach
Massacre of the Innocents (detail), 1515,
Dresden, Gemäldegalerie Alte Meister

nothing, imagine nothing, that not only will I understand it, but even if I do not see it, I will penetrate it in depth, I will sense it."

Classical rhetoric also defines enumerations by anaphora and enumerations by *asyndeton* or *polysyndeton*.

Anaphora is the repetition of the same word at the beginning of every phrase, or in the case of poetry, at the beginning of every verse. This does not always establish a list (see for example in Jacopone da Todi, where he simply reiterates an invocation: "O son, son, son,—son, loving lily!—Son, who gives counsel—to my anguished heart?—Son, of merry eye,—son, why do you answer not?—Son, why do you hide—from the breast that suckled you?"). Sometimes instead it is actually the start of a list, as in "Liberté" by **Eluard** or in "Possibility" by **Wisława Szymborska**.

Asyndeton is the typical modality of a list with no conjunctions linking the elements of a phrase; see for example the classic opening words of *Orlando Furioso*: "Of ladies, knights, arms, loves, I sing—of courtesies, and bold deeds". The opposite of *asyndeton*, but a mechanism allowing for lists all the same, is *polysyndeton*, which can be seen for example in Milton's *Paradise Lost* (II, 949–950), where the first verse starts with an *asyndeton* followed by a *polysyndeton* that also dominates the second verse: "With head, hands, wings, or feet pursues his way / And swims or sinks, or wades, or creeps, or flyes."

But in traditional rhetoric there is no interesting definition of what strikes us as the dizzying voraciousness of the list, especially of fairly long lists of different things (albeit rendered homogeneous by a single universe of discourse, such as drink or money) as found in the *Carmina burana* or as we can see, centuries later, in this short passage from Calvino's *The Nonexistent Knight* ("You must sympathize: we are country girls ... apart from religious services, tridua, novenas, work in the fields, threshing, the vintage, the whipping of servants, incest, fires, hangings, invading armies, sack, rape, and pestilence, we have seen nothing.") or in the classic enumerations of **Milton, Villon, Lee Masters**, or **Montale**.

Luca Signorelli
The Damned (detail), 1499-1504,
Orvieto, Duomo,
Cappella di San Brizio

pages 138-139: Martin van Meytens (school of)
*The Arrival of Isabella of Parma on
the Occasion of Her Wedding to Joseph II*, 1760,
Vienna, Schönbrunn Palace

CARMINA BURANA
"WHEN WE ARE AT THE TAVERN",
CARMEN 196

The mistress and the master drink
the soldier and the cleric drink
that man and that woman drink
the servant drinks with the maid
the fast man drinks, so does the slow
the white man drinks, so does the black
the stay-at-home drinks, so does the
   wanderer
the fool drinks, so does the scholar.
The poor drink, and the sick
the exile and the unknown
the boy, the greybeard
the bishop, the deacon
sister, brother
old woman, mother
that woman, this man
they drink by the hundred, by the thousand.

Large sums of money last too short a time
when everybody drinks without moderation
   and limit
even though they drink with a happy heart;
in this everyone sponges on us and it will
   make us poor.
Damnation to those who sponge on us!
Put not their names in the book of Just.

CARMINA BURANA
"VERSES ON MONEY",
CARMEN 11

Everywhere, nowadays, the sole ruler is
   money
Money loves a gentleman and seems to be
   his servant,
Money loves the government and fears
   pennilessness,
Money is worshipped by abbot and friar,
Money reigns supreme above the black-
   frocked prior,
Money advises those who sit at council,
Money brings peace, but also war, if he so
   chooses,
Money causes conflict and can ruin the
   wealthy,
Money can instantly make the mendicant rich,
Money buys and sells, what it gives it takes
   right back,
Money is an adulator but later becomes a
   traitor,
Money always lies, only rarely is it sincere,
Money makes a perjurer of both healthy and
   sick,
Money is dreamt of by the miser and yearned
   for by the greedy,
Money turns lying whores and prostitutes
   into ladies,
Money turns the poor slut into a rich queen.
Money turns even valiant knights into
   rapacious beasts,
Money makes more thieves than there are
   stars in the night sky,
If money is put on trial, rarely does it lose,
If money wins the trial even the judge, deeply
   moved,
Pardons it and justifies the ill-gotten gains.
But money, impudent money, doesn't deny
   the crime,
Instead, all present immediately offer to be
   its guarantors.
If money opens its mouth, the poor man's the
   one to suffer,
Money placates all torments and soothes all
   suffering,
Money brings death and renders even the
   wise man blind.
Money makes even madmen and the
   demented seem smart.

Pieter Bruegel the Younger
Fair with a Theatrical Performance (detail), 1562,
St. Petersburg, Hermitage

With money, you have doctors, but also
treacherous friends,
Money, at its table, has bountiful plates of
food.
Money gives you exquisite dishes and well-
prepared fish,
Money drinks French and other fine foreign
wines.
Money dons very noble and precious garb,
Money, dressed to the nines, is more
resplendent than anything,
Money has diamonds that are the pride
of India.
Money loves to see peoples' backs bent.

Money vilifies and betrays all cities.
Money is worshipped, and heals the sick,
Money, like rouge, masks all imperfections.
Money brings honor to those entirely without
valor,
Money sours all that is sweet and dear,
Money makes the deaf hear and the crippled
walk.
About money I'm willing to say things I can't
keep inside:
Money often seems to celebrate at the altar,
Money is heard singing a solo, or singing with
the chorus,
Money is seen crying as it feigns a sermon,
But behind that mask it's sneering at the trick
it's pulled over.
Without him no one is loved, obeyed or
honored,
With money, even the evil feel at ease.
Above all, it's money that rules, and reigns
everywhere supreme.
Only wisdom flees from and distains it.

JOHN MILTON
PARADISE LOST, BOOK I, VV. 476-634 (1667)

[...]
Nor had they yet among the Sons of Eve
Got them new names, till, wandring o'er
  the earth,
Through God's high sufferance for the trial
  of man,
By falsities and lies the greatest part
Of mankind they corrupted to forsake
God their Creator, and th' invisible
Glory of him that made them, to transform
Oft to the image of a brute, adorn'd
With gay religions full of pomp and gold,
And devils to adore for deities:
Then were they known to men by various
  names,
And various idols through the Heathen world.
  Say, Muse, their names then known, who
  first, who last,
Rous'd from the slumber, on that fiery couch,
At their great emperor's call, as next in worth
Came singly where he stood on the bare strand,
While the promiscuous crowd stood yet aloof!
  The chief were those who from the pit of
  Hell,
Roaming to seek their prey on earth, durst fix
Their seats long after next the seat of God,
Their altars by his altar; gods ador'd
Among the nations round; and durst abide
Jehovah thundering out of Sion, thron'd
Between the Cherubim: yea, often plac'd
Within his sanctuary itself their shrines,
Abominations, and with cursed things
His holy rites and solemn feasts profan'd
And with their darkness durst affront his light.
  First, Moloch, horrid king, besmear'd with
  blood
Of human sacrifice, and parents' tears;
Though for the noise of drums and timbrels
  loud
Their children's cries unheard, pass'd that
  past through fire
To his grim idol. Him the Ammonite
Worship in Rabba and her watery plain,

Peter Paul Rubens
The Fall of the Rebel Angels, c. 1620,
Munich, Alte Pinakothek

In Argob and in Basan, to the stream
Of utmost Arnon: nor content with such
Audacious neighbourhood, the wisest heart
Of Salomon he led by fraud to build
His temple right against the temple of God,
On that opprobrious hill; and made his grove
The pleasant valley of Hinnom, Tophet thence
And black Gehenna call'd, the type of Hell.
  Next, Chemos, the obscene dread of
  Moab's sons,
For Aroer to Nebo, and the wild
Of southmost Abarim, in Hesebon
And Heronaim, Seon's realm, beyond
The flowery dale of Sibma clad with vines,
And Eleale to th' Asphaltick pool.
Peor his other name, when he entic'd
Israel in Sittim, on their march from Nile,
To do him wanton rites, which cost them woe.
Yet thence his lustful Orgies he enlarg'd,
Even to that hill of scandal, by the grove
Of Moloch homicide, lust hard by hate;
Till good Josiah drove them thence to Hell.
  With these came they, who, from the
  bordering flood
Of old Euphrates to the brook that parts
Egypt from Syrian ground, had general
  names
Of Baalim and Ashtaroth; those male,
These Feminine: for Spirits, when they please,
Can either sex assume, or both; so soft
And uncompounded is their essence pure;
Not tied or manacled with joint or limb,
Nor founded on the brittle strength of bones,
Like cumbrous flesh; but, in what shape they
  choose,
Dilated or condens'd, bright or obscure,
Can execute their aery purposes,
And works of love or enmity fulfil.
For those the race of Israel oft forsook
Their living strength, and unfrequented left
His righteous altar, bowing lowly down
To bestial gods; for which their heads as low
Bow'd down in battle, sunk before the spear
Of despicable foes. With these in troop
Came Astoreth, whom the Phœnicians call'd
Astarte, queen of Heaven, with crescent
  horns:
To whose bright image nightly by the moon
Sidonian Virgins paid their vows and songs:
In Sion also not unsung, where stood,
Her temple on the offensive mountain, built

By that uxorious king, whose heart, though
    large,
Beguil'd by fair idolatresses, fell
To idols foul.
Thammuz came next behind,
Whose annual wound in Lebanon allur'd
The Syrian damsels to lament his fate
In amorous ditties all a summer's day;
While smooth Adonis from his native rock
Ran purple to the sea, suppos'd with blood
Of Thammuz yearly wounded: the love-tale
Infected Sion's daughters with like heat;
Whose wanton passions in the sacred porch
Ezekiel saw, when, by the vision led,
His eye survey'd the dark idolatries
Of alienated Judah. Next came one
Who mourn'd in earnest, when the captive
    ark
Maim'd his brute image, head and hands lopt
    off
In his own temple, on the grunsel-edge,
Where he fell flat, and sham'd his worshipers:
Dagon his name, sea-monster, upward man
And downward fish: yet had his temple high
Rear'd in Azotus, dreaded through the coast
Of Palestine, in Gath and Ascalon,
And Accaron and Gaza's frontier-bounds.
Him follow'd Rimmon. whose delightful seat
Was fair Damascus, on the fertile banks
Of Abbana and Pharphar, lucid streams.
He also against the house of God was bold!
A Leper once he lost, and gain'd a king;
Ahaz, his sottish conquerour, whom he drew
God's altar to disparage and displace,
For one of Syrian mode, whereon to burn
His odious offerings, and adore the Gods
Whom he had vanquish'd. After these
    appear'd
A crew, who, under names of old renown,
Osiris, Isis, Orus, and their train,
With monstrous shapes and sorceries abus'd
Fanatic Egypt and her priests, to seek
Their wandering gods, disguis'd in brutish
    forms
Rather then human. Nor did Israel 'scape
The infection, when their borrow'd gold
    compos'd
The calf in Oreb, and the rebel king
Doubled that sin in Bethel and in Dan,
Likening his Maker to the grazed ox;
Jehovah, who in one night, when he pass'd

From Egypt marching, equal with one stroke
Both her first-born, and all her bleating gods.
Belial came last, than whom a spirit more
    lewd
Fell not from Heaven, or more gross to love
Vice for itself; to him no temple stood
Or altar smok'd; yet who more oft than he
In temples and at altars, when the priest
Turns atheist, as did Ely's sons, who fill'd
With lust and violence the house of God?
In courts and palaces he also reigns,
And in luxurious cities, where the noise
Of riot ascends above their loftiest towers,
And injury and outrage; and when night
Darkens the streets, then wander forth the
    sons
Of Belial, flown with insolence and wine.
Witness the streets of Sodom, and that night
In Gibeah, when the hospitable door
Expos'd a matron, to avoid worse rape.
These were the prime in order and in might:
The rest were long to tell [...]

Daniele da Volterra (Daniele Ricciarelli)
Moses on Mount Sinai, 1545-1555,
Dresden, Staatliche Kunstsammlungen, Gemäldegalerie

FRANÇOIS VILLON
BALLADS FROM FRANÇOIS VILLON
"THE BALLAD OF DEAD LADIES"
(1489)

Tell me now in what hidden way is
Lady Flora the lovely Roman?
Where's Hipparchia, and where is Thais,
Neither of them the fairer woman?
Where is Echo, beheld of no man,
Only heard on river and mere,—
She whose beauty was more than human?...
But where are the snows of yester-year?

Where's Héloise, the learned nun,
For whose sake Abeillard, I ween,
Lost manhood and put priesthood on?
(From Love he won such dule and teen!)
And where, I pray you, is the Queen
Who willed that Buridan should steer
Sewed in a sack's mouth down the Seine?...
But where are the snows of yester-year?

EUGENIO MONTALE
COLLECTED POEMS, 1920-1954
"KEEPSAKE" (1939)

Fanfan returns the victor; Molly's sold
at auction: a reflector fries.
Surcouf strides the quarterdeck,
Gaspard counts his money in his hole.
Snow fell in the limpid afternoon,
the Cicada flies back to his nest.
Fatinitza agonizes in a lapse of memory,
A shout is all that's left of Tonio.
False Spaniards play *The Brigands*
at the castle; but the bloodcurdling
alarm squeals in a pocket.
The Marchese del Grillo's sent
into the street again; unhappy Zeffirino
returns a clerk; the Druggist stands,
and the matches strike on the floor.
The Musketeers desert the convent,
Van Schlisch hurries to his horse,
Takimini fans herself, the Doll gets wound.
(Imary goes back to his apartment.)
Thrilling La Rivaudière and Pitou
lie askance. Friday dreams
of his green islands and won't dance.

A Dance at the Castle
illustration from Christine de Pizan's
The Book of the City of Ladies, **1405,**
Chantilly, Musée Condé

EDGAR LEE MASTERS
THE SPOON RIVER ANTHOLOGY
"THE HILL" (1916)

Where are Elmer, Herman, Bert, Toni and Charley,
The weak of will, the strong of arm, the
    clown, the boozer, the fighter?
All, all, are sleeping on the hill.

One passed in a fever,
One was burned in a mine,
One was killed in a brawl,
One died in a jail,
One fell from a bridge toiling for children
    and wife—
All, all are sleeping, sleeping, sleeping on the hill.

Where are Ella, Kate, Mag, Lizzie and Edith,
The tender heart, the simple soul, the loud,
    the proud, the happy one?—
All, all, are sleeping on the hill.

One died in shameful child-birth,
One of a thwarted love,
One at the hands of a brute in a brothel,
One of a broken pride, in the search for
    heart's desire,
One after life in far-away London and Paris
Was brought to her little space by Ella and
    Kate and Mag—
All, all are sleeping, sleeping, sleeping on the hill.

Where are Uncle Isaac and Aunt Emily,
And old Towny Kincaid and Sevigne Houghton,
And Major Walker who had talked
With venerable men of the revolution?—
All, all, are sleeping on the hill.

They brought them dead sons from the war,
And daughters whom life had crushed,
And their children fatherless, crying—
All, all are sleeping, sleeping, sleeping on the hill.

Old Jewish Cemetery,
Prague

PAUL ÉLUARD
"LIBERTY"
(1945)

On my school notebooks
On my desk and on the trees
On the powdery snow
I write your name

On the pages read
On all the blank pages
Stone, blood, paper or ash
I write your name

On the gilt images
On the warriors' weapons
On the king's crown
I write your name

On the jungle and the desert
On the nests and the briers
On the echo of my youth
I write your name

On all my blue scarves
On the damp sunlit swamps
On the living moonlit lake
I write your name

On the fields, on the horizon
On the birds' wings
And on the shadowy mill
I write your name

On every daybreak breeze
On the sea, on the boats

On the demented peaks
I write your name

On the froth of the cloud
On the sweat of the storm
On the dense, flat rain
I write your name

On the scintillating forms
On the colorful bells
On the physical truth
I write your name

On the elevated paths
On the deployed roads
On the overcrowded city
  square
I write your name

On the lit lamp
On the spent lamp
On my reunited reasonings
I write your name

On the bisected fruit
Of my mirror and my room
On my bed, my empty shell
I write your name

On my dog, sweet gourmand
On his piqued ears
On his blundering paws
I write your name

On the latch of my door
On those familiar objects

On the torrent of a bonfire
I write your name

On all comfortable flesh
On the foreheads of my
  friends
On all outstretched hands
I write your name

On the windowpane of
  surprises
On the expectant lips
Far deeper than silence
I write your name

On my ruined hiding-places
On my sunken lighthouses
On my walls and my
  boredom
I write your name

On absence without desire
On naked solitude
On death's march
I write your name

And by the power of a word
I regain my life
I was born to know you
To name you

Liberty.

WISŁAWA SZYMBORSKA
"POSSIBILITIES"
(1985)

I prefer movies.
I prefer cats.
I prefer the oaks along the Warta.
I prefer Dickens to Dostoyevsky.
I prefer myself liking people
to myself loving mankind.
I prefer keeping a needle and thread on hand,
    just in case.
I prefer the color green.
I prefer not to maintain
that reason is to blame for everything.
I prefer exceptions.
I prefer to leave early.
I prefer talking to doctors about something
    else.
I prefer the old fine-lined illustrations.
I prefer the absurdity of writing poems
to the absurdity of not writing poems.
I prefer, where love's concerned, nonspecific
    anniversaries
that can be celebrated every day.

I prefer moralists
who promise me nothing.
I prefer cunning kindness to the over-trustful
    kind.
I prefer the earth in civvies.
I prefer conquered to conquering countries.
I prefer having some reservations.
I prefer the hell of chaos to the hell of order.
I prefer Grimms' fairy tales to the
    newspapers' front pages.
I prefer leaves without flowers to flowers
    without leaves.
I prefer dogs with uncropped tails.
I prefer light eyes, since mine are dark.
I prefer desk drawers.
I prefer many things that I haven't mentioned
    here
to many things I've also left unsaid.
I prefer zeroes on the loose
to those lined up behind a cipher.
I prefer the time of insects to the time of stars.
I prefer to knock on wood.
I prefer not to ask how much longer and when.
I prefer keeping in mind even the possibility
that existence has its own reason for being.

10. LISTS OF MIRABILIA

Pliny's *Natural History* (a prototype of all ancient and medieval encyclopaedias) is a collection of about 20,000 facts and about 500 sources. At first sight it looks like an authentic congeries that naturally is not in alphabetic order but does not even seem to correspond to a systematic plan—and so it would merely be a list. Yet, if we examine the index carefully, we see that the work starts from the heavens, then deals with geography, demography and ethnography, followed by anthropology and human physiology, zoology, botany, agriculture, horticulture, natural pharmacopeia, medicine and magic, before moving on to mineralogy, architecture and the plastic arts—establishing a sort of hierarchy from the original to the derived, and from the natural to the artificial.

It seems that medieval encyclopaedias also had extremely vague
classificatory criteria and represent simple lists of disconnected
information. In his *Etymologies*, **Isidore of Seville** considers the seven
liberal arts, grammar, rhetoric, dialectics, music, arithmetic, geometry,
astronomy, medicine, ecclesiastical law, books, and offices, languages,
people, and armies, words, man, animals, the world, buildings, stones
and metals, agriculture, wars, games, the theatre, ships, clothing, the
home and domestic tasks—and one wonders what order can underlie
such a list, in which for example the part about animals is divided
into Beasts, Small Animals, Snakes, Worms, Fish, Birds and Small
Winged Animals, while the crocodile is classified among the Fish.
But in Isidore's day basic education was divided into Trivium and

Jan Bruegel the Elder (school of)
Allegory of Fire, 1607-1608,
Paris, Musée du Louvre

page 152: *A Greyhound*, from Bartholomaeus Anglicus'
On the Properties of Things, ms. 993, fol. 254v., c. 1416,
Reims, Bibliothèque municipale

page 153: Jacob Savery the Elder
The Animals Entering the Ark, 17th century,
private collection

Quadrivium, and in fact Isidore devotes the first books to these subjects, with the inclusion of medicine. The chapters that follow, on ecclesiastical laws and offices, are present because he was also writing for the learned, jurists, and monks. Immediately after, there comes another order: this begins in Book VII with God, the angels and the saints before moving on to man and the animals, while from Book XIII he considers the world and its parts, winds, waters and mountains. Finally, in Book XV we come to inanimate but artificial things, i.e., to the various arts. Although Isidore juxtaposes two criteria syncretistically, he does not accumulate at random and in the second part he follows a decreasing order of dignity, from God down to domestic utensils.

Hence these encyclopaedias presumed (or still looked for) a form, also because their organization had a *mnemonic function*: things in a given order help us to remember them, to remember the place they occupied in the image of the world. But this happened, if it happened, only for highly specialized readers. For the others the fascinating thing (one that still fascinates us) was probably the list of *mirabilia*, like the ones that appeared in many Hellenic collections such as the *De Mirabilibus* attributed to **Aristotle** (of which the anthology gives only 14 prodigies out of the 178 listed), the list of portents and monstrous beings in Isidore of Seville, in the *Liber monstrorum diversi generibus*, in Mandeville's *Travels*, in **Marbodus of Rennes'** list of gems, or in Gervase of Tilbury's *Otia imperialia*, where among other things the author mentions the magnet, Agrigentine salt, asbestos, the Egyptian fig, the fruits of Pentapolis, the stone that follows the cycle of the moon, the meat of Naples that cannot rot, the baths of Pozzuoli, the upside-down bean, the gates of hell, the Holy Face of Edessa, the combat of beetles, hot sands, the windows at which ladies appear, water that never boils, silk, dolphins, mermaids, the fox, the equinocephali, bearded women, the phoenix, men with eight feet, nocturnal larvae, the crow's egg in the stork's nest, and birds born of trees ...

The list of *mirabilia* takes on a purely poetic function in modern authors who use ancient information knowing that the lists refer to nothing existent and are pure catalogues of the imagination, enjoyable solely because they are cases of *flatus vocis*. And so, in his

Book of Imaginary Beings, Borges lists pygmies, dragons, Abtu and Anet, the elephant that foretold the birth of Buddha, elves, sylphs, the banshee, Haokah, god of thunder, gnomes, Lilith, the Chinese fox, Youwarkee, the Cheshire cat and the Kilkenny cats, nymphs, the double, Fatistocalón, the angels and demons of Swedenborg, the Lamed Wufniks, brownies, Valkyries, the Norns, the demons of Hebraism, Hochigan, the Eloi and the Morlocks, trolls, fairies, lamias, lemurs, the Kuyata, satyrs, the heavenly cockerel, the rain bird and so on.

ARISTOTLE [?] (IV CENT. B.C.) "DE MIRABILIBUS AUSCULTATIONIBUS", CHAPTERS 7-20

Men say that in Egypt the sandpipers fly into the mouths of crocodiles, and cleanse their teeth, pulling out the pieces of flesh, which stick in their snouts, while the crocodiles are pleased, and do them no harm.

Men say that the hedgehogs in Byzantium perceive when north or south winds are blowing, and immediately change their holes; and, when the winds are southerly, make their holes opening out of the ground, but, when they are northerly, out of the walls. The she-goats in Cephallenia do not drink, as it appears, like other quadrupeds; but daily turning their faces towards the sea, open their mouths, and take in the breezes.

Men say that in Syria herds of wild asses are led by one male. When one of the younger males copulates with one of the females, the alpha male grows irate, and chases the other until he catches him, bends him onto his rear hooves, and bites his genitalia off.*

Men say that tortoises, when they have eaten part of a viper, eat marjoram as an antidote, and, if the creature fails to find it at once, it dies; that many of the country-folk, wishing to prove whether this is true, whenever they see it acting in this manner, pluck up the marjoram, and when they have done so, the tortoise is presently seen dying.

Men say that the genitalia of male weasels are unlike that of any other animal, but are extremely hard, almost as if they were bone, as sometimes is the case. It seems that these are among the best remedies for urinary difficulty; they are administered after being scraped clean.*

Men say that the bird called the woodpecker climbs upon trees like a lizard, both hanging from and standing on the branches. It is further stated that it feeds upon the grubs out of trees, and digs so deeply into the trees, in its search for the grubs, that it even brings the trees down.

Men say that the pelicans dig up the mussels that are found in the rivers, and swallow them; then, when they have devoured a large quantity of these, they vomit them up again, and thereupon eat the meat of the mussels, but do not touch the shells.

Men say that in Cyllene in Arcadia the blackbirds are born white, which happens nowhere else, and that they give utterance to various sounds, and go forth by the light of the moon; but that, if any one should attempt to capture them by day, they are caught with great difficulty.

It is stated by certain persons that what is called flower-honey is produced in Melos and Knidos, and that, while fragrant in smell, it lasts for only a short time; and that in it bee-bread is produced.

In some parts of Cappadocia they say that the honey is made without a honey-comb, and that in consistency it resembles olive-oil. At Trapezus in Pontus the honey gathered from the box-tree is produced, having an oppressive smell, and they say that this drives out of their senses those who are sound in mind, while it completely cures those who suffer from epilepsy.

Men say that in Lydia also the honey is gathered from the trees in abundance, and that the inhabitants form out of it balls without wax, cutting off portions by very violent rubbing to make use of it. It is produced indeed in Thrace likewise, not so solid, but as it were of a sandy nature. They say that all honey when congealed preserves an equal volume, not like water and all other liquids.

The grass of Chalcis and almonds are most useful for making honey; for they say that a very large quantity is produced by them.

Fantastic Animals of Egypt, **from Robinet Testard's** *Livre des merveilles du monde, ou Secret de l'histoire naturelle,* **fol. 15v, c. 1480-1485, Paris, Bibliothèque Nationale de France**

* Paragraphs marked with an asterisk appeared in the original Latin in this English-language edition; translations here are by Alta L. Price.

ISIDORE OF SEVILLE (570-636)
THE ETYMOLOGIES OF ISIDORE OF SEVILLE
FROM BOOK XI, "THE HUMAN BEING AND PORTENTS," III, 6-27

There is a difference between a "portent" (*portentum*) and "an unnatural being" (*portentuosus*). Portents are beings of transformed appearance, as, for instance, is said to have happened when in Umbria a woman gave birth to a serpent. Whence Lucan says (*Civil War* 1.563): "And the child terrified its own mother."
But an unnatural being strictly speaking takes the form of a slight mutation, as for instance in the case of someone born with six fingers.

Portents, then, or unnatural beings, exist in some cases in the form of a size of the whole body that surpasses common human nature, as in the case of Tityos who, as Homer witnesses, covered nine jugers (i.e. about six acres) when lying prostrate; in other cases in the form of a smallness of the whole body, as in dwarfs (*nanus*), or those whom the Greeks call pygmies (*pygmaeus*), because they are a cubit tall. Others are so called due to the size of the parts of their bodies, as for instance a misshapen head, or due to superfluous parts of their limbs, as in the case of two-headed and three-headed individuals, or in the case of the *cynodontes* (i.e. "dog-toothed" people), who have a pair of projecting fangs. Yet others are so called due to missing parts of the body, individuals in whom one corresponding part is deficient compared with the other, as when one hand is compared with the other hand and one foot with the other foot. Others due to a cutting off, as in

Jacopo Bassano
Animals Boarding Noah's Ark, 1570-1579,
Madrid, Museo del Prado

the case of those born without a head, whom the Greeks call *steresios* [from the Greek root for "deprivation"]. [...] Others in the form of *praenumeria*, when only the head or a leg is born.

Others, who are transformed in a part of the body, as for instance those who have the features of a lion or of a dog, or the head or body of a bull, as they relate in the case of the Minotaur born of Pasiphae [...]. Others become a portent due to a complete transformation into a different creature, as in the story of a woman who gave birth to a calf. Others, who have a change in the position of features without any transformation, such as those with eyes in their chest or forehead, or ears above their temples, or, as Aristotle relates, someone who had his liver on the left side

and his spleen on the right. Others, because of a joined begetting, as when in one hand several fingers are found joined at birth and fused together, and in the other hand fewer— and likewise with the feet. Others, with a feature that is premature and untimely, as those who are born with teeth or a beard or white hair. Others, with a complex of several oddities [...] Others, from a mixing of sexes, like those they call the "androgynes" [...] Hermaphrodites are so named because both sexes appear in them.... These, having a male right breast and a female left breast, in sexual intercourse sire and bear children in turn.

Just as, in individual nations, there are instances of monstrous people, so in the whole of humankind there are certain monstrous races, like the Giants, the Cynocephali (i.e. "dog-headed people"), the Cyclopes, and others. Giants (*Gigantes*) are so called according to the etymology of a Greek term; the Greeks suppose that they are [...]

Kaspar Memberger
The Animals Entering the Ark, 1588,
Vienna, Kunsthistorisches Museum, Gemäldegalerie

"earthborn," because in their fable the parent Earth begot them as like itself, with their immense mass [as the term's Greek roots mean "earth" and "offspring," hence "offspring of the earth"]. However, those whose parentage is uncertain are also commonly called "sons of the earth." But some, inexperienced with Holy Scripture (i.e. Genesis 6:4), falsely suppose that apostate angels lay with the daughters of humans before the Flood, and that from this the Giants were born—that is, excessively large and powerful men—and filed the earth. The Cynocephali are so called because they have dogs' heads, and their barking indeed reveals that they are rather beasts than humans. These originate in India. India also produces the *Cyclopes*, and they are called Cyclops because they are believed to have a single eye in the middle of their foreheads. [...] People believe that the Blemmyans in Libya are born as trunks without heads, and having their mouth and eyes in their chest, and that another race is born without necks and having their eyes in their shoulders. Moreover, people write about the monstrous faces of nations in the far East: some with no noses, having completely flat faces and a shapeless countenance; some with a lower lip so protruding that when they are sleeping it protects the whole face from the heat of the sun; some with mouths grown shut, taking in nourishment only through a small opening by means of hollow straws. Some are said to have no tongues, using nods or gestures in place of words. They tell of the Panotians of Scythia, who have such huge ears that they cover all the body [...]. The Artabatitans of

Nathaniel Currier
Noah's Ark, 19th century,
New York, Brooklyn Museum of Art

French School
Noah's Ark, copy from a 12th-century manuscript,
Paris, Bibliothèque des Arts Decoratifs

Ethiopia are said to walk on all fours, like cattle; none passes the age of forty.
The Satyrs are little people with hooked noses; they have horns on their foreheads, and feet like goats'—the kind of creature that Saint Anthony saw in the wilderness. When questioned by the servant of God, this Satyr is said to have responded [...] "I am one of the mortals that dwell in the desert, whom the pagans, deluded by their fickle error, worship as Fauns and Satyrs." There are also said to be a kind of wild men, whom some call Fauns of the fig. The race of Sciopodes are said to live in Ethiopia; they have only one leg, and are wonderfully speedy. The Greeks call them [...] "shade-footed ones" because when it is hot they lie on their backs on the ground and are shaded by the great size of their feet.
The Antipodes in Libya have the soles of their feet twisted behind their legs, and eight toes on each foot. The Hippopodes are in Scythia, and have a human form and horses' hooves. In India there are said to be a race [...] who are twelve feet tall. There, too, is a race a cubit tall [...] they live in the mountainous regions of India, near the Ocean. They also claim that in the same India is a race of women who conceive when they are five years old and do not live beyond eight.

MARBODUS, BISHOP OF RENNES (1035-1123)
LIBELLVS DE LAPIDIBVS PRECIOSIS NVPER EDITVS "MARVELOUS GEMS"

Jasper is useful against lightning and thunder. Chalcedony is a protective stone, and, worn in a necklace or ring, cures lunacy ... In his book *De lapidibus*, Aristotle writes: "An emerald, hung around one's neck or worn on one's finger, protects against a suspected case of epilepsy." This is why noblemen are advised to hang emeralds 'round their children's necks, such that they do succumb to this illness ... Sard [a type of carnelian], when worn around the neck or finger as a gem weighing twenty grains of barley, prevents one from horrible and distressing nightmares, and also protects against spells and curses. Chrysolite, a thick and glossy stone somewhat similar to gold, wards off all sorts of snakes. Applied upon gold powder and then washed, it forms a protective talisman against nighttime fears; drilled with a hole, strung upon hair from a donkey's mane, and tied around the left arm, it wards off demons... Beryl is a large, polished stone. Carve a lobster into this gem, and under it a crow, and place the entire stone atop a small bunch of herbal Sabina sealed in gold. Once consecrated and worn by married couples, this talisman protects them from all illness and has medicinal properties to cure all diseases of the eye. If you put this stone in water and give the infusion to someone to drink, that person will be cleansed and re-energized, and his liver will be freed from all pain. It is useful to carry this stone at all times, and anyone who wears it will be victorious, defeating all his enemies. It is found in India, much like emerald, but is a paler stone. When one wears topaz, not even an enemy can do him any harm. It should be kept in the home to ward off evildoers. If one wears jacinth around the neck or finger, he may venture into a diseased region and still not fall sick; rather, he will be honored by all and his wishes will come to pass. Immersed in water and given to a barren wife to drink, amethyst will immediately make the woman pregnant. Agate aids women who have had a miscarriage, and immediately brings about a successful birth. Sard is a good talisman, and very helpful for women. Carve a vine or climbing ivy into the stone. Onyx enables anyone who has had a vision to properly interpret it. Carnelian, worn around the neck or finger, mitigates the effects of anger and conflict. It brings freedom to the chaste, and those who consecrate this gem following the proper procedure will be completely freed. But the stone must be prepared as follows: carve a scarab into it, and under its belly carve a man. It must then be placed vertically,

Saint Stephen's Reliquary, **9th century**
Vienna, Kunsthistorisches Museum

consecrated, and worn upon a gold fibula; when placed in a spot specially prepared and adorned as if for a ritual, it will unleash the full glory granted it by God. Jasper symbolizes the strength of faith. Sapphire symbolizes sublime, heavenly hope. Chalcedony harbors the flame of intimate love; emerald represents the courageous prophecy of faith against all adversity; sardonyx [banded agate] symbolizes the humility of the saints and virtues; sard reverently represents the blood of martyrs; chrysolite symbolizes the a spiritual sermon amid miracles; beryl represents the perfect works of preachers, and topaz symbolizes their ardent contemplation; jacinth symbolizes the heavenly ascension of the [Church] doctors and the humbling descension of the ill to the realm of mortal humans. Amethyst represents the humble spirit's memory of the heavenly kingdom. Thus each gemstone has specific properties, because—as all gems that adorned the foundations of the City of God, atop His holy mountain, are perfect—all stones are refulgent with light and spiritual grace.

11. COLLECTIONS AND TREASURES

A museum catalogue is an example of a practical list which refers to objects that exist in a predetermined place, and as such it is necessarily finite. But how should we consider a museum in itself, or any kind of collection? Except for extremely rare cases of collections that contain *all* the objects of a certain type (for example, all, and I mean all, the works of a given artist), a collection is always open and could always be increased with the addition of some other element. Especially if the collection is based, as was the case with Roman patricians, medieval lords, or modern galleries and museums, on a taste for accumulation and expansion ad infinitum.

DAVID · TENIERS · F.

page 164: Hubert Robert
View of the Grand Gallery of the Louvre, circa 1789,
1789-1799,
Paris, Musée du Louvre

page 165: Alexandre Brun
Visit to the Salon Carré at the Louvre, circa 1880,
20th century,
Paris, Musée du Louvre

pages 166-167: David Teniers the Younger
Archduke Leopold Wilhelm in his Gallery, c. 1650,
Madrid, Museo del Prado

Damien Hirst
Anatomy of an Angel and *The Abyss*, 2008,
London, Sotheby's

What is more, save for highly specialized cases (again: all and exclusively the works of painter such-and-such) collections always verge on the incongruous. A space traveller unaware of our concept of art would wonder why the Louvre contains trifles in common use such as vases, plates or salt cellars, icons of a goddess such as the Venus de Milo, representations of landscapes, portraits of normal people, grave goods and mummies, portrayals of monstrous creatures, objects of worship, images of human beings suffering torture, accounts of battles, nudes calculated to arouse sexual attraction and even archaeological finds.

But we do not need to imagine a visitor from space. In 1923 Paul Valéry expressed his irritation with museums:[1] "I don't like museums much. There are some admirable ones, but none is delightful. The ideas of classification, of conservation and public utility, which are correct and clear, have little to do with delights [...] I find myself in a tumult of frozen creatures, each of which demands, without obtaining it, the inexistence of all the others [...] A strange organized disorder spreads out before me. I am seized by a holy dread. My gait becomes religious. My voice changes, becoming a little higher as if I were in church, but lower than it is in life. Soon I no longer know what I came to do in this waxen solitude, redolent of the temple and the salon, the cemetery and school [...] What an effort, I tell myself, what barbarities! All this is inhuman. It is not pure. This onset of independent and inimical marvels, and the more inimical the more they resemble one another, is paradoxical [...] The ear would not bear ten orchestras playing at once. The spirit cannot follow many distinct operations, there are no simultaneous arguments. But here the eye [...] as soon as it perceives, finds itself obliged to admit a portrait and a seascape, a kitchen and a triumph, characters in the most diverse poses and conditions, and not just this, it must also embrace in the same glance harmonies and ways of painting that elude comparison with one another [...] productions that devour one another [...] But our heritage crushes us. Modern man, exhausted by the enormousness of his technical means, is impoverished by the very excess of his own riches [...] An excessive capital and therefore a useless one."

Perhaps Valéry was in a bad mood that day, given that fourteen years later he was to write for the façade of the Palais de Chaillot verses in honour of the museum exhibition (*Choses rares et choses belles—ici savamment assemblées—instruisent l'oeil à regarder—comme jamais ancore vues—toutes choses qui sont au monde*). But as far as the traditional museum is concerned he certainly grasped three characteristics: (i) it is a silent, dark, unfriendly ambience, (ii) where the lack of context for single works made it hard to perceive them individually or memorize them all, and (iii) its voraciousness was oppressive. Today developments in museum organization have ensured that Valéry's first two objections no longer apply: museums have become bright, sunny, friendly, welcoming, and the distribution of the rooms almost always favours the relationship between the work and its context. But we are still left with the problem of the third characteristic, in fact people visit museums precisely because such institutions are voracious by definition. This is because they spring from private collections, and private collections spring from rapine, the spoils of war. Pliny (*Nat. Hist.* 37, 13-14) says: "It was Pompey's victory that created the fashion for pearls and gems, as those of Scipio and Manlius created the fad for tooled silverware, Attalic cloths and triclinia adorned with bronze; and as that of Lucius Mummius created the fashion for Corinthian vases and paintings." From this booty (or, if you prefer, the right of conquest) sprang the accumulation of important objects, and a pride in increasing that accumulation.

According to Krysztof Pomian,[2] while at first people collected religiously, and in private places, grave-goods (we need only think of the treasures buried with the pharaohs), or gifts received from the temple, collection very soon turned to objects that he calls "semiophoric", in other words things—often over and above their selling value—that were signs, witnesses to something else, to the past they come from, to an exotic world of which they are the only documents, to the invisible world.

While we know little of the collections of the Roman patricians, we have more information about the medieval taste for accumulation. In the **"treasuries"** of the period we find relics, precious stones,

Joseph Cornell
Untitled (Pharmacy), 1943,
Paris, Collection Mrs. Marcel Duchamp

curious, surprising, marvellous and unexpected items. Many of these treasures have now disappeared or have been dispersed, such as the Duc de Berry's renowned collection, or that of the Abbey of Saint-Denis whose abbot in the 12th century was the great Suger, a refined collector, a devotee of gems, pearls, ivories, golden candelabra, historiated altarpieces, and a man who had made a sort of religion and a mystico-philosophical theory out of the collection of precious objects. The best of Suger's collection was dispersed during the French Revolution, and the abbot-bishop's famed chalice is now in London. But most of the surviving part is in the Louvre.

The most venerated marvels of the medieval treasuries were the relics. The cult of relics is not just a Christian phenomenon, and Pliny tells us of relics that were dear to the Greco-Roman world: Orpheus' lyre, Helen's sandal, or the bones of the monster that attacked Andromeda. The presence of a relic was a boon for a city or a church in the Middle Ages, because it was not just a sacred object but also a valuable tourist attraction.

In St. Vitus' Cathedral, in Prague, you can find the craniums of St. Adalbert and St. Wenceslas, St. Stephen's sword, a fragment of the Cross, the table cloth used for the Last Supper, one of St. Margaret's teeth, a fragment of St. Vitalius' shinbone, one of St. Sophia's ribs, St. Eoban's chin, Moses' rod and the Virgin's dress. The catalogue of the Duc de Berry's fabulous collection, now dispersed, included St. Joseph's engagement ring, but in Vienna you can still admire a piece of the manger in Bethlehem, St. Stephen's purse, the spear that struck Jesus in the side (plus a nail from the Cross), Charlemagne's sword, one of John the Baptist's teeth, one of St. Anne's arm bones, the chains of the apostles, a piece of John the Baptist's robes, and another piece of the tablecloth used for the Last Supper. Nor should we forget the larynx of St. Charles Borromeo to be found in the treasury of Milan Cathedral. Indeed, on consulting that cathedral's inventory (*l'Inventario dei paramenti e delle suppellettili sacre del Duomo*

Arman (Armand Fernandez)
La poubelle de Bernard Venet, 1970,
Collection Bernard Venet

di Milano), we realize that—apart from splendid regalia, vases, ivories, and gold—the various sacristies hold some thorns from the Crown of Thorns, a piece of the Cross, various bits and pieces of St. Agnes, St. Agatha, St. Catherine, St. Praxedes and of the Saints Simplicianus, Caius, and Gerontius.

The fact is that even an unbeliever cannot resist the fascination of two portents. First of all the object itself, those anonymous, yellowing pieces of cartilage, mystically repugnant, pathetic,

Clasp of an Ecclesiastical Cope with the Annunciation, 9th century, Aachen, Treasury of the Dom

Martin-Guillaume Biennais *Hand of Justice (Hand of Saint-Denis),* 1804, Paris, Musée du Louvre

and mysterious; the scraps of clothing, from goodness knows what period, faded, discoloured, threadbare, sometimes rolled up in a phial like some strange message in a bottle, material that is often crumbling away to blend in with the fabric and the metal or the bone they lie in. And in the second place the containers, often incredibly precious, sometimes constructed by a pious bricoleur who used bits of other relics, in the form of towers, little cathedrals with pinnacles and cupolas, not to mention certain Baroque relics (the finest are in Vienna), which are a forest of tiny sculptures, and look like clocks, music boxes, or magical boxes. Some will remind lovers of modern art of Joseph Cornell's surrealist boxes, Arman's cabinets full of

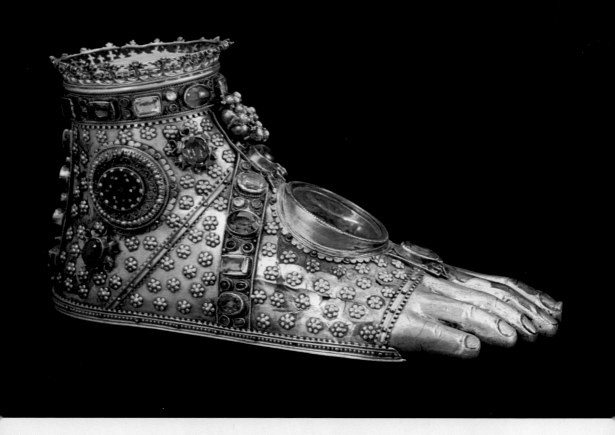

glasses and watches, or those of Damien Hirst—all secular reliquaries, but they reveal the same taste for worn out, dusty materials, or in any case for a kind of mad accumulation

The ancient chronicles say that in the 12th century a German cathedral held the cranium of John the Baptist at the age of twelve. Even without ever having seen it, we can imagine the pinkish streaks against the greyish background, the arabesques of crumbling, corroded cranial seams, the display cabinet that contains it, adorned with blue enamel like the altar of Verdun and the little cushion in yellowing silk covered with withered roses, deprived of air for two thousand years, immobilized in a vacuum, before the Baptist grew up and the headsman's sword took that other, older cranium, which is now kept in San Silvestro in Capite in Rome, although a previous

Foot Reliquary of One of the Holy Innocents from Basel Cathedral, Osvald Uberlinger, 1450, Zürich, Schweizerisches Landesmuseum

tradition would have us believe it was in Amiens Cathedral. In any event, the skull kept in Rome would be minus the jawbone, conserved in the Cathedral of San Lorenzo in Viterbo. The plate that held the Baptist's head is in Genoa, in the treasury of the Cathedral of San Lorenzo, together with the saint's ashes, but a part of these ashes are also kept in the ancient Church of the Benedictine Monastery in Loano, while a finger is apparently in the Museo dell'Opera in Florence Cathedral, an arm in Siena Cathedral, and the jawbone in San Lorenzo in Viterbo. Of the teeth, one is in Ragusa Cathedral and another, together with a lock of hair, in Monza.

The search for precious stones and their diverse types is one of the favourite amusements of treasury enthusiasts, because it is not only a matter of recognizing diamonds or rubies or emeralds, but also those stones always mentioned in the sacred texts, such as opal, chrysophrase, beryl, agate, jasper, and sardonyx. To put it briefly, you have to be able to recognize the good stones from the fakes: still in the Milan treasury there is a large silver statue of St. Charles Borromeo, from the Baroque period, and, since the patrons or donors thought silver was still too cheap a material, the statue bears a pectoral cross that is aglitter with gems. According to the catalogue, some are genuine, others are merely coloured crystals. But our curiosity regarding mere commodities should not distract us from the enjoyment felt by the original collectors, who sought to achieve an overall effect of sparkling, sumptuous wealth.

The same taste for the accumulation of gems, where the pleasure taken in the precious material is indistinguishable from the aesthetic pleasure taken in the form given it, is found in modern decadent authors such as **Huysmans** and **Wilde**, where the former, whom Wilde imitated fairly shamelessly, made no secret of the medieval origins of his tastes.

1. "Le problème des musées", now in *Oeuvres*, Paris, Pleiade II, pp. 1290 ff.
2. "Collezione", in *Enciclopedia* iii (Turin, Einaudi, 1978).

DESCRIPTION OF CONQUES CHURCH TREASURE
FROM MARCEL AUBERT,
THE CHURCH OF CONQUES, 1954

The Pépin Reliquary [...] This is the oldest piece in the treasury. Historian Charles de Linas was the first to trace it back to Pépin, son of Louis the Debonair, King of Aquitaine from 817 to 838. It is a rectangular coffer covered with a four-sided, sloping roof of gilt wood. It has a filigreed border with gemstones and framed intaglios. On one side is a depiction of Christ on the Cross between the Virgin and Saint John, with the sun and moon overhead [...]

The Gold Statue of Saint Foy [...] This is the treasury's most famous object, and is one of the most valuable works of goldsmithery from the Middle Ages. It depicts the patron saint of Conques majestically seated upon a throne [...] the figure is plated entirely in gold; her head is modeled in gold leaf, crowned by a richly worked band of jewels, and her large eyes are made of white enamel with dark blue pupils [...] This statue predates Bernard of Angers' first visit to Conques, in 1013, and according to what he wrote in the first book of his *Miracles of Saint Foy*, chapters XVI and XVII, it replaced an older statue, made around the time a local blind man named Guibert recovered his sight. At the beginning of chapter II of his book, Bernard explains that this miracle happened some thirty years before his arrival—therefore, around 983. Because the new statue was completed thanks to the donations that poured into the church after Guibert's cure, we can date it around 985. Its style imitated that of reliquary statues from Auvergne, the oldest of which M. Brehier has shown was a gilt Virgin in Majesty made by Cleric Aleaume, goldsmith and architect, with the help of his brother Adam, on behalf of Stephen II, bishop of Clermont and abbot of Conques, around 946. Throughout the Middle Ages, the so-called

Majesté de sainte Foy ("Majesty of Saint Foy") was the most widely venerated treasury object, and remains covered by the jewels and precious stones with which successive generations of pilgrims adorned it. On the back, a vermeil plate depicts Christ in Majesty; older than the statue itself, it is likely a fragment of an eighth-century altarpiece. There is also a thirteenth-century triptych on the figure's chest, and on her knees is a plaque depicting a woman under a tripartite archway; it also includes fragments from a tooled gospel cover depicting Christ surrounded by evangelical symbols, cut into pieces and set into different parts of the reliquary's body. According to [historian Camille] Enlart, the pearl belt with translucent enamel dates back to the early fourteenth century, and was made in Paris, perhaps by the workshop of Guillaume Julien, and nailed to the figure's knees, chest, and shoulders. Some flowers on the belt are a translucent green, strewn with yellow spots, while others are a translucent blue with alternating yellow and red stamens. A round vermeil plaque nailed to each side of the saint's feet, on the chair legs, represents the Lamb of God and Christ on the Cross between the Virgin and Saint John; it dates back to the late fourteenth or early fifteenth century. The saint's large, sumptuously jeweled necklace also dates back to the fifteenth century. In the sixteenth century, her hands and forearms were redone, perhaps by Antoine Frechrieu, an artisan from Rodez. The base step and feet are both modern, as are the four spheres under the chair's trellis support and the iron frame in which the statue sits. It includes many precious stones—emeralds, onyx, sapphires, amethysts, agates, pearls—and two cameos, one portraying Diana; it also features antique carved stones, a Carolingian intaglio depicting Christ on the Cross between the Virgin and Saint John, and, on the reverse, a rock-crystal cabochon at the top of the chair. Many other jewels enrich this extraordinary piece of goldsmithery that, in a cavity on the reverse, holds Saint Foy's skull behind a silver plaque [...]

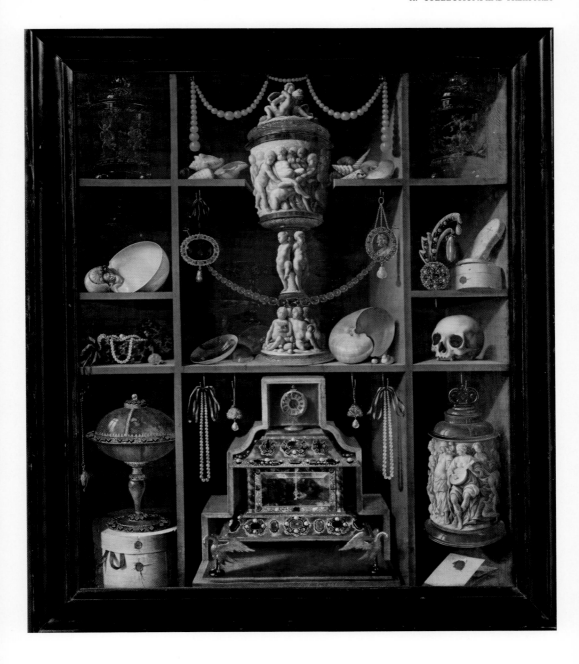

Johann Georg Hainz (Hinz)
Collector's Cabinet, 1666,
Hamburg, Hamburger Kunsthalle

The Bégon Reliquary [...] This shrine—also known as the Lantern of Saint Vincent, after a church deacon martyred in Agen whose remains were left at Conques—houses the saint's relics in the shape of an octagonal bell tower upon square base, topped by a ribbed spire. It is made of wood plated with sheets of partially gilt silver. At its base is an almost illegible inscription; nevertheless, from the remaining letters one can decipher the name of the famous abbot Bégon (1087-1107). The octagonal portion is decorated with six repoussé plaques with a portrait bust, surrounded and topped by glass through which the relics can be seen. The square base is decorated with relief figures, two of which—Christ and Saint John the Baptist— had been cut and mounted on the Pépin Reliquary, and were subsequently returned to the Bégon Reliquary. A third, circular medallion depicts David defeating the lion, but it is executed more skillfully, in a style more advanced than others; I therefore think it was executed after the Abbacy of Bégon, but still in the first half of the twelfth century, and then applied to this shrine.

The Reliquary of Pope Paschal II [...] Made of wood and covered in leaves of partially gilt silver, this reliquary features a flat, rectangular coffer mounted on a chamfered base. The front depicts Christ on the Cross between the Virgin and Saint John, with the sun and moon high above the cross. The reverse features an interlacing pattern. An inscription reads *Me firi jussit Bego clemens cui Dominus sit*, "Bégon made me, may the Lord be merciful unto him." Another inscription indicates for whose relics it was executed: *Ab anno Domini incarnatione millesimo centesimo Pascalis Dominus Papa II a Roma misit reliquias de cruce Christi and sepulcro sanctorum ejus atque plurimorum*, "

In the 1100 year of the Incarnation, Paschal II, pope, sent the relics of the cross and tomb of Christ, and several saints, from Rome." This reliquary was intended, as the aforementioned altar inscription attests, to house the relics sent to Conques in 1100 by Pope Paschal II (1099-1118); it was executed under the abbacy of Bégon (1087-1107), most likely just after 1100.

Past interventions have altered its original form: the Crucifixion may have come from a tooled gospel book cover; at the bottom one can still see a partially destroyed inscription (*sit reliquias de...*); it features a filigreed and vertically striped coupée band within a diamond-shaped plaque. It dates back to the thirteenth century, and the cavity housing the relic was taken from another monument.

The so-called Charlemagne's A [...] According to tradition, this reliquary—formed in the shape of a capital letter *A*—was donated by Charlemagne; however, in reality, its current form dates only to the abbacy of Bégon, whose name it bears on the left side: *Abbas formavit Bego reliqiiias locavit*, "Abbot Bégon made me and placed the relics herein." It is made of gilt oak covered in vermeil, filigree, cabochons, precious stones, and enamel plaques. The reliquary is located at the top of the letter, in a circular case; its center is decorated with a large cabochon crystal, inlaid with antique intaglio, surrounded by filigree on a gold background, and features small plaques of cloisonné enamel that date back to the early fourteenth century. One of the plaquettes, toward the bottom, is different from the rest: it resembles some of the finer works of Parisian goldsmith Guillaume Julien, and has been attributed to him or his workshop. Lower down is a cross decorated with horizontal bands of silver foliage and inscriptions, added at a later

Treasury of Hagenbach, 275 A.D.
Speyer, Historisches Museum
der Pfalz

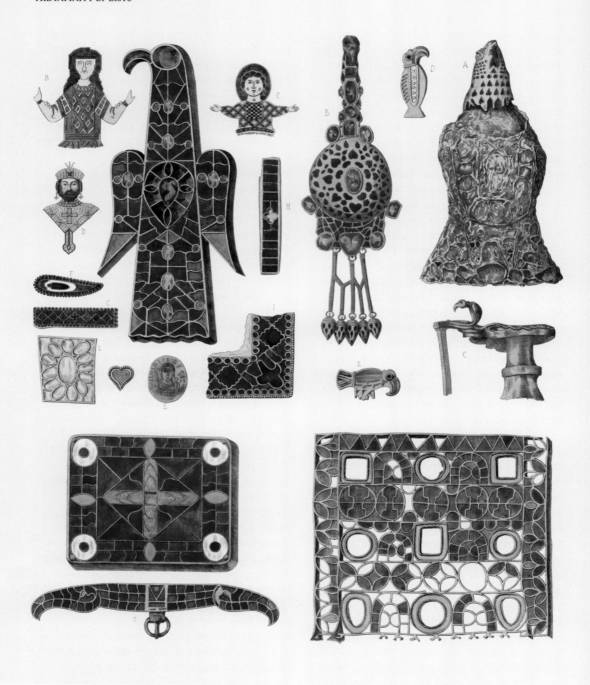

Charles de Linas
*Merovingian Goldsmithing, the Works
of Saint Eligius*, 1863,
Paris, Bibliothèque de l'Institut

Chalice
10th-11th century,
Paris, Musée du Louvre

Chalice of Abbot Pélage
Spain, 12th century,
Paris, Musée du Louvre

Chalice
Chapelle aux armes
de France, 1675-1676,
Paris, Musée du Louvre

Chalice
Siena,
late 14th century,
Paris, Musée du Louvre

Luigi Valadier
Chalice, c. 1770-1780,
Paris, Musée du Louvre

Matteo d'Ambrogio, Chalice
c. 1370-1390,
Paris, Musée du Louvre

Chalice: a scene from the
Passion; Saint Vincent;
Angels bearing an heraldic
shield to Lara, Catalonia,
mid-14th century,
Paris, Musée du Louvre

Chalice from the treasury of
the Ariège, 14th century,
Paris, Musée du Louvre

Glass chalice
France, c. 1550,
Paris, Musée du Louvre

Chalice, treasury
of Saint-Denis, c. 1600,
Paris, Musée du Louvre

date. The horizontal arm of the cross features two small repoussé silver friezes depicting angels holding censers.

Phylacteries. The treasury features two phylacteries: one has five sections, the other has six; both are made of wood covered in silver leaf; they were made in different periods, but both date back to abbacy of Bégon. Both are decorated with cloisonnés from the sixth or seventh century, several fragments of a frieze with gemstones and filigree, and various other parts, some of which postdate the Renaissance.

The Saint Foy Coffer [...] After a fire set by Protestants in 1561, the pillars of the apse had to be reinforced, and were enclosed in a wall of masonry. When that wall was demolished on April 21, 1875, a hidden cavity was discovered; it housed a wooden coffer, covered in leather and decorative enamel discs, which contained the relics of Saint Foy. A few years later, it was skillfully restored by the Poussielgue Workshop, and the original leather was reapplied to a new backing. The chest, four decorative medallions, and the angles on the reverse side were all restored: a hole had been drilled through the center, and was repaired in a style to match the original; missing pieces were replaced as well, since many had found their way into private collections—such as the Collection Carraud, now at the Bargello Museum in Florence. It also featured a copper enamel decorative disc reminiscent of the shrine of Bellac (in Haute-Vienne), with arabesques, griffins, fantastic animals, and many pairs of birds facing one another—all in white, green, turquoise, and ultramarine tones. Two of these discs bear inscriptions attesting to the fact that the chest was executed under abbot Boniface, Bégon's successor, who ran the abbey from 1107 to 1119: the disc on the left side of the back reads *Scrinia Concharum monster opus undique clarum*, "The Conques coffers exhibit excellent craftsmanship in all details"; the disc on the left side of the front reads *Bone ornamentum Hoc facii monimentum sit*, "May this ornament be a commemoration of Boniface." The black leather cover of the coffer is studded with small silver nails forming the outlines of roses and jewels.

Several pieces of the treasury date back to the thirteenth century: a *double-cross reliquary* [...] a seated statuette of the *Virgin with Child* on her lap, in gilt silver [...] a *reliquary arm of Saint George* in gilt silver atop a wood core, dating back to the late twelfth or early thirteenth century, and likely executed in the same workshop [...] two enamel *gémellions*, decorated with charming female figures, musicians, and dancers, and coats of arms, as well as a triptych forming two reliquaries [...] the latter are filigreed, and house the relics of saints whose names are inscribed on the exterior.

Two gilt silver *reliquary heads* date to the fourteenth century: their face and neck are covered in painted canvas, and they contain the skulls of Saint Marse and Saint Libérate. A small silver shrine of Saint Foy, largely rebuilt by the Poussielgue Workshop, is from the same period. A monstrance with a six-lobed circular top and two spiral arms, each depicting a small angel, dates back to the fifteenth century; its base—decorated with scenes from the Flagellation, the Descent into limbo, the Resurrection, and the Last Judgment—dates back to the fourteenth century.

Several other *footed reliquaries* date back to the fifteenth century, as does a beautiful gilt silver *statuette of Saint Foy* [...] She is shown standing, wearing a long dress and mantle: in her right hand she holds a sword and grill, the instruments of her torture; in her left hand is the palm of martyrdom that Bernard Gaulejac attributes to Pierre Frechrieu and Huc Lenfan, goldsmiths from Villefranche-de-Rouergue, who likely executed the piece between 1493 and 1497. There is also a large *processional cross* [...] attributed to the same workshop and likely executed between 1498 and 1512. It is decorated with gemstones and intaglios, and at its center is a depiction of Christ between the Virgin and Saint John on the arms of the cross; the Eternal Father is depicted at the top of the cross, and on the back we see Saint Foy with the four evangelists. The octagonal nexus is decorated with statues of Saint Andrew, Saint Bartholomew, Saint Matthew, Saint John the Baptist, Saint Paul, Saint Simon, Saint John the Evangelist, and Saint Peter.

In 1879, the Bishop of Rodez donated a piece of the True Cross, also housed in a reliquary. *A Gospel bound in a Silver Cover*[...] dates back to the sixteenth century. It is decorated with figures of Christ, the Virgin, and Saint John, depicted in relief against a background of foliage; Gaulejac attributes it to the Frechrieu workshop in Rodez. There is also a seventeenth-century *silver repoussé chalice*, a modern chasuble with a section of embroidery on the back dated to the twelfth century, and many sixteenth-century *tapestries.* The latter depict four scenes from the martyrdom of Saint Foy and Saint Caprais, as well as landscapes scenes and greenery. This hall was built in 1910 to house the treasury of the old abbey, and has been transformed by recent renovations.

French School
Reliquary of Saint Foy, c. 980,
Conques, Cathedral of Saint Foy

SOME OBJECTS IN THE IMPERIAL TREASURY OF VIENNA

In the Sacred Treasury are: the bag of King Stephen of Hungary; Charlemagne's pendent; a reliquary containing a relic of Saint Hedwig; an *Adoration of the Magi*; a monstrance (of gilt silver, rock crystal, chrysophrase, amethyst, sapphires, garnets, coral, ruby, pearls, turquoise, and artificial stones); parchment miniatures; a reliquary of rock crystal and velvet; a patch of silk said to belong to Stephen King of Hungary; a chalice in gilt copper; a gilt silver chalice; a scene of the Holy Family with Angels (a bas-relief in stone); ten beads of ivory and agate, with a silver pendent depicting the Vanities; a Saint Christopher (a bas-relief in copper); a reliquary cross of King Louis the Great of Hungary; a chasuble with Christ on the Cross; the sculpted head of a woman; a wooden reliquary bust of Saint Catherine; a *Lamentation of Christ* (tapestry); various ornaments made of silk, brocade, and silver; a monstrance; a chalice with artificial red and blue stones; two red chasubles; a papal ornament; a silver lamé pendant with miniatures on parchment depicting the crucifixion and the serpent; a prayer book of Emperor Ferdinand II; discipline books from empresses Anne and Eleanor; a pilgrim's staff (a bamboo cane with finely worked handle depicting scenes from the Old Testament and images of the apostles); crucifixes; two candelabra; a golden rose (vase with dragon feet); an altarpiece (with the relics of Saint Laurent, Saint Nicolas, Saint Christine, Saint Deocharius, Saint Habundus, Saint Joan, and Saint Dorothy, accompanied by Saint Victor, Saint Jerome,

Reliquary, Magny-les-Hameaux, Musée de Port-Royal des Champs

Reliquary urn with pebbles from the Holy Land, 17th century, Paris, Musée des Civilisations de l'Europe et de la Méditerranée

and 11,000 Virgins); a miter; an *Annunciation* with shepherds (in gilt silver, ebony, enamel, pearls, rubies, and diamonds); a monstrance containing various relics of Christ; a reliquary bust of Saint Valérien topped with wax and containing a relic of Saint Maurice; a reliquary altarpiece that belonged to Empress Anne; a monstrance representing Christ in the Garden of Olives; a reliquary topped with the bust of Saint Tiburce; a reliquary in wax containing a relic of Saint Crispin; an altarpiece with a bone relic of Saint Timothy; an altarpiece reliquary depicting the group of the crucifixion; two monstrances with thorns from the crown of Christ; a coffer containing a relic of Saint Felix; a monstrance with the relics of Saint Stanislaus; a monstrance with a fragment from Christ's scepter (and relics of Saints Peter, Maximilian, and Sigmund); other altarpieces (with relics of Saints Matthew, Lucius, Candide, Eustace, Mary Magdalene, Cecil, Valentine, Zosima, Amanda, Laurent, Jean, Thecles, Verena, Albert, and Udalrich); monstrances with relics of Saint Mary Magdalene and two anonymous saints; a monstrance with relics of saints Sebastian, Apollinaire and a group of anonymous saints; a monstrance depicting saints and the Virgin with the Infant Jesus (in silver bas-relief with ebony and bronze trim); an altarpiece with the relics of Saints Stephen, Lucy, Luke, Bartholomew, Lawrence, Matthew, Gregory, and Blaise; a relief depicting the Rest on the Flight to Egypt; a relief depicting the body of Christ carried by two angels; a sculpted Calvary inspired by the work of Giambologna; a depiction of Christ in a small temple (in ivory, ebony, partially gilt silver, and carbuncle, with a capsule crowning the temple containing a fragment of the column from Christ's flagellation, and drawers with various other relics in the base); an ivory Virgin and Child; a reproduction of the Risen Christ by Michelangelo; 68 Baroque and Rococo works; 19 nineteenth-century works.

The secular part of the treasury contains 186 objects, including: the baptismal clothes of the Hapsburg family; the crown of Emperor Rudolf II; a globe of imperial Austria and two other objects dated 1546; a cup of agate from the fourth century AD which was sometimes identified with the Holy Grail; a unicorn horn (which is a narwhal tusk); 38 objects of jewelry and souvenirs, including the cradle of the King of Rome; 29 works from the treasury of the Duke of Burgundy with adornments of the Knights of the Golden Fleece; 35 insignia, jewels, and relics of the Holy Roman Empire with the crown, scepter, globe, sword, imperial cross, and Holy Lance; a piece of the True Cross; the bag of Saint Etienne; Charlemagne's sword; a piece of the holy crèche; a tooth of Saint John the Baptist; an arm bone of Saint Anne; a chain of the apostles; and a fragment of the tablecloth from the Last Supper.

Reliquary with the Agnus Dei in white wax with the Pontiff's coat of arms, **19th century, Paris, Musée des Civilisations de l'Europe et de la Méditerranée**

Gustave Moreau
The Pretenders, 1862-1898,
Paris, Musée Gustave Moreau

JORIS-KARL HUYSMANS
AGAINST THE GRAIN
FROM CHAPTER 5 (1884)

The man bowed and deposited the buckler on the pinewood floor of the dining room. It oscillated and wavered, revealing the serpentine head of a tortoise which, suddenly terrified, retreated into its shell.

This tortoise was a fancy which had seized Des Esseintes some time before his departure from Paris. Examining an Oriental rug, one day, in reflected light, and following the silver gleams which fell on its web of plum violet and alladin yellow, it suddenly occurred to him how much it would be improved if he could place on it some object whose deep color might enhance the vividness of its tints. Possessed by this idea, he had been strolling aimlessly along the streets, when suddenly he found himself gazing at the very object of his wishes. There, in a shop window on the Palais Royal, lay a huge tortoise in a large basin. He had purchased it. Then he had sat a long time, with eyes half-shut, studying the effect.

Decidedly, the Ethiopic black, the harsh Sienna tone of this shell dulled the rug's reflections without adding to it. The dominant silver gleams in it barely sparkled, crawling with lack-lustre tones of dead zinc against the edges of the hard, tarnished shell.

He bit his nails while he studied a method of removing these discords and reconciling the determined opposition of the tones. He finally discovered that his first inspiration, which was to animate the fire of the weave by setting it off against some dark object, was erroneous. In fact, this rug was too new, too petulant and gaudy. The colors were not sufficiently subdued. He must reverse the process, dull the tones, and extinguish them by the contrast of a striking object, which would eclipse all else and cast a golden light on the pale silver.

Thus stated, the problem was easier to solve. He therefore decided to glaze the shell of the tortoise with gold.

The tortoise, just returned by the lapidary, shone brilliantly, softening the tones of the rug and casting on it a gorgeous reflection which resembled the irradiations from the scales of a barbaric Visigoth shield.

At first Des Esseintes was enchanted with this effect. Then he reflected that this gigantic jewel was only in outline, that it would not really be complete until it had been incrusted with rare stones.

From a Japanese collection he chose a design representing a cluster of flowers emanating spindle-like, from a slender stalk. Taking it to a jeweler, he sketched a border to enclose this bouquet in an oval frame, and informed the amazed lapidary that every petal and every leaf was to be designed with jewels and mounted on the scales of the tortoise. The choice of stones made him pause. The diamond has become notoriously common since every tradesman has taken to wearing it on his little finger. The oriental emeralds and rubies are less vulgarized and cast brilliant, rutilant flames, but they remind one of the green and red antennae of certain omnibuses which carry signal lights of these colors. As for topazes, whether sparkling or dim, they are cheap stones, precious only to women of the middle class who like to have jewel cases on their dressing-tables. And then, although the Church has preserved for the amethyst a sacerdotal character which is at once unctuous and solemn, this stone, too, is abused on the blood-red ears and veined hands of butchers' wives who love to adorn themselves inexpensively with real and heavy jewels. Only the sapphire, among all these stones, has kept its fires undefiled by any taint of commercialism. Its sparks, crackling in its limpid, cold depths have in some way protected its shy and proud nobility from pollution. Unfortunately, its fresh fire does not sparkle in artificial light: the blue retreats and seems to fall asleep, only awakening to shine at daybreak.

None of these satisfied Des Esseintes at all. They were too civilized and familiar. He let trickle through his fingers still more

Patena
date unknown (between 1st century B.C. and 9th century A.D.)
Paris, Musée du Louvre

astonishing and bizarre stones, and finally selected a number of real and artificial ones which, used together, should produce a fascinating and disconcerting harmony.

This is how he composed his bouquet of flowers: the leaves were set with jewels of a pronounced, distinct green; the chrysoberyls of asparagus green; the chrysolites of leek green; the olivines of olive green. They hung from branches of almandine and *ouwarovite* of a violet red, darting spangles of a hard brilliance like tartar micas gleaming through forest depths.

For the flowers, separated from the stalk and removed from the bottom of the sheaf, he used blue cinder. But he formally waived that oriental turquoise used for brooches and rings which, like the banal pearl and the odious coral, serves to delight people of no importance. He chose occidental turquoises exclusively, stones which, properly speaking, are only a fossil ivory impregnated with coppery substances whose sea blue is choked, opaque, sulphurous, as though yellowed by bile.

This done, he could now set the petals of his flowers with transparent stones which had morbid and vitreous sparks, feverish and sharp lights.

He composed them entirely with Ceylon snap-dragons, cymophanes and blue chalcedony. These three stones darted mysterious and perverse scintillations, painfully torn from the frozen depths of their troubled waters. The snap-dragon of a greenish grey, streaked with concentric veins which seem to stir and change constantly, according to the dispositions of light.

The cymophane, whose azure waves float over the milky tint swimming in its depths. The blue chalcedony which kindles with bluish phosphorescent fires against a dead brown, chocolate background.

The lapidary made a note of the places where the stones were to be inlaid. "And the border of the shell?" he asked Des Esseintes. At first he had thought of some opals and hydrophanes; but these stones, interesting

for their hesitating colors, for the evasions of their flames, are too refractory and faithless; the opal has a quite rheumatic sensitiveness; the play of its rays alters according to the humidity, the warmth or cold; as for the hydrophane, it only burns in water and only consents to kindle its embers when moistened. He finally decided on minerals whose reflections vary; for the Compostelle hyacinth, mahogany red; the beryl, glaucous green; the balas ruby, vinegar rose; the Sudermanian ruby, pale slate. Their feeble sparklings sufficed to light the darkness of the shell and preserved the values of the flowering stones which they encircled with a slender garland of vague fires.

Des Esseintes now watched the tortoise squatting in a corner of the dining room, shining in the shadow.

He was perfectly happy. His eyes gleamed with pleasure at the resplendencies of the flaming corrollae against the gold background. Then, he grew hungry—a thing that rarely if ever happened to him—and dipped his toast, spread with a special butter, in a cup of tea, a flawless blend of Siafayoune, Moyoutann and Khansky—yellow teas which had come from China to Russia by special caravans. This liquid perfume he drank in those Chinese porcelains called egg-shell, so light and diaphanous they are. And, as an accompaniment to these adorable cups, he used a service of solid silver, slightly gilded; the silver showed faintly under the fatigued layer of gold, which gave it an aged, quite exhausted and moribund tint.

After he had finished his tea, he returned to his study and had the servant carry in the tortoise which stubbornly refused to budge. The snow was falling. By the lamp light, he saw the icy patterns on the bluish windows, and the hoar-frost, like melted sugar, scintillating in the stumps of bottles spotted with gold.

A deep silence enveloped the cottage drooping in shadow.

Des Esseintes fell into revery. The fireplace

piled with logs gave forth a smell of burning wood. He opened the window slightly.

Like a high tapestry of black ermine, the sky rose before him, black flecked with white. An icy wind swept past, accelerated the crazy flight of the snow, and reversed the color order.

The heraldic tapestry of heaven returned, became a true ermine, a white flecked with black, in its turn, by the specks of darkness dispersed among the flakes.

He closed the window. This abrupt transition from torrid warmth to cold winter affected him. He crouched near the fire and it occurred to him that he needed a cordial to revive his flagging spirits.

He went to the dining room where, built in one of the panels, was a closet containing a number of tiny casks, ranged side by side, and resting on small stands of sandal wood.

This collection of barrels he called his mouth organ.

A stem could connect all the spigots and control them by a single movement, so that once attached, he had only to press a button concealed in the woodwork to turn on all the taps at the same time and fill the mugs placed underneath.

The organ was now open. The stops labelled flute, horn, celestial voice, were pulled out, ready to be placed. Des Esseintes sipped here and there, enjoying the inner symphonies, succeeded in procuring sensations in his throat analogous to those which music gives to the ear.

Moreover, each liquor corresponded, according to his thinking, to the sound of some instrument. Dry curacoa, for example, to the clarinet whose tone is sourish and velvety; *kummel* to the oboe whose sonorous notes snuffle; mint and anisette to the flute, at once sugary and peppery, puling and sweet; while, to complete the orchestra, *kirschwasser* has the furious ring of the trumpet; gin and whiskey burn the palate with their strident crashings of trombones and cornets; brandy storms with the deafening hubbub of tubas; while the thunder-claps of the cymbals and the furiously beaten drum roll in the mouth by means of the *rakis de Chio*.

He also thought that the comparison could be continued, that quartets of string instruments could play under the palate, with the violin simulated by old brandy, fumous and fine, piercing and frail; the tenor violin by rum, louder and more sonorous; the cello by the lacerating and lingering ratafia, melancholy and caressing; with the double-bass, full-bodied, solid and dark as the old bitters. If one wished to form a quintet, one could even add a fifth instrument with the vibrant taste, the silvery detached and shrill note of dry cumin imitating the harp.

The comparison was further prolonged. Tone relationships existed in the music of liquors; to cite but one note, benedictine represents, so to speak, the minor key of that major key of alcohols which are designated in commercial scores, under the name of green Chartreuse.

These principles once admitted, he succeeded, after numerous experiments, in enjoying silent melodies on his tongue, mute funeral marches, in hearing, in his mouth, solos of mint, duos of ratafia and rum.

He was even able to transfer to his palate real pieces of music, following the composer step by step, rendering his thought, his effects, his nuances, by combinations or contrasts of liquors, by approximative and skilled mixtures.

At other times, he himself composed melodies, executed pastorals with mild black-currant which evoked, in his throat, the trillings of nightingales; with the tender chouva cocoa which sang saccharine songs like "The romance of Estelle" and the "Ah! Shall I tell you, mama," of past days.

But on this evening Des Esseintes was not inclined to listen to this music. He confined himself to sounding one note on the keyboard of his organ, by swallowing a little glass of genuine Irish whiskey.

OSCAR WILDE
THE PICTURE OF DORIAN GRAY
FROM CHAPTER XI (1890)

On one occasion he took up the study of jewels, and appeared at a costume ball as Anne de Joyeuse, Admiral of France, in a dress covered with five hundred and sixty pearls. This taste enthralled him for years, and, indeed, may be said never to have left him. He would often spend a whole day settling and resettling in their cases the various stones that he had collected, such as the olive-green chrysoberyl that turns red by lamplight, the cymophane with its wirelike line of silver, the pistachio-coloured peridot, rose-pink and wine-yellow topazes, carbuncles of fiery scarlet with tremulous, four-rayed stars, flame-red cinnamon-stones, orange and violet spinels, and amethysts with their alternate layers of ruby and sapphire. He loved the red gold of the sunstone, and the moonstone's pearly whiteness, and the broken rainbow of the milky opal. He procured from Amsterdam three emeralds of extraordinary size and richness of colour, and had a turquoise *de la vieille roche* that was the envy of all the connoisseurs.

He discovered wonderful stories, also, about jewels. In Alphonso's Clericalis Disciplina a serpent was mentioned with eyes of real jacinth, and in the romantic history of Alexander, the Conqueror of Emathia was said to have found in the vale of Jordan snakes "with collars of real emeralds growing on their backs." There was a gem in the brain of the dragon, Philostratus told us, and "by the exhibition of golden letters and a scarlet robe" the monster could be thrown into a magical sleep and slain. According to the great alchemist, Pierre de Boniface, the diamond rendered a man invisible, and the agate of India made him eloquent. The cornelian appeased anger, and the hyacinth provoked sleep, and the amethyst drove away the fumes of wine. The garnet cast out demons, and the hydropicus deprived the

moon of her colour. The selenite waxed and waned with the moon, and the meloceus, that discovers thieves, could be affected only by the blood of kids. Leonardus Camillus had seen a white stone taken from the brain of a newly killed toad, that was a certain antidote against poison. The bezoar, that was found in the heart of the Arabian deer, was a charm that could cure the plague. In the nests of Arabian birds was the aspilates, that, according to Democritus, kept the wearer from any danger by fire.

The King of Ceilan rode through his city with a large ruby in his hand, as the ceremony of his coronation. The gates of the palace of John the Priest were "made of sardius, with the horn of the horned snake inwrought, so that no man might bring poison within." Over the gable were "two golden apples, in which were two carbuncles," so that the gold might shine by day and the carbuncles by night. In Lodge's strange romance "A Margarite of America," it was stated that in the chamber of the queen one could behold "all the chaste ladies of the world, inchased out of silver, looking through fair mirrours of chrysolites, carbuncles, sapphires, and greene emeraults." Marco Polo had seen the inhabitants of Zipangu place rose-coloured pearls in the mouths of the dead. A sea-monster had been enamoured of the pearl that the diver brought to King Perozes, and had slain the thief, and mourned for seven moons over its loss. When the Huns lured the king into the great pit, he flung it away—Procopius tells the story—nor was it ever found again, though the Emperor Anastasius offered five hundred-weight of gold pieces for it. The King of Malabar had shown to a certain Venetian a rosary of three hundred and four pearls, one for every god that he worshipped.

When the Duke de Valentinois, son of Alexander VI, visited Louis XII of France, his horse was loaded with gold leaves, according to Brantome, and his cap had double rows of rubies that threw out a great light. Charles of England had ridden in stirrups hung with four hundred

and twenty-one diamonds. Richard II had a coat, valued at thirty thousand marks, which was covered with balas rubies. Hall described Henry VIII, on his way to the Tower previous to his coronation, as wearing "a jacket of raised gold, the placard embroidered with diamonds and other rich stones, and a great bauderike about his neck of large balasses." The favourites of James I wore ear-rings of emeralds set in gold filigrane. Edward II gave to Piers Gaveston a suit of red-gold armour studded with jacinths, a collar of gold roses set with turquoise-stones, and a skull-cap *parsemé* with pearls. Henry II wore jewelled gloves reaching to the elbow, and had a hawk-glove sewn with twelve rubies and fifty-two great orients. The ducal hat of Charles the Rash, the last Duke of Burgundy of his race, was hung with pear-shaped pearls and studded with sapphires.

Gustave Moreau
Jupiter and Semele, 1895,
Paris, Musée Gustave Moreau

Gustav Klimt
Adele Bloch–Bauer I, 1907,
New York, Neue Galerie

12. THE WUNDERKAMMER

At a certain point in the history of collecting a caesura occurs. From the Renaissance onward marvels were no longer those from distant lands (which gradually, at least from the end of the 15th century, were no longer the stuff of legend but reality), curiosities or the relics of saints, but the wonders of the human body and its recesses that had been secret until then. Within the framework of this secular and scientific standpoint, a change came about regarding the taste for portents. First they had been seen as premonitory signs of some extraordinary event—and in this sense the *Prodigiorum ac ostentorum chronicon* of Conrad Lycosthenes (1557) is still a renowned example. But now people began to see them as objects of *scientific curiosity*, or at least pre-scientific curiosity. Now there is talk of physic, even though the concept of "physic" is still bizarre, and *Physica Curiosa* was the title of the monumental work (one thousand six hundred pages with dozens and dozens of engravings) by the Jesuit Caspar Schott (1662), which contains a description of all the "physical" monstrosities known at the time. The text deals only occasionally with exotic animals like elephants and giraffes, but is more interested in freaks of nature, and certain creatures that the sailors or travellers who saw them from a distance (and who superimposed upon them memories of tales about legendary monsters) found similar to monsters of the bestiaries. As a result, normal dugongs were taken for mermaids.

Among the many books on this subject we might mention *Des monstres et prodiges* by Ambroise Paré (1573), the *Historium animalium* by Conrad Gessner (1551-1558), the *Monstrorum historia* by Ulisse Aldrovandi (1642), the *Historia naturalis* by John Johnston (1653),

*A collection
of beetles and insects*

Large-Eared Man

Man with the Head of a Crane

Bishop-fish

Jonah and the Whale
in Conrad Lycosthenes's
Prodigiorum ac ostentorum chronicon, 1557

and *De monstris* by Fortunato Liceti (1665). While they indulged in the representation of monsters these authors made a fundamental contribution to the development of the biological sciences.

These books, brimming with illustrations, are repertories or lists of extraordinary things. Their equivalent in the world of objects were the *Wunderkammern*, or wonder cabinets, or cabinets of curiosities, the forerunners of our natural science museums, where some tried to collect systematically all the things that ought to be known, while others collected things that seemed extraordinary or unheard of, including bizarre objects or amazing items such as a stuffed crocodile, which usually hung from a keystone dominating the entire room. In many of these collections, such as the one put together by Peter the Great in St. Petersburg, monstrous foetuses were carefully preserved in spirits. The waxworks in the Museo della Specola in Florence are a collection of anatomical marvels, hyper-realistic masterpieces of bodies eviscerated and laid bare, in a symphony of tones ranging from pink to dark red and thence down to the browns of intestines, livers, lungs, stomachs and spleens.

Most of that which remains of the *Wunderkammern* are pictorial representations or etchings in their catalogues. Sometimes they were made up of hundreds of tiny shelves holding stones, shells, the skeletons of curious animals and sometimes masterpieces of the taxidermist's art capable of producing non-existent animals. Other times they are cupboards, like miniature museums, full of compartments containing items that, removed from their original context, seem to tell senseless or incongruous stories.

From illustrated catalogues such as the *Museum Celeberrimum* by de Sepibus (1678) and the *Museum Kircherianum* by Bonanni (1709) we learn that in the collection put together by Kircher in the Collegio Romano there were ancient statues, pagan cult objects, amulets, Chinese idols, votive tables, two tablets showing the fifty incarnations of Brahma, Roman tomb inscriptions, lanterns, rings, seals, buckles, armillas, weights, bells, stones and fossils with strange images produced by nature engraved on their surface, exotic objects *ex variis orbis plagis collectum*, containing the belts of Brazilian natives adorned with the teeth of devoured victims, exotic birds and other stuffed animals, a

book from Malabar made of palm leaves, Turkish artefacts, Chinese scales, barbarian weapons, Indian fruits, the foot of an Egyptian mummy, foetuses from forty days to seven months, skeletons of eagles, hoopoes, magpies, thrushes, Brazilian monkeys, cats and mice, moles, porcupines, frogs, chameleons, sharks, as well as marine plants, a seal's tooth, a crocodile, an armadillo, a tarantula, a hippo's head, a rhinoceros horn, a monstrous dog in a vase preserved in a balsamic solution, giants' bones, musical and mathematical instruments, experimental projects on perpetual motion, automatons and other devices along the lines of the machines made by Archimedes and Heron of Alexandria, cochleas, an octagonal catoptric device that multiplied a little model elephant so that "it restores the image of a herd of elephants that seemed to have been collected from all of Asia and Africa", hydraulic

Ole Worm's Cabinet of Curiosities
engraved frontispiece of *Museum Wormianum,*
seu Historia Rerum Rarorium, Ledine 1665

machines, telescopes and microscopes with microscopic observations of insects, globes, armillary spheres, astrolabes, planispheres, solar, hydraulic, mechanical and magnetic clocks, lenses, hourglasses, instruments for measuring temperature and humidity, various paintings and images of mountainous precipices, winding channels in valleys, wooded labyrinths, foaming waves, whirlpools, hills, architectural perspectives, ruins, ancient monuments, battles, massacres, duels, triumphs, palaces, biblical mysteries, and effigies of gods.

In its lunatic eclecticism the *Wunderkammer* was intended to symbolize a dream of total scientific knowledge utopistically portrayed by **Francis Bacon** in his *New Atlantis*: except that his house of marvels was not a collection of natural finds but that of the products by which human ingenuity had at his time subjugated and modified nature.

A Visit to Pharmacist Ferrante Imperato's Museum of Natural History, engraving 1678, Milan, private collection

Frans Francken the Younger
Collection of Art and Curiosities, c. 1636,
Vienna, Kunsthistorisches Museum, Gemäldegalerie

A la Ronde
collection of the Parminter cousins,
18th century

pages 208-209: Domenico Remps
Cabinet of Curiosities, 17th century,
Florence, Museo dell'Opificio delle Pietre Dure

FRANCIS BACON
THE NEW ATLANTIS
(1627)

"The end of our foundation is the knowledge of causes, and secret motions of things; and the enlarging of the bounds of human empire, to the effecting of all things possible.

"The preparations and instruments are these: [...]

"We have dispensatories or shops of medicines; wherein you may easily think, if we have such variety of plants, and living creatures, more than you have in Europe (for we know what you have), the simples, drugs, and ingredients of medicines, must likewise be in so much the greater variety. We have them likewise of divers ages, and long fermentations. And for their preparations, we have not only all manner of exquisite distillations, and separations, and especially by gentle heats, and percolations through divers strainers, yea, and substances; but also exact forms of composition, whereby they incorporate almost as they were natural simples.

"We have also divers mechanical arts, which you have not; and stuffs made by them, as papers, linen, silks, tissues, dainty works of feathers of wonderful lustre, excellent dyes, and many others, and shops likewise as well for such as are not brought into vulgar use among us, as for those that are. For you must know, that of the things before recited, many of them are grown into use throughout the kingdom, but yet, if they did flow from our invention, we have of them also for patterns and principals.

"We have also furnaces of great diversities, and that keep great diversity of heats; fierce and quick, strong and constant, soft and mild, blown, quiet, dry, moist, and the like. But above all we have heats, in imitation of the sun's and heavenly bodies' heats, that pass divers inequalities, and as it were orbs, progresses, and returns whereby we produce admirable effects. Besides, we have heats of dungs, and of bellies and maws of living creatures and of their bloods and bodies, and of hays and herbs laid up moist, of lime unquenched, and such like. Instruments also which generate heat only by motion. And farther, places for strong insulations; and, again, places under the earth, which by nature or art yield heat. These divers heats we use as the nature of the operation which we intend requireth.

"We have also perspective houses, where we make demonstrations of all lights and radiations and of all colors; and out of things uncolored and transparent we can represent unto you all several colors, not in rainbows, as it is in gems and prisms, but of themselves single. We represent also all multiplications of light, which we carry to great distance, and make so sharp as to discern small points and lines. Also all colorations of light: all delusions and deceits of the sight, in figures, magnitudes, motions, colors; all demonstrations of shadows. We find also divers means, yet unknown to you, of producing of light, originally from divers bodies. We procure means of seeing objects afar off, as in the heaven and remote places; and represent things near as afar off, and things afar off as near; making feigned distances. We have also helps for the sight far above spectacles and glasses in use; we have also glasses and means to see small and minute bodies, perfectly and distinctly; as the shapes and colors of small flies and worms, grains, and flaws in gems which cannot otherwise be seen, observations in urine and blood not otherwise to be seen. We make artificial rainbows, halos, and circles about light. We represent also all manner of reflections, refractions, and multiplications of visual beams of objects.

"We have also precious stones, of all kinds, many of them of great beauty and to you unknown, crystals likewise, and glasses of divers kind; and among them some of metals vitrificated, and other materials, besides those of which you make glass. Also a number of fossils and imperfect minerals, which you have not. Likewise loadstones of prodigious

Mark Dion and Robert Williams
Theatrum Mundi: Armarium, 2001,
Cambridge, University of Cambridge,
Jesus College Chapel
© Mark Dion & Robert Williams 2001

virtue, and other rare stones, both natural and artificial.

"We have also sound-houses, where we practise and demonstrate all sounds and their generation. We have harmony which you have not, of quarter-sounds and lesser slides of sounds. Divers instruments of music likewise to you unknown, some sweeter than any you have; with bells and rings that are dainty and sweet. We represent small sounds as great and deep, likewise great sounds extenuate and sharp; we make divers tremblings and warblings of sounds, which in their original are entire. We represent and imitate all articulate sounds and letters, and the voices and notes of beasts and birds. We have certain helps which, set to the ear, do further the hearing greatly; we have also divers strange and artificial echoes, reflecting the voice many times, and, as it were, tossing it; and some that give back the voice louder than it came, some shriller and some deeper; yea, some rendering the voice, differing in the letters or articulate sound from that they receive. We have all means to convey sounds in trunks and pipes, in strange lines and distances.

"We have also perfume-houses, wherewith we join also practices of taste. We multiply smells which may seem strange: we imitate smells, making all smells to breathe out of other mixtures than those that give them. We make divers imitations of taste likewise, so that they will deceive any man's taste. And in this house we contain also a confiture-house, where we make all sweetmeats, dry and moist, and divers pleasant wines, milks, broths, and salads, far in greater variety than you have.

"We have also engine-houses, where are prepared engines and instruments for all sorts of motions. There we imitate and practise to make swifter motions than any you have, either out of your muskets or any engine that you have; and to make them and multiply them more easily and with small force, by wheels and other means, and to make them stronger and more violent than yours are, exceeding your greatest cannons and basilisks. We represent also ordnance and instruments of war and engines of all kinds; and likewise new mixtures and compositions of gunpowder, wild-fires burning in water and unquenchable, also fire-works of all variety, both for pleasure and use. We imitate also flights of birds; we have some degrees of flying in the air. We have ships and boats for going under water and brooking of seas, also swimming-girdles and supporters. We have divers curious clocks and other like motions of return, and some perpetual motions. We imitate also motions of living creatures by images of men, beasts, birds, fishes, and serpents; we have also a great number of other various motions, strange for equality, fineness, and subtilty.

"We have also a mathematical-house, where are represented all instruments, as well of geometry as astronomy, exquisitely made.

"We have also houses of deceits of the senses, where we represent all manner of feats of juggling, false apparitions, impostures and illusions, and their fallacies. And surely you will easily believe that we, that have so many things truly natural which induce admiration, could in a world of particulars deceive the senses if we would disguise those things, and labor to make them more miraculous. But we do hate all impostures and lies, insomuch as we have severely forbidden it to all our fellows, under pain of ignominy and fines, that they do not show any natural work or thing adorned or swelling, but only pure as it is, and without all affectation of strangeness.

"These are, my son, the riches of Salomon's House."

pages 212-213:
**Main hall from the Museo del Tempo
Ozzano Taro (PR), Museo Ettore Guatelli**

André Breton
Un bas déchiré, 1941,
New York, Pierre Matisse Gallery Corporation

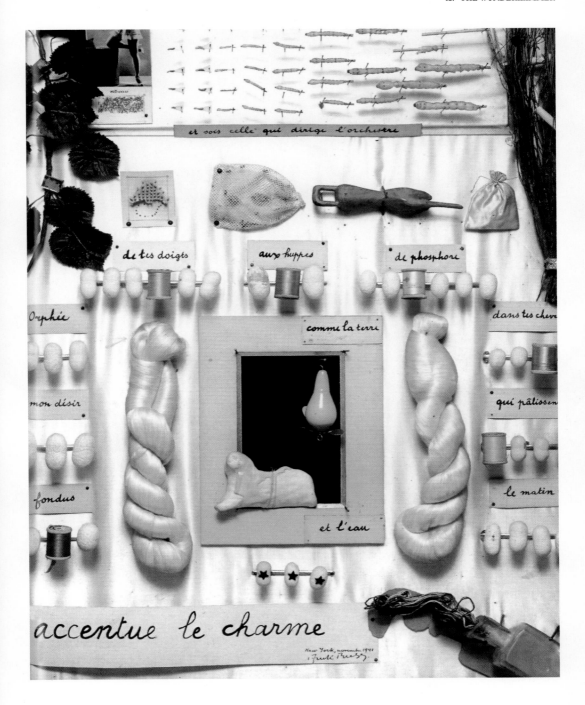

13. DEFINITION BY LIST OF PROPERTIES VERSUS DEFINITION BY ESSENCE

We have seen lists of inexpressible quantities (the number of warriors before Troy, the number of angels in God's presence, the number of pictures in a museum, the number of places in the universe). But it has often been observed how lists can regard an infinity of properties that may be attributed to the same object. In this sense the opposition between form and list refers to two ways of knowing and defining things.

The dream of every philosophy and science from the days of ancient Greece onwards has been to know and define things by essence and, since Aristotle, definition by essence has been that which is capable of defining a given thing as an individual of a given species and this in its turn as an element of a given genus. Without getting involved in logical subtleties, defining a man as a featherless biped means seeing him as a particular species (without feathers) of the larger genus of bipeds, which in its turn is a species of the genus of animals, in their turn a species of the genus of living things. Likewise, defining man as a rational mortal animal means seeing him as a species of the mortal animals (members of which include donkeys and horses), which are in their turn a species of living things.[1]

If we think about it, this is the same procedure followed by modern taxonomy when it defines the tiger or the platypus. Naturally the system of classes and subclasses is more complex, and so the tiger would belong to the species Felis Tigris, of the genus Felis, family of the Felids, Suborder of the Fissipedia, order of the Carnivora,

Nicolas de Largillière
Study of Hands, c. 1715,
Paris, Musée du Louvre

subclass of the Placentalia, class of the Mammals; while the platypus would belong to a family of monotreme mammals.

But, from its discovery onwards, eighty years passed before the platypus was defined as a monotreme mammal; in the course of that time it had to be decided how and where to classify it, and until that moment it remained, rather disturbingly, something the size of a mole, with little eyes, front paws with four claws united by a membrane (bigger than the one uniting the claws of the hind paws), with a tail, a duck's bill, paws that it used to swim and to dig its burrow, and with the capacity to produce eggs and feed its young with milk from its mammary glands.

This is exactly what a non-scientist would say about the animal upon observing it. And it is worth noting that through this (incomplete) description by list of properties, a person would still be able to tell a platypus from an ox, whereas saying that it is a monotreme mammal would enable no one to recognize it should they come across one.

On the other hand if a child asks his mother what a tiger is and what it is like, she would be unlikely to reply that it is a mammal of the suborder Placentalia or a fissiped carnivore, but would probably say that it is a ferocious wild beast that looks like a cat but is bigger, very agile, yellow with black stripes, lives in the jungle, occasionally a man-eater, and so on. A good description for recognizing and, if necessary, avoiding a tiger.

We use definition by properties when we do not have a definition by essence or if this last does not satisfy us. Hence it is proper either to a primitive culture that has still to construct a hierarchy of genera and species, or to a mature culture (maybe even one in crisis) that is bent on casting doubt on all previous definitions.

According to Aristotle, definition by properties is definition by accident. Whereas definition by essence takes substances into consideration, and we presume we know which and how many they are (for example, living, animal or vegetal), definition by properties

Ernst Haeckel
Ascidia, lithograph n. 85
Kunstformen der Natur ("Art Forms of Nature"), 1899

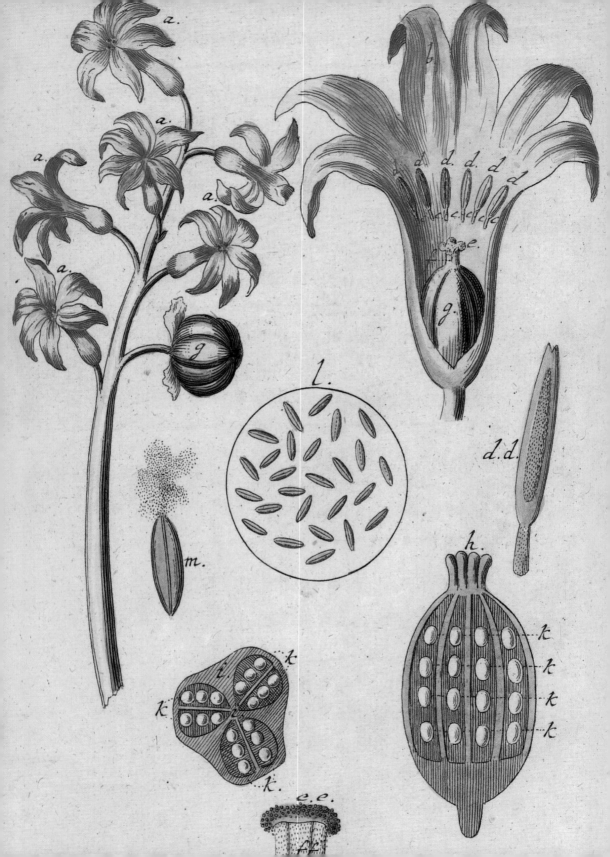

takes into consideration every possible accident: so, in the case of the tiger, it must not only be able to say that it is a quadruped, similar to a big cat, striped, but also that a tiger called Shere Khan was Mowgli's enemy in Kipling's *The Jungle Book*, that there are differences between the Bengal tiger and the Chinese tiger, the Indochinese tiger and the Malaysian tiger (and perhaps even that a given tiger was in the Coliseum on such and such a day in Nero's time, with its muzzle pointing west, and that another tiger was killed on 24 May 1846 by an English major called Ferguson, and so on).

The reality is that we seldom give definitions by essence, but more frequently by lists of properties. And this is why all the lists that define something through a non-finite series of properties, even though apparently vertiginous, seem to be closer to the way in which in everyday life (and not in science departments) we define and recognize things.

Naturally, a list by properties can also be given in an evaluative sense. We have already mentioned the eulogy of Tyre in Ezekiel, and we might add the eulogy to England in **Shakespeare**'s *Richard II*.

A typical example of the evaluative list by properties is the topos of the *laudatio puellae*, in other words the representation of beautiful women (of which the noblest example is "The Song of Songs" in **Solomon**). But we also come across it in a modern author such as **Rubén Dario**, in his *Canto a la Argentina*, which is a veritable explosion of encomiastic lists in the style of Whitman.

Similarly there is the *vituperatio puellae* (or *dominae*), the description of ugly women, as for example in **Marot**, or (but this will appear in the anthology under lists by excess) in **Burton**, and the self-description of ugly men, as in the renowned tirade on Cyrano's nose in **Rostand**.

---

1. We shall not tackle here the age-old problem of *specific difference* by virtue of which man can be distinguished as a rational animal as opposed to the other irrational animals. On this see my *Semiotics and the Philosophy of Language* (Bloomington, Indiana University Press and London, Macmillan, 1984), ch. 2. For the platypus see my *Kant and the Platypus* (New York, Harcourt and London, Secker & Warburg, 1999).

De la poussière de l'Hyacinthe bleue,
plate XXII, in Martin Froben Ledermüller,
Amusement microscopique, 1764, Nuremberg

WILLIAM SHAKESPEARE
KING RICHARD II
ACT II, SCENE II (C. 1595)

London. A room in Ely-house.

GAUNT *on a couch; the* DUKE OF YORK,
the EARL OF NORTHUMBERLAND, *and others.*

[...]
Gaunt.
[...]
This royal throne of kings, this scepter'd isle,
This earth of majesty, this seat of Mars,
This other Eden, demi-paradise;
This fortress built by Nature for herself
Against infection and the hand of war,
This happy breed of men, this little world,
This precious stone set in the silver sea,
Which serves it in the office of a wall,
Or as a moat defensive to a house,
Against the envy of less happier lands,
This blessèd plot, this earth, this realm,
    this England,
This nurse, this teeming womb of royal kings,
Fear'd by their breed and famous by their
    birth,
Renowned for their deeds as far from home,
For Christian service and true chivalry,
As is the sepulchre in stubborn Jewry,
Of the world's ransom, blessed Mary's Son,
This land of such dear souls, this dear dear
    land,
Dear for her reputation through the world,
Is now leased out—I die pronouncing it—
Like to a tenement or pelting farm:
England, bound in with the triumphant sea
Whose rocky shore beats back the envious
    siege
Of watery Neptune, is now bound in with
    shame,
With inky blots and rotten parchment bonds:
That England, that was wont to conquer others,
Hath made a shameful conquest of itself.
Ah, would the scandal vanish with my life,
How happy then were my ensuing death!

SONG OF SONGS
THE KING JAMES BIBLE
BOOK 22: SONG OF SOLOMON, 1:15FF

Behold, thou art fair, my love; behold, thou
art fair; thou hast doves' eyes within thy
locks: thy hair is as a flock of goats, that
appear from mount Gilead.
Thy teeth are like a flock of sheep that are
even shorn, which came up from the washing;
whereof every one bear twins, and none is
barren among them.
Thy lips are like a thread of scarlet, and thy
speech is comely: thy temples are like a
piece of a pomegranate within thy locks.
Thy neck is like the tower of David builded
for an armoury, whereon there hang a
thousand bucklers, all shields of mighty men.
Thy two breasts are like two young roes that
are twins, which feed among the lilies.
Until the day break, and the shadows flee
away, I will get me to the mountain of myrrh,
and to the hill of frankincense.
Thou art all fair, my love; there is no spot in
thee.
[...]
How fair is thy love, my sister, my spouse!
how much better is thy love than wine! and
the smell of thine ointments than all spices!
Thy lips, O my spouse, drop as the
honeycomb: honey and milk are under thy
tongue; and the smell of thy garments is like
the smell of Lebanon.
A garden inclosed is my sister, my spouse;
a spring shut up, a fountain sealed.
Thy plants are an orchard of pomegranates,
with pleasant fruits; camphire, with spikenard,
Spikenard and saffron; calamus and cinnamon,
with all trees of frankincense; myrrh and
aloes, with all the chief spices:
A fountain of gardens, a well of living waters,
and streams from Lebanon.
[...]
Thou art beautiful, O my love, as Tirzah,
comely as Jerusalem, terrible as an army
with banners.

Turn away thine eyes from me, for they have overcome me: thy hair is as a flock of goats that appear from Gilead.

Thy teeth are as a flock of sheep which go up from the washing, whereof every one beareth twins, and there is not one barren among them. As a piece of a pomegranate are thy temples within thy locks.

[...]

Who is she that looketh forth as the morning, fair as the moon, clear as the sun, and terrible as an army with banners?

[...]

How beautiful are thy feet with shoes, O prince's daughter! the joints of thy thighs are like jewels, the work of the hands of a cunning workman. Thy navel is like a round goblet, which wanteth not liquor: thy belly is like an heap of wheat set about with lilies.

Thy two breasts are like two young roes that are twins.

Thy neck is as a tower of ivory; thine eyes like the fishpools in Heshbon, by the gate of Bathrabbim: thy nose is as the tower of Lebanon which looketh toward Damascus. Thine head upon thee is like Carmel, and the hair of thine head like purple; the king is held in the galleries.

How fair and how pleasant art thou, O love, for delights!

This thy stature is like to a palm tree, and thy breasts to clusters of grapes.

I said, I will go up to the palm tree, I will take hold of the boughs thereof: now also thy breasts shall be as clusters of the vine, and the smell of thy nose like apples.

RUBÉN DARÍO
CANTO A LA ARGENTINA
(1886-1916)

I sing the praises of woman's
beauty and grace. Just as,
with singular mastery, the
good gardener uses the
rustic art of
cuttings and grafts,
cross-pollinations and hybrids,
to create n'er-before-seen roses,
chrysanthemums, and hyacinths,
with rare scent and appearance,
resplendent petals,
distinct colors and shapes.
Similarly, the Argentine woman,
created of a different lifeblood,
is a splendid, animate blossom—
shining, scented, towering.

Waltz of Vienna,
dark eyes of Spain,
thick, curly black eyelashes
of the Latina siren;
skin of Albion,
white as lily-flesh,
blushing, angelic face
of a queen;
her flowing elegance
is a favorite in Paris,
and her luminous fragrance
comes straight from the heart of the land.

Distilled concentrate of various charms,
blend of essences and strengths,
Nordic gold, marble terraces,
mixture of pearl and iris,
sculptural music, a vision
of the most spellbinding martyrdom,
voluptuousness, fantastic illusion,
all-soothing sweetness
or all-consuming passion,
leonine lover or endearing enemy—
such is the triumphant native Venus.

CLÉMENT MAROT
BLAZON OF THE UGLY LITTLE TIT
(1535)

Little tit with nothing but skin,
scrawny flag flapping limply about,
large tit, long tit,
squished tit, bread-like tit,
pointy-nippled tit,
like the tip of a funnel,
you jounce about at every move,
no need to be pushed...
Tit, one might say he who fondles you
knows he's knee-deep in it.
Roasted tit, hanging tit,
shriveled tit, tit that squirts
mud in lieu of milk.
The devil summons you to the
infernal family, to nurse his daughter.
Tit to be tossed over the shoulder,
like a broad old-fashioned shawl,
if you're glimpsed, men feel they need
to handle you with gloves,
so as not to stain themselves. And they take
you,
tit, to slap the ugly nose of she
who has you dangling under her pits.

pages 224-225: Domenico Ghirlandaio
The Birth of the Virgin, 1486-1490,
Florence, Santa Maria Novella

ROBERT BURTON
THE ANATOMY OF MELANCHOLY
VOL. III (1621)

Love is blind, as the saying is, Cupid's blind,
and so are all his followers. *Quisquis amat
ranam, ranam putat esse Dianam* [whosoever
loves a frog, thinks that frog Diana]. Every
lover admires his mistress, though she be
very deformed of herself, ill-favoured,
wrinkled, pimpled, pale, red, yellow, tanned,
tallow-faced, have a swollen juggler's platter
face, or a thin, lean, chitty face, have clouds
in her face, be crooked, dry, bald, goggle-
eyed, blear-eyed, or with staring eyes, she
looks like a squis'd cat, hold her head still
awry, heavy, dull, hollow-eyed, black or
yellow about the eyes, or squint-eyed,
sparrow-mouthed, Persian hook-nosed, have
a sharp fox nose, a red nose, China flat, great
nose, *nare simo patuloque* [snub, flat nose],
a nose like a promontory, gubber-tushed,
rotten teeth, black, uneven, brown teeth,
beetle browed, a witch's beard, her breath
stink all over the room, her nose drip winter
and summer, with a Bavarian poke under her
chin, a sharp chin, lave eared, with a long
crane's neck, which stands awry too, *pendulis
mammis* [pendulous breasts], "her dugs like
two double jugs," or else no dugs, in that
other extreme, bloody fallen fingers, she have
filthy, long unpared nails, scabbed hands
or wrists, a tanned skin, a rotten carcass,
crooked back, she stoops, is lame, splay-
footed, "as slender in the middle as a cow
in the waist," gouty legs, her ankles hang
over her shoes, her feet stink, she breed lice,
a mere changeling, a very monster, an oaf
imperfect, her whole complexion savours,
a harsh voice, incondite gesture, vile gait,
a vast virago, or an ugly tit, a slug, a fat
fustilugs, a truss, a long lean rawbone,
a skeleton, a sneaker (*si qua latent meliora
puta* [to think what remains unseen is better]),
and to thy judgment looks like a merd in a
lantern, whom thou couldst not fancy for a
world, but hatest, loathest, and wouldst have

spit in her face, or blow thy nose in her bosom, *remedium amoris* [a remedy for love] to another man, a dowdy, a slut, a scold, a nasty, rank, rammy, filthy, beastly quean, dishonest peradventure, obscene, base, beggarly, rude, foolish, untaught, peevish, Irus' daughter, Thersites' sister, Grobians' scholar, if he love her once, he admires her for all this, he takes no notice of any such errors, or imperfections of body or mind, *Ipsa hæc—delectant, veluti Balbinum Polypus Agnæ* [but then again, Balbinus loved Hagna's polyp]; he had rather have her than any woman in the world.

Francisco de Goya
The Witches' Sabbath (detail),
1819-1823, Madrid, Museo del Prado

EDMOND ROSTAND
CYRANO DE BERGERAC
ACT I, SCENE 1.IV (1897)

CYRANO [TO THE VISCOUNT].

Ah no! young blade! That was a trifle short!
You might have said at least a hundred things
By varying the tone, ... like this, suppose, ...
Aggressive: "Sir, if I had such a nose
I'd amputate it!" Friendly: "When you sup
It must annoy you, dipping in your cup;
You need a drinking-bowl of special shape!"
Descriptive: "'Tis a rock! ... a peak! ... a cape!
—A cape, forsooth! 'Tis a peninsular!"
Curious: "How serves that oblong capsular?
For scissor-sheath? Or pot to hold your ink?"
Gracious: "You love the little birds, I think?
I see you've managed with a fond research
To find their tiny claws a roomy perch!"
Truculent: "When you smoke your pipe ...
suppose
That the tobacco-smoke spouts from your
nose—
Do not the neighbors, as the fumes rise higher,
Cry terror-struck: 'The chimney is afire'?"
Considerate: "Take care, ... your head bowed
low
By such a weight ... lest head o'er heels you go!"

Tender: "Pray get a small umbrella made,
Lest its bright color in the sun should fade!"
Pedantic: "That beast Aristophanes
Names Hippocamelelephantoles
Must have possessed just such a solid lump
Of flesh and bone, beneath his forehead's
bump!"
Cavalier: "The last fashion, friend, that hook?
To hang your hat on? 'Tis a useful crook!"
Emphatic: "No wind, O majestic nose,
Can give *thee* cold!—save when the mistral
blows!"
Dramatic: "When it bleeds, what a Red Sea!"
Admiring: "Sign for a perfumery!"
Lyric: "Is this a conch? ... a Triton you?"
Simple: "When is the monument on view?"
Rustic: "That thing a nose? Marry-come-up!
'Tis a dwarf pumpkin, or a prize turnip!"
Military: "Point against cavalry!"
Practical: "Put it in a lottery!
Assuredly 'twould be the biggest prize!"
Or ... parodying Pyramus' sighs ...
"Behold the nose that mars the harmony
Of its master's phiz! blushing its treachery!"
—Such, my dear sir, is what you might have said,
Had you of wit or letters the least jot:
But, O most lamentable man!—of wit
You never had an atom, and of letters
You have three letters only!—they spell Ass!

Giancarlo Vitali
La "coda" dell'ermellino ("The Ermine's Tail"), 1999,
collection of the artist

Max Beckmann
Women's Bath, 1919,
Berlin, Staatliche Museen zu Berlin, Nationalgalerie

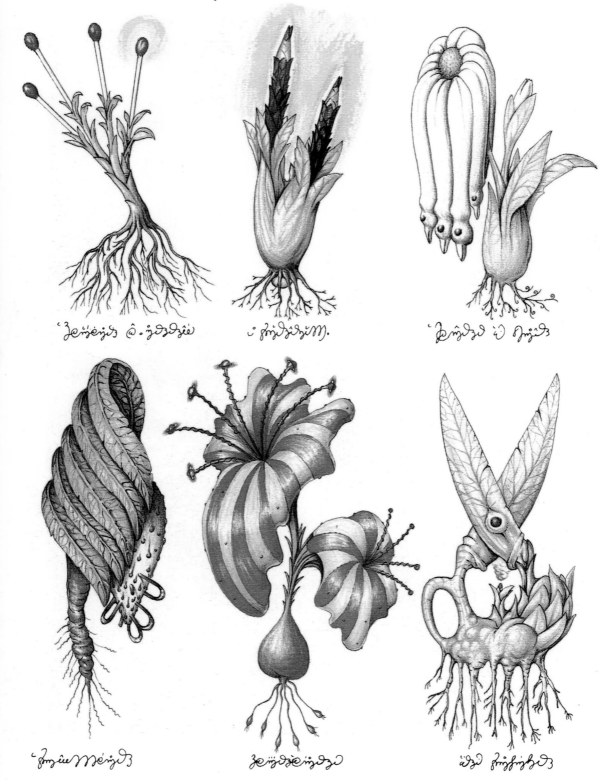

14.   THE ARISTOTELIAN TELESCOPE

A semantic representation by essence presupposes as a background a tree of the genealogical type, a series of embedded classes and subclasses so that the creation of the supporting structure precedes the identification of individuals, genera and species, and all of them can obtain an identity solely thanks to that structure. To return to the platypus, for eighty years it was known through the gradual discovery of apparently contradictory properties (such as laying eggs and nursing its young) until scientific taxonomies identified (almost *ad hoc*) the subclass of the monotreme mammals. In semiotics these are known as dictionary definitions: you make a dictionary definition of a dog if you say that it is an animal of the Canidae family, which are placental, fissiped, carnivorous mammals. In point of fact no "flesh and blood" dictionary (of the type we use habitually) is made of dictionary definitions in the semiotic sense: even if a dictionary contained the definition given here above (but it seldom does so with such precision) it would add other properties that distinguish dogs as quadrupeds, man's best friend, omnivorous, and so on—and probably it would also at least mention the better known breeds. A representation by accumulation or series of properties does not presuppose a dictionary but a kind of on-going encyclopaedia, never finished, and never definitively capable of taking the rigid form of a tree.

The immensity of the encyclopaedia frightened the compilers of the first dictionaries: in the 17th century the renowned Italian *Dizionario della Crusca*, unable to take advantage of scientific taxonomies

Luigi Serafini
Illuminated miniature from the *Codex Seraphinianus*,
Milan, F.M. Ricci, 1981

Johann Joachim Becher
Classification of Known Substances,
plate from the *Opuscola chymica rariora,*
1719, Nuremberg

elaborated later, defined the dog as a "known animal". Only the Baroque mentality, with its taste for the boundless and the extraordinary, could conceive of encyclopaedic structures that listed infinite properties.

In defining the superiority of the German language Georg Philipp Harsdörfer (*Frauenzimmer Gesprächspiele*, 1641) did not write an orderly treaty on linguistics but stated that [German] "speaks with the tongues of nature, expressing most perceptibly all sounds [...] It thunders with the heavens, flashes with the swift clouds, glitters like hail, whistles with the wind, foams with the waves, clatters like locks, resounds with the air, detonates with cannons, roars like the lion, lows like the ox, snarls like the bear, bells like the deer, bleats like the sheep, grunts like the pig, barks like the dog, neighs like the horse, hisses like the serpent, meows like the cat, honks like the goose, croaks like the frog, buzzes like the hornet, squawks like the chicken, clacks its beak like the stork, caws like the crow, twitters like the swallow, and chirps like the sparrow [...]".

In his *Cannocchiale aristotelico,* or *The Aristotelian Telescope* (1665), Emanuele Tesauro proposes the model of the metaphor as a way to discover hitherto unknown relationships between the known data. Hence it is a question of constituting a repertory of known things, on running through which the metaphoric imagination can discover new relationships. In this way Tesauro works out the idea of a Categorical Index—which would be an enormous dictionary were it not for the fact that it only has the apparent form of the dictionary, given that the quantity of properties it lists is such that we suspect that it is not limited to those mentioned. He presents his index (with Baroque satisfaction for the *marvellous* idea) as a "truly secret secret", an inexhaustible mine of infinite metaphors and ingenious concepts given that ingenuity is none other than the capacity to "penetrate objects that are hidden under different categories and to make comparisons between them"—in other words the capacity to unearth analogies and similarities that would have passed unnoticed if everything had remained classified in its own category.

It was therefore a matter of recording in a book the ten Aristotelian categories (Substance and the nine Accidents), and listing its Members under each category and under each member the Things "subjacent to them".

Here we can do little more than provide some brief examples from the catalogue that Tesauro gives us (apparently susceptible to constant extension), but members of the category of Substance include Divine Persons, Ideas, Gods of Fable, Angels, Demons, and Sprites, members of the Heavens include Wandering Stars, the Zodiac, Vapours, Exhalations, Meteors, Comets, Lightning and the Winds; the category of Earth lists Fields, Wildernesses, Mountains, Hills and Promontories; that of Bodies includes Stones, Gems, Metals, and Grasses; while Mathematics includes Globes, Compasses, Squares, and so on.

Likewise in the category of Quantities, for Quantity of Volume we find listed the Small, the Great, the Long and the Short; for Quantity of Weight the Light and the Heavy; for Quality, under Seeing we find the Visible and the Invisible, the Apparent, the Beautiful and the Deformed, the Clear and the Obscure, Black and White; under Smell, Aroma and Stink—and so on with the categories of Relation, Action and Affection, Position, Time, Place and State.

When we go to look for the Things subjacent to these members, under the category of Quantity, in the member Quantity of Volume, among small Things we find the angel who stands on a pinhead, incorporeal forms, the pole as the motionless point of the sphere, zenith and nadir; among Elementary Things the spark of fire, the drop of water, the scruple of stone, the grain of sand, the gem and the atom; among Human things, the embryo, the abortus, the pygmy and the dwarf; among the Animals, the ant and the flea; among the Plants mustard seed and the breadcrumb; among the Sciences the mathematical point, in Architecture the tip of the pyramid.

This list certainly seems to have neither rhyme nor reason, like all the Baroque attempts to encapsulate the global content of a body of knowledge. In *Technica curiosa* (1664) and in *Joco-seriorium naturae et artis sive magiae naturalis centuriae tres* (1665) Caspar Schott mentions a work of 1653, whose author's name he says he has forgotten, but who apparently presented in Rome an *Artificium* comprising forty-

Robinet Testard
image from Mattheaus Platearius's *The Book of
Simple Medicine*, Ms. Fr. VI n. 1, fol. 166v, c. 1470,
St. Petersburg, National Library

four fundamental classes all of which are worth listing here, giving in brackets only a few examples: "1. Elements (fire, wind, smoke, ash, hell, purgatory, and the centre of the Earth). 2. Heavenly entities (stars, lightning, rainbow...). 3. Intellectual entities (God, Jesus, discourse, opinion, suspicion, soul, stratagem or spectre). 4. Secular states (emperor, barons, plebeians). 5. Ecclesiastical states. 6. Craftsmen (painter or sailor). 7. Instruments. 8. Affections (love, justice, lust). 9. Religion. 10. Sacramental confession. 11. Tribunal. 12. Army. 13. Medicine (doctor, hunger, enema). 14. Brute beasts. 15. Birds. 16. Reptiles and fish. 17. Parts of animals. 18. Furnishings. 19. Foods. 20. Drinks and liquids (wine, beer, water, butter, wax, resin). 21. Clothing. 22. Silk fabrics. 23. Wools. 24. Canvas and other woven fabrics. 25. Nautical and aromas (ship, cinnamon, anchor, chocolate). 26. Metals and coins. 27. Various artefacts. 28. Stones. 29. Jewels. 30. Trees and fruits. 31. Public places. 32. Weights and measures. 33. Numerals. 39. Time. 40. Adjectives. 41. Adverbs. 42. Prepositions. 43. Persons (pronouns, titles such as His Eminence the Cardinal). 44. Travelling (hay, road, robber)."

Around 1660 a manuscript by Athanasius Kircher was produced (*Novum Inventum*)[1] which explains how it is possible to reduce the various languages of the world to a single code, which contemplated a dictionary of 1,620 "words", and in which the author attempted to establish a list of 54 fundamental categories that could be written down through iconograms. The 54 categories also constituted a remarkably heterogeneous list, including divine, angelic and celestial entities, elements, human beings, animals, vegetables, minerals, drinks, clothing, weights, numbers, hours, cities, foods, family, actions such as seeing or giving, adjectives, adverbs, and the months of the year.

In these lists the lack of a systematic spirit testifies to the effort made by the encyclopaedist to elude an arid classification by genera and species. It is this still-disordered accumulation (or barely ordered, as in Tesauro, under the rubrics of the ten categories and their members)

De la Cochenille, plate XXVIII, in Martin Froben Ledermüller, *Amusement microscopique*, Nuremberg, 1764

that would later allow the discovery of unexpected relations between the objects of knowledge. The "hotchpotch" is the price we pay not to attain completeness but to avoid the poverty of all arborescent classifications.

We should note the experience that Tesauro gains from his storehouse of properties. If we wanted to find a good metaphor for a dwarf (but for Tesauro finding metaphors meant, in the Aristotelian sense, knowing new determinations of things or rather all that could be said about a given object), we could go to the aforementioned Index of Categories and look up the definitions of Myrmidon, or a Mouse born of a mountain. But this index is joined by another that for every small thing and, gradually, according to which of the ten categories we consult, decides (for Quantity) what thing the small thing can be measured against or what parts it has; for Quality whether it is visible or what deformations it may present; for Relation to whom or what it is related, whether it is material and of what form; for Action and Passion how much it can or cannot do, and so on. And if we want to know how to measure a small thing, the Index should refer us, for example, to the Geometrical Finger.

In this way, as we proceed through every category, we find that with regard to the dwarf (and the list takes up three pages of the *Cannocchiale*) we might say that it is something shorter than its own name, more embryo than man, a human fragment, far smaller than a finger, with so little substance as to have no colour, who would succumb in a fight with a fly, so much so that it is impossible to understand whether he sits, stands, or lies down ...

But even though it seems to be based upon relationship of dependence from species to genus, the model of a definition by properties is not the tree but what Deleuze and Guattari[2] have called the *rhizome*, that subterranean modification of the stalk of a vegetable in which every point can be connected to any other point, in which there are no points or positions but only lines of connection. And so a rhizome can be broken at any point only to pick up again by following its own line; it is detachable, reversible; it has no centre, it connects any point with any other point, it is not genealogical like

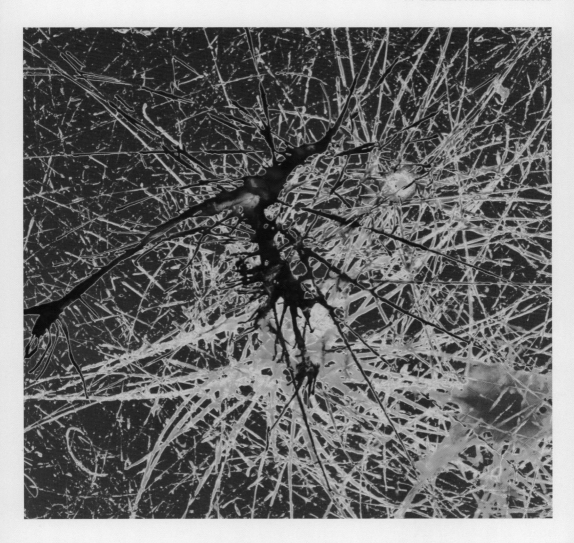

Nerve cells

a root, it is not hierarchic, it is acentric and in principle it has neither
a beginning nor an end …

The homology with the rhizome obliges us to think also of
territorial and architectonic lists. Earlier we remarked how difficult
it is to imagine a pictorial list given that the picture frame limits
space and, so to speak, prevents us from thinking of an "etcetera";
but we did grant that it is possible to suggest (and we have seen how)
an incalculable continuity beyond the limits of the frame.

Likewise we ought to say that there is no architectonic "etcetera",
since every architectonic edifice circumscribes and delimits its own
space, and exists precisely because it separates an internal living space
from the space surrounding it. This holds not only for buildings but
also for cities once delimited by walls, or those that spread out in
a star shape from around a central square (like the ideal cities of
the 16th century). But it was the same with the form of the Roman
castrum, a square subdivided by vertical and horizontal lines, and

in fact we commonly talk of city and outskirts, city and district, city and surrounding territory.

Yet when we leave the city built around a central square and move on to the American city that spreads out from "Main Street", we find that this spinal column of the city can be infinitely prolonged, and gradually cities spring up where the centre fades seamlessly into suburbs that get bigger day by day so that sometimes it is difficult to say where the city ends and the rest of the territory begins. This eventually leads us to the "city-territory", the main example of which is Los Angeles, which has no centre and is practically the outskirts of itself. Los Angeles is an "etcetera" city and so, if we wish to accept the metaphor, it is a "list-city" rather than a "form-city".

A "list-city" is shaped like an *open maze*. Certainly, the classical structure of a maze is that of a delimited space. But it is a closed space structured in such a way that those who enter it feel that it is impossible to find the way out. The maze is a form, but for those who enter one it represents the experience of the impossibility of getting out and hence of endless wandering—and this is the source of its appeal and of the fear it can strike into people. Paradoxically, the maze is a non-linear list, which rewinds itself like a ball of wool, and again the homology with the structure of a rhizome tells us something about this Achilles' shield as infinite as the catalogue of ships.

1. See Caterina Marrone, "Lingua universale e scrittura segreta nell'opera di Kircher", in Casciato et al., eds., *Enciclopedia in Roma barocca* (Venice, Marsilio), and U. Eco, *The Search for a Perfect Language* (Oxford, Blackwell, 1995), page 203 ff.
2. Gilles Deleuze, Félix Guattari, *Mille Plateaux, Capitalisme et schizophrénie 2* (Paris, Minuit, 1980).

Ronan-Jim Sévellec
Un incertain reposoir, 1996,
Paris, collection of the artist

Bird's-eye
view of Los Angeles

242

15. EXCESS, FROM RABELAIS ONWARDS

It seems that in the Baroque period on the one hand people strove to find definitions by essence that were less rigid than those of medieval logic, but on the other hand the taste for the marvellous led to the transformation of every taxonomy into lists, every tree into a labyrinth. In reality, however, lists were already being used during the Renaissance to strike the first blows at the world order sanctioned by the great medieval *summae*.

In effect, and we have said this about encyclopaedias, throughout classical and medieval times the list is almost a *pis aller*, and just underneath its surface we always glimpse the outline of a possible order, the desire to give things a form. With the modern world, instead, the list is conceived out of a taste for *deformation*.

A phantasmagorical collection of all forms of devilish ugliness is found in *Baldus* (1517). Written by Teofilo Folengo under the pseudonym of Merlin Cocai, *Baldus* is a heroic-comic, grotesque, goliardic poem, and is both a parody of Dante's *Comedy* and a forerunner of **Rabelais'** *Gargantua and Pantagruel*. Among the main character's and his friends' various picaresque adventures there is, in the second part (Book 19), a battle with a host of devils, who appear in a collage of animal forms: bat, dog, goose, serpent, ox, ass, billy goat, with tusks, blood dripping down their breasts, fetid slobber, and sulphurous emissions from their sphincters. In the end Baldus and his friends chop the devils into such small pieces than when Beelzebub tries to reassemble the one hundred and seventy thousand chunks he has been reduced

Richard Dadd
The Fairy Feller's Master-Stroke, 1855-1864,
London, Tate Gallery

Bernard Palissy (school of)
Palissy-ware plate, late 16th century,
Paris, Musée du Louvre

pages 246-247: Jan Bruegel the Elder
Allegory of Air, 1621,
Paris, Musée du Louvre

to, he glues together foxes without tails, bears and pigs with horns, mastiffs with three paws, bulls with four horns, wolves' mouths in giants' heads, birds with the beak of an owl and the limbs of a frog … It is not difficult to see in this collage capable of producing an infinity of creatures a verbal equivalent of Hieronymous Bosch's visions of hell—and how Bosch's infernos do not represent a simple taste for the fantastic and the teratological but are an allusion to the vices of the day, the corruption of social mores, and the disintegration of a world.

The author whose enormous lists seem made in contempt of the requirements for order that inspired the learned doctors of the Sorbonne of his day was Rabelais. There was no obvious reason to list the many unheard of ways of cleaning one's backside, the many adjectives used to qualify the male organ, the many ways of flaying one's enemies, the many useless books in the Abbey of Saint Victor's, the many kinds of snakes, or the many games that Gargantua knew how to play (and God only knows how he found the time to play them all): at flush, at love, at primero, at chess, at the beast, at Reynard the fox, at the rifle, at the squares, at trump, at the cows, at the prick and spare not, at the lottery, at the hundred, at the chance or mumchance, at the peeny, at three dice or maniest bleaks, at the unfortunate woman, at the tables, at the fib, at nivinivinack, at the pass ten, at the lurch, at one-and-thirty, at doublets or queen's game, at post and pair, odd or even, at the faily, at the French trictrac, at three hundred, at the long tables or ferkeering, at the unlucky man, at feldown, at the last couple in hell, at tod's body, at the hock, at needs must, at the surly, at the dames or draughts, at the lansquenet, at bob and mow, at the cuckoo, at primus secundus, at puff, or let him speak that hath it, at mark-knife, at the keys, at take nothing and throw out, at span-counter, at the marriage, at even or odd, at the frolic or jackdaw, at cross or pile, at the opinion, at ball and huckle-bones, at who doth the one, doth the other, at ivory balls, at the billiards, at the sequences, at bob and hit, at the ivory bundles, at the owl, at the tarots, at the charming of the hare, at losing load him, at pull yet a little, at he's gulled and esto, at trudgepig, at the torture,

at the magatapies, at the handruff, at the horn, at the click, at the
flowered or Shrovetide ox, at honours, at the madge-owlet, at pinch
without laughing, at tilt at weeky, at prickle me tickle me, at ninepins,
at the unshoeing of the ass, at the cock quintin, at the cocksess, at tip
and hurl, at hari hohi, at the flat bowls, at I set me down, at the veer
and turn, at earl beardy, at rogue and ruffian, at the old mode, at
bumbatch touch, at draw the spit, at the mysterious trough, at put
out, at the short bowls, at gossip lend me your sack, at the dapple-
grey, at the ramcod ball, at cock and crank it, at thrust out the harlot,
at break-pot, at Marseilles figs, at my desire, at nicknamry, at twirly
whirlytrill, at stick and hole, at the rush bundles, at boke or him, or
flaying the fox, at the short staff, at the branching it, at the whirling
gig, at trill madam, or grapple my lady, at hide and seek, or are you
all hid?, at the cat selling, at blow the coal, at the picket, at the re-
wedding, at the blank, at the quick and dead judge, at the pilferers,
at unoven the iron, at the caveson, at the false clown, at prison bars,
at the flints, or at the nine stones, at have at the nuts, at to the crutch
hulch back, at cherry-pit, at the Sanct is found, at rub and rice, at
hinch, pinch and laugh not, at whiptop, at the leek, at the casting
top, at bumdockdousse, at the hobgoblins, at the loose gig, at the O
wonderful, at the hoop, at the soily smutchy, at the sow, at fast and
loose, at belly to belly, at scutchbreech, at the dales or straths, at the
broom-besom, at the twigs, at St. Cosme, I come to adore thee, at the
quoits, at I'm for that, at the lusty brown boy, at I take you napping,
at greedy glutton, at fair and softly passeth Lent, at the morris dance,
at the forked oak, at feeby, at truss, at the whole frisk and gambol, at
the wolf's tail, at battabum, or riding of the at bum to buss, or nose
in breech, wild mare, at Geordie, give me my lance, at Hind the
ploughman, at swaggy, waggy or shoggyshou, at the good mawkin,
at stook and rook, shear and threave, the dead beast, at climb the ladder,
Billy, at the birch, at the dying hog, at the muss, at the salt doup, at
the dilly dilly darling, at the pretty pigeon, at ox moudy, at barley
break, at purpose in purpose, at the bavine, at nine less, at the bush
leap, at blind-man-buff, at crossing, at the fallen bridges, at bo-peep,
at bridled nick, at the hardit arsepursy, at the white, at butts, at the

harrowers nest, at thwack swinge him, at forward hey, at apple, pear, plum, at the fig, at mumgi, at gunshot crack, at the toad, at mustard peel, at the cricket, at the gome, at the pounding stick, at the relapse, at jack and the box, at jog breech, or prick him forward, at the queens, at the trades, at knockpate, at heads and points, at the Cornish c(h)ough, at the vine-tree hug, at the crane-dance, at black be thy fall, at slash and cut, at ho the distaff, at bobbing, or flirt on the nose, at Joan Thomson, at the bolting cloth, at the larks, at the oat's seed, at fillipping,

It is the beginning of a poetics of the list for the list, written for the love of lists, of the list *by excess*.

Adriaen van Utrecht
Birds of the Basse-Cour, 17th century,
Paris, Musée du Louvre

Suzi Gablik
Tropism #12, 1972,
Washington DC, Smithsonian
American Art Museum

Only a taste for excess could have led a Baroque fabulist such as Giambattista Basile, in his *The Tale of Tales or the Entertainment for Little Ones*, in telling of how seven brothers are turned into seven doves for their sister's fault, has them explode in a scolding that is none other than a volley of names of birds: "Have you eaten the brains of a cat, O sister, that you have driven our advice from your mind? Behold us, turned to birds, a prey to the talons of kites, hawks, and falcons! Behold us made companions of water-hens, snipes, goldfinches, woodpeckers, jays, owls, magpies, jackdaws, rooks, starlings, woodcocks, cocks, hens and chickens, turkey-cocks, blackbirds, thrushes, chaffinches, tomtits, jenny-wrens, lapwings, linnets, greenfinches, crossbills, flycatchers, larks, plovers, kingfishers, wagtails, redbreasts, redfinches, sparrows, ducks, fieldfares, woodpigeons and bullfinches!"

It is for love of excess that **Burton** was to describe an ugly woman by accumulating a disproportionate number of depictions and insults, or when **Marino** (*Adonis* 10, 136-138), in producing a deluge of verses on the products of human artifice, was to say:

Look around, astrolabes and almanacs, traps, rasps and picklocks, cages, bedlam, tabards, shell cases and sacks, labyrinths, plumb-rules and levels, dice, cards, ball, board and chessmen and rattles and pulleys and gimlets, reels, winders, parrels, clocks, alembics, decanters, bellows and crucibles, look, bags and blisters full of wind, and swollen bubbles of soap, towers of smoke, nettle leaves, pumpkin flowers, and green and yellow feathers, spiders, scarabs, crickets, ants, wasps, mosquitoes, fireflies and moths, mice, cats, silkworms and a hundred such extravaganzas of devices and animals; all these you see and other strange phantasms again in massive ranks, are the whims of human ingenuity, fantasies, mad, chimerical frenzies. There are mills and moving vanes, pulleys, winches and all kinds of wheels; others are shaped like fish, others like birds, various, since brains are various.

It is out of the taste for excess that **Hugo**, in suggesting the mammoth dimensions of the Republican Convention, explodes in page after page of names, so that what could be an archive register becomes a mind-boggling experience. And a somewhat "rhetorical" example of the rhetoric of excess is to be found in **Kipling**'s letter to his son.

At this point we find ourselves faced with two trends, both present in the history of lists but even more so in modern and post-modern literature. There is a list *coherent by excess* that nonetheless puts together entities that have some form of kinship among them; and there are lists, which in principle are not necessarily required to be excessively long, which are an assembly of things deliberately devoid of any apparent reciprocal relationship, so much so that such cases have been referred to as *chaotic enumeration*.[1]

1. Cf. Leo Spitzer, *La enumeración caotica en la poesia moderna* (Buenos Aires, Faculdad de Filosofía y Letras, 1945).

**FRANÇOIS RABELAIS
FIVE BOOKS OF THE
LIVES, HEROIC DEEDS
AND SAYINGS OF
GARGANTUA AND HIS
SON PANTAGRUEL
BOOK III, CHAPTER 26
(1532-1534)
HOW PANURGE
CONSULTETH WITH
FRIAR JOHN OF THE
FUNNELS**

Panurge was indeed very
much troubled in mind and
disquieted at the words of
Herr Trippa, and therefore, as
he passed by the little village
of Huymes, after he had
made his address to Friar
John, in pecking at, rubbing,
and scratching his own left
ear, he said unto him, Keep
me a little jovial and merry,
my dear and sweet bully, for
I find my brains altogether
metagrabolized and
confounded, and my spirits
in a most dunsical puzzle at
the bitter talk of this devilish,
hellish, damned fool.
Hearken, my dainty cod.

Mellow C.
Varnished C.
Resolute C.
Lead-coloured C.
Renowned C.
Cabbage-like C.
Knurled C.
Matted C.
Courteous C.
Suborned C.
Genitive C.
Fertile C.
Desired C.
Gigantal C.
Whizzing C.

Stuffed C.
Oval C.
Neat C.
Speckled C.
Claustral C.
Common C.
Finely metalled C.
Virile C.
Brisk C.
Arabian-like C.
Stayed C.
Quick C.
Trussed-up Grey-hound-like C.
Massive C.
Bearlike C.
Manual C.
Partitional C.
Mounted C.
Absolute C.
Patronymic C.
Sleeked C.
Well-set C.
Cockney C.
Diapered C.
Gemel C.
Auromercuriated C.
Spotted C.
Turkish C.
Robust C.
Master C.
Burning C.
Appetizing C.
Seeded C.
Thwacking C.
Succourable C.
Lusty C.
Urgent C.
Redoubtable C.
Jupped C.
Handsome C.
Affable C.
Milked C.
Prompt C.
Memorable C.
Calfeted C.
Fortunate C.
Palpable C.

Raised C.
Boxwood C.
Barbable C.
Odd C.
Latten C.
Tragical C.
Steeled C.
Unbridled C.
Transpontine C.
Stale C.
Hooked C.
Digestive C.
Orange-tawny C.
Researched C.
Active C.
Embroidered C.
Encompassed C.
Vital C.
Glazed C.
Strouting out C.
Magistral C.
Interlarded C.
Jolly C.
Monachal C.
Burgher-like C.
Lively C.
Subtle C.
Empowdered C.
Gerundive C.
Hammering C.
Ebonized C.
Franked C.
Clashing C.
Brasiliated C.
Polished C.
Tingling C.
Organized C.
Powdered Beef C.
Usual C.
Passable C.
Positive C.
Exquisite C.
Trunkified C.
Spared C.
Trim C.
Furious C.
Bold C.

Succulent C.
Packed C.
Lascivious C.
Factious C.
Hooded C.
Gluttonous C.
Clammy C.
Fat C.
Boulting C.
New-vamped C.
High-prized C.
Snorting C.
Improved C.
Requisite C.
Pilfering C.
Malling C.
Laycod C.
Shaking C.
Sounding C.

Hand-filling C.
Bobbing C.
Battled C.
Insuperable C.
Chiveted C.
Burly C.
Agreeable C.
Fumbling C.
Seditious C.
Formidable C.
Topsyturvying C.
Wardian C.
Profitable C.
Raging C.
Protective C.
Notable C.
Piled up C.
Twinkling C.
Musculous C.

Filled up C.
Able C.
Subsidiary C.
Manly C.
Algoristical C.
Satiric C.
Idle C.
Odoriferous C.
Repercussive C.
Membrous C.
Pranked C.
Convulsive C.
Strong C.
Jocund C.
Restorative C.
Twin C.
Routing C.
Masculinating C.
Belabouring C.

Pieter Bruegel the Younger
Peasant Wedding, 1568,
Ghent, Museum voor Schone Kunsten

Verbeeck family
A Grotesque Wedding Feast, 16th century,
Private collection

FRANÇOIS RABELAIS
FIVE BOOKS OF THE LIVES, HEROIC DEEDS AND SAYINGS OF GARGANTUA AND HIS SON PANTAGRUEL
BOOK II, CHAPTER 16 (1532-1534)
OF THE QUALITIES AND CONDITIONS OF PANURGE

Panurge was of a middle stature, not too high nor too low, and had somewhat an aquiline nose, made like the handle of a razor. He was at that time five and thirty years old or thereabouts, fine to gild like a leaden dagger—for he was a notable cheater and coney-catcher—he was a very gallant and proper man of his person, only that he was a little lecherous, and naturally subject to a kind of disease which at that time they called lack of money—it is an incomparable grief, yet, notwithstanding, he had three score and three tricks to come by it at his need, of which the most honourable and most ordinary was in manner of thieving, secret purloining and filching, for he was a wicked lewd rogue, a cozener, drinker, roister, rover, and a very dissolute and debauched fellow, if there were any in Paris; otherwise, and in all matters else, the best and most virtuous man in the world; and he was still contriving some plot, and devising mischief against the sergeants and the watch.
At one time he assembled three or four especial good hacksters and roaring boys, made them in the evening drink like Templars, afterwards led them till they came under St. Genevieve, or about the college of Navarre, and, at the hour that the watch was coming up that way—which he knew by putting his sword upon the pavement, and his ear by it, and, when he heard his sword shake, it was an infallible sign that the watch was near at that instant—then he and his companions took a tumbrel or dung-cart, and gave it the brangle, hurling it with all their force down the hill, and so overthrew all the poor watchmen like pigs, and then ran away upon the other side; for in less than two days he knew all the streets, lanes, and turnings in Paris as well as his Deus det.

At another time he made in some fair place, where the said watch was to pass, a train of gunpowder, and, at the very instant that they went along, set fire to it, and then made himself sport to see what good grace they had in running away, thinking that St. Anthony's fire had caught them by the legs. As for the poor masters of arts, he did persecute them above all others. When he encountered with any of them upon the street, he would not never fail to put some trick or other upon them, sometimes putting the bit of a fried turd in their graduate hoods, at other times pinning on little foxtails or hares'-ears behind them, or some such other roguish prank. One day that they were appointed all to meet in the Fodder Street (Sorbonne), he made a Borbonesa tart, or filthy and slovenly compound, made of store of garlic, of assafoetida, of castoreum, of dogs' turds very warm, which he steeped, tempered, and liquefied in the corrupt matter of pocky boils and pestiferous botches; and, very early in the morning therewith anointed all the pavement, in such sort that the devil could not have endured it, which made all these good people there to lay up their gorges, and vomit what was upon their stomachs before all the world, as if they had flayed the fox; and ten or twelve of them died of the plague, fourteen became lepers, eighteen grew lousy, and about seven and twenty had the pox, but he did not care a button for it. He commonly carried a whip under his gown, wherewith he whipped without remission the pages whom he found carrying wine to their masters, to make them mend their pace. In his coat he had above six and twenty little fobs and pockets always full; one with some lead-water, and a little knife as sharp as a glover's needle, wherewith he used to cut purses; another with some kind of bitter stuff, which he threw into the eyes of those he met; another with clotburrs, penned with little geese' or capon's feathers, which he cast upon the gowns and caps of honest people, and often made them fair horns, which they wore about all the city, sometimes all their life. Very often, also, upon the women's French hoods would he stick in the hind part somewhat made in the shape of a man's member. In another, he had a great many little horns full of fleas and lice, which he borrowed from the beggars of St. Innocent, and cast them with small canes or quills to write with into the necks of the daintiest gentlewomen that he could find, yea, even in the church, for he never seated himself above in the choir, but always sat in the body of the church amongst the women, both at mass, at vespers, and at sermon. In another, he used to have good store of hooks and buckles, wherewith he would couple men and women together that sat in company close to one another, but especially those that wore gowns of crimson taffeties, that, when they were about to go away, they might rend all their gowns. In another, he had a squib furnished with tinder, matches, stones to strike fire, and all other tackling necessary for it. In another, two or three burning glasses, wherewith he made both men and women sometimes mad, and in the church put them quite out of countenance; for he said that there was but an antistrophe, or little more difference than of a literal inversion, between a woman folle a la messe and molle a la fesse, that is, foolish at the mass and of a pliant buttock. In another, he had a good deal of needles and thread, wherewith he did a thousand little devilish pranks. One time, at the entry of the palace unto the great hall, where a certain grey friar or cordelier was to say mass to the counsellors, he did help to apparel him and put on his vestments, but in the accoutring of him he sewed on his alb, surplice, or stole, to his gown and shirt, and then withdrew himself when the said lords of the court or counsellors came to hear the said mass; but when it came to the Ite, missa est, that the poor frater would have laid by his stole or surplice, as the fashion then was, he plucked off withal both his frock and shirt, which were well sewed together, and thereby stripping himself up to the very shoulders showed his bel vedere to all the world, together with his Don Cypriano, which was no small one, as you may imagine. And the friar still kept haling, but so much the more did he discover himself and lay open his back parts, till one of the lords of the court said, How now! what's the matter? Will this fair father make us here an offering of his tail to kiss it? Nay, St. Anthony's fire kiss it for us! From thenceforth it was ordained that the poor fathers should never disrobe themselves any more before the world, but in their vestry-room, or sextry, as they call it; especially in the presence of women, lest it should tempt them to the sin of longing and disordinate desire. The people then asked why it was the friars had so long and large genitories? The said Panurge resolved the problem very neatly, saying, That which makes asses to have such great ears is that their dams did put no biggins on their heads, as Alliaco mentioneth in his Suppositions. By the like reason, that which makes the genitories or generation-tools of those so fair fraters so long is, for that they wear no bottomed breeches, and therefore their jolly member, having no impediment, hangeth dangling at liberty as far as it can reach, with a wiggle-waggle down to their knees, as women carry their paternoster beads, and the cause wherefore they have it so correspondently great is, that in this constant wig-wagging the humours of the body descend into the said member. For, according to the Legists, agitation and continual motion is cause of attraction.

Item, he had another pocket full of itching powder, called stone-alum, whereof he would cast some into the backs of those women whom he judged to be most beautiful and stately, which did so ticklishly gall them, that some would strip themselves in the open view of the world, and others dance like a cock upon hot embers, or a drumstick on a tabor. Others, again, ran about the streets, and he would run after them. To such as were in the stripping vein he would very civilly come to offer his attendance, and cover them with his cloak, like a courteous and very gracious man. Item, in another he had a little leather bottle full of old oil, wherewith, when he saw any man or woman in a rich new handsome suit, he would grease, smutch, and spoil all the best parts of it under colour and pretence of touching them, saying, This is good cloth; this is good satin; good taffeties! Madam, God give you all that your noble heart desireth! You have a new suit, pretty sir;—and you a new gown, sweet mistress;—God give you joy of it, and maintain you in all prosperity! And with this would lay his hand upon their shoulder, at which touch such a villainous spot was left behind, so enormously engraven to perpetuity in the very soul, body, and reputation, that the devil himself could never have taken it away. Then, upon his departing, he would say, Madam, take heed you do not fall, for there is a filthy great hole before you, whereinto if you put your foot, you will quite spoil yourself.

Another he had all full of euphorbium, very finely pulverized. In that powder did he lay a fair handkerchief curiously wrought, which he had stolen from a pretty seamstress of the palace, in taking away a louse from off her bosom which he had put there himself, and, when he came into the company of some good ladies, he would trifle them into a discourse of some fine workmanship of bone-lace, then immediately put his hand into their bosom, asking them, And this work, is it of Flanders, or of Hainault? and then drew out his handkerchief, and said, Hold, hold, look what work here is, it is of Foutignan or of Fontarabia, and shaking it hard at their nose, made them sneeze for four hours without ceasing. In the meanwhile he would fart like a horse, and the women would laugh and say, How now, do you fart, Panurge? No, no, madam, said he, I do but tune my tail to the plain song of the music which you make with your nose. In another he had a picklock, a pelican, a crampiron, a crook, and some other iron tools, wherewith there was no door nor coffer which he would not pick open.

FRANÇOIS RABELAIS
FIVE BOOKS OF THE LIVES, HEROIC DEEDS AND SAYINGS OF GARGANTUA AND HIS SON PANTAGRUEL
BOOK I, CHAPTER 13 (1532-1534)
HOW GARGANTUA'S WONDERFUL UNDERSTANDING BECAME KNOWN TO HIS FATHER GRANGOUSIER, BY THE INVENTION OF A TORCHECUL OR WIPEBREECH

About the end of the fifth year, Grangousier returning from the conquest of the Canarians, went by the way to see his son Gargantua. There was he filled with joy, as such a father might be at the sight of such a child of his: and whilst he kissed and embraced him, he asked many childish questions of him about divers matters, and drank very freely with him and with his governesses, of whom in great earnest he asked, amongst other things, whether they had been careful to keep him clean and sweet. To this Gargantua answered, that he had taken such a course for that himself, that in all the country there was not to be found a cleanlier boy than he. How is that? said Grangousier. I have, answered Gargantua, by a long and curious experience, found out a means to wipe my bum, the most lordly, the most excellent, and the most convenient that ever was seen. What is that? said Grangousier, how is it? I will tell you by-and-by, said Gargantua. Once I did wipe me with a gentle-woman's velvet mask, and found it to be good; for the softness of the silk was very voluptuous and pleasant to my fundament. Another time with one of their hoods, and in like manner that was comfortable. At another time with a lady's neckerchief, and after that I wiped me with some ear-pieces of hers made of crimson satin, but there was such a number of golden spangles in them (turdy round things, a pox take them) that they fetched away all the skin of my tail with a vengeance. Now I wish St. Antony's fire burn the bum-gut of the goldsmith that made them, and of her that wore them! This hurt I cured by wiping myself with a page's cap, garnished with a feather after the Switzers' fashion.

Afterwards, in dunging behind a bush, I found a March-cat, and with it I wiped my breech, but her claws were so sharp that they scratched and exulcerated all my perinee. Of this I recovered the next morning thereafter, by wiping myself with my mother's gloves, of a most excellent perfume and scent of the Arabian Benin. After that I wiped me with sage, with fennel, with anet, with marjoram, with roses, with gourd-leaves, with beets, with colewort, with leaves of the vine-tree, with mallows, wool-blade, which is a tail-scarlet, with lettuce, and with spinach leaves. All this did very great good to my leg. Then with mercury, with parsley, with nettles, with comfrey, but that gave me the bloody flux of Lombardy, which I healed by wiping me with my braguette. Then I wiped my tail in the sheets, in the coverlet, in the curtains, with a cushion, with arras hangings, with a green carpet, with a table-cloth, with a napkin, with a handkerchief, with a combing-cloth; in all which I found more pleasure than do the mangy dogs when you rub them. Yea, but, said Grangousier, which torchecul did you find to be the best? I was coming to it, said Gargantua, and by-and-by shall you hear the tu autem, and know the whole mystery and knot of the matter. I wiped myself with hay, with straw, with thatch-rushes, with flax, with wool, with paper, but,

Who his foul tail with paper wipes,
Shall at his ballocks leave some chips.

What, said Grangousier, my little rogue, hast thou been at the pot, that thou dost rhyme already? Yes, yes, my lord the king, answered Gargantua, I can rhyme gallantly, and rhyme till I become hoarse with rheum. Hark, what our privy says to the skiters:
Shittard,
Squirtard,
Crackard,
Turdous,
Thy bung
Hath flung
Some dung

Barcelóna: Imprenta de Llorens, Palma de Sta. Catalina, 6.

On us:
Filthard,
Cackard,
Stinkard,
St. Antony's fire seize on thy toane [bone?],
If thy
Dirty
Dounby
Thou do not wipe, ere thou be gone.

Will you have any more of it? Yes, yes,
answered Grangousier. Then, said Gargantua,

A Roundelay.

In shitting yes'day I did know
The sess I to my arse did owe:
The smell was such came from that slunk,
That I was with it all bestunk:
O had but then some brave Signor
Brought her to me I waited for,
In shitting!

I would have cleft her watergap,
And join'd it close to my flipflap,
Whilst she had with her fingers guarded
My foul nockandrow, all bemerded
In shitting.

Now say that I can do nothing! By the Merdi,
they are not of my making, but I heard them
of this good old grandam, that you see here,
and ever since have retained them in the
budget of my memory.
Let us return to our purpose, said
Grangousier. What, said Gargantua, to skite?
No, said Grangousier, but to wipe our tail.
But, said Gargantua, will not you be content
to pay a puncheon of Breton wine, if I do not
blank and gravel you in this matter, and put
you to a non-plus? Yes, truly, said Grangousier.
There is no need of wiping one's tail, said
Gargantua, but when it is foul; foul it cannot
be, unless one have been a-skiting; skite then
we must before we wipe our tails. O my pretty
little waggish boy, said Grangousier, what an
excellent wit thou hast? I will make thee very

shortly proceed doctor in the jovial quirks
of gay learning, and that, by G—, for thou
hast more wit than age. Now, I prithee, go on
in this torcheculative, or wipe-bummatory
discourse, and by my beard I swear, for one
puncheon, thou shalt have threescore pipes,
I mean of the good Breton wine, not that
which grows in Britain, but in the good
country of Verron. Afterwards I wiped my
bum, said Gargantua, with a kerchief, with
a pillow, with a pantoufle, with a pouch,
with a pannier, but that was a wicked and
unpleasant torchecul; then with a hat. Of
hats, note that some are shorn, and others
shaggy, some velveted, others covered with
taffeties, and others with satin. The best of
all these is the shaggy hat, for it makes a very
neat abstersion of the fecal matter.
Afterwards I wiped my tail with a hen, with
a cock, with a pullet, with a calf's skin, with a
hare, with a pigeon, with a cormorant, with
an attorney's bag, with a montero, with a coif,
with a falconer's lure. But, to conclude, I say
and maintain, that of all torcheculs, arsewisps,
bumfodders, tail-napkins, bunghole cleansers,
and wipe-breeches, there is none in the world
comparable to the neck of a goose, that is well
downed, if you hold her head betwixt your legs.
And believe me therein upon mine honour, for
you will thereby feel in your nockhole a most
wonderful pleasure, both in regard of the
softness of the said down and of the temperate
heat of the goose, which is easily communicated
to the bum-gut and the rest of the inwards,
in so far as to come even to the regions of
the heart and brains. And think not that the
felicity of the heroes and demigods in the
Elysian fields consisteth either in their asphodel,
ambrosia, or nectar, as our old women here
used to say; but in this, according to my
judgment, that they wipe their tails with the
neck of a goose, holding her head betwixt
their legs, and such is the opinion of Master
John of Scotland, alias Scotus.

page 263: Goliard Figures

FRANÇOIS RABELAIS
**FIVE BOOKS OF THE LIVES, HEROIC
DEEDS AND SAYINGS OF GARGANTUA
AND HIS SON PANTAGRUEL
BOOK II, CHAPTER 56. (1532-1534)
HOW THE MEN AND WOMEN OF THE
RELIGIOUS ORDER OF THELEME
WERE APPARELLED**

The ladies at the foundation of this order were apparelled after their own pleasure and liking; but, since that of their own accord and free will they have reformed themselves, their accoutrement is in manner as followeth. They wore stockings of scarlet crimson, or ingrained purple dye, which reached just three inches above the knee, having a list beautified with exquisite embroideries and rare incisions of the cutter's art. Their garters were of the colour of their bracelets, and circled the knee a little both over and under. Their shoes, pumps, and slippers were either of red, violet, or crimson-velvet, pinked and jagged like lobster waddles. Next to their smock they put on the pretty kirtle or vasquin of pure silk camlet: above that went the taffety or tabby farthingale, of white, red, tawny, grey, or of any other colour. Above this taffety petticoat they had another of cloth of tissue or brocade, embroidered with fine gold and interlaced with needlework, or as they thought good, and according to the temperature and disposition of the weather had their upper coats of satin, damask, or velvet, and those either orange, tawny, green, ash-coloured, blue, yellow, bright red, crimson, or white, and so forth; or had them of cloth of gold, cloth of silver, or some other choice stuff, enriched with purl, or embroidered according to the dignity of the festival days and times wherein they wore them.
Their gowns, being still correspondent to the season, were either of cloth of gold frizzled with a silver-raised work; of red satin, covered with gold purl; of tabby, or taffety, white, blue, black, tawny, &c., of silk serge, silk camlet, velvet, cloth of silver, silver tissue, cloth of gold, gold wire, figured velvet, or figured

satin tinselled and overcast with golden threads, in divers variously purfled draughts. In the summer some days instead of gowns they wore light handsome mantles, made either of the stuff of the aforesaid attire, or like Moresco rugs, of violet velvet frizzled, with a raised work of gold upon silver purl, or with a knotted cord-work of gold embroidery, everywhere garnished with little Indian pearls. They always carried a fair panache, or plume of feathers, of the colour of their muff, bravely adorned and tricked out with glistering spangles of gold. In the winter time they had their taffety gowns of all colours, as above-named, and those lined with the rich furrings of hind-wolves, or speckled lynxes, black-spotted weasels, martlet skins of Calabria, sables, and other costly furs of an inestimable value. Their beads, rings, bracelets, collars, carcanets, and neck-chains were all of precious stones, such as carbuncles, rubies, baleus, diamonds, sapphires, emeralds, turquoises, garnets, agates, beryls, and excellent margarites. Their head-dressing also varied with the season of the year, according to which they decked themselves. In winter it was of the French fashion; in the spring, of the Spanish; in summer, of the fashion of Tuscany, except only upon the holy days and Sundays, at which times they were accoutred in the French mode, because they accounted it more honourable and better befitting the garb of a matronal pudicity.
The men were apparelled after their fashion. Their stockings were of tamine or of cloth serge, of white, black, scarlet, or some other ingrained colour. Their breeches were of velvet, of the same colour with their stockings, or very near, embroidered and cut according to their fancy. Their doublet was of cloth of gold, of cloth of silver, of velvet, satin, damask, taffeties, &c., of the same colours, cut, embroidered, and suitably trimmed up in perfection. The points were of silk of the same colours; the tags were of gold well enamelled. Their coats and jerkins were of cloth of gold, cloth of silver, gold, tissue or velvet

Giovanni and Gentile Bellini
Saint Mark Preaching in Alexandria, c. 1507,
Milan, Pinacoteca di Brera

embroidered, as they thought fit. Their gowns were every whit as costly as those of the ladies. Their girdles were of silks, of the colour of their doublets. Every one had a gallant sword by his side, the hilt and handle whereof were gilt, and the scabbard of velvet, of the colour of his breeches, with a chape of gold, and pure goldsmith's work. The dagger was of the same. Their caps or bonnets were of black velvet, adorned with jewels and buttons of gold. Upon that they wore a white plume, most prettily and minion-like parted by so many rows of gold spangles, at the end whereof hung dangling in a more sparkling resplendency fair rubies, emeralds, diamonds, &c., but there was such a sympathy betwixt the gallants and the ladies, that every day they were apparelled in the same livery. And that they might not miss, there were certain gentlemen appointed to tell the youths every morning what vestments the ladies would on that day wear: for all was done according to the pleasure of the ladies. In these so handsome clothes, and habiliments so rich, think not that either one or other of either sex did waste any time at all; for the masters of the wardrobes had all their raiments and apparel so ready for every morning, and the chamber-ladies so well skilled, that in a trice they would be dressed and completely in their clothes from head to foot. And to have those accoutrements with the more conveniency, there was about the wood of Theleme a row of houses of the extent of half a league, very neat and cleanly, wherein dwelt the goldsmiths, lapidaries, jewellers, embroiderers, tailors, gold-drawers, velvet-weavers, tapestry-makers and upholsterers, who wrought there every one in his own trade, and all for the aforesaid jolly friars and nuns of the new stamp.

Albert Seba
Serpents and Lizards, illustration from
Locuplestissimi Rerum Naturalium Thesauri,
Amsterdam, c. 1740

FRANÇOIS RABELAIS
FIVE BOOKS OF THE LIVES, HEROIC DEEDS AND SAYINGS OF GARGANTUA AND HIS SON PANTAGRUEL
BOOK IV, CHAPTER 64 (1532-1534)
SNAKES, SNAKES

I have cleared my eyesight, said Gymnast.
I have broke my fast, said Eusthenes;
so that for this whole day I shall be secure
from the danger of my spittle.
Asps.
Black wag leg-flies.
Domeses.
Amphisbenes.
Spanish flies.
Dryinades.
Anerudutes.
Catoblepes.
Dragons.
Abedissimons.
Horned snakes.
Elopes.
Alhartrafz.
Caterpillars.
Enhydrides.
Ammobates.
Crocodiles.
Falvises.
Apimaos.
Toads.
Galeotes.
Alhatrabans.
Nightmares.
Harmenes.
Aractes.
Mad dogs.
Handons.
Asterions.
Colotes.
Icles.
Alcharates.
Cychriodes.
Jarraries.
Arges.
Cafezates.
Ilicines.

Spiders.	Sucking water-snakes.	Phalanges.
Cauhares.	Cockatrices.	Hornworms.
Pharaoh's mice.	Mouse-serpents.	Scolopendres.
Starry lizards.	Dipsades.	Penphredons.
Snakes.	Shrew-mice.	Scalavotins.
Kesudures.	Miliares.	Tarantulas.
Attelabes.	Salamanders.	Pinetree-worms.
Cuhersks.	Stinkfish.	Solofuidars.
Sea-hares.	Megalaunes.	Blind worms.
Ascalabotes.	Slowworms.	Ruteles.
Two-tongued adders.	Stuphes.	Deaf-asps.
Chalcidic newts.	Spitting-asps.	Tetragnathias.
Haemorrhoids.	Stellions.	Worms.
Amphibious serpents.	Sabrins.	Horseleeches.
Footed serpents.	Porphyri.	Teristales.
Basilisks.	Scorpenes.	Rhagions.
Manticores.	Blood-sucking flies.	Salt-haters.
Fitches.	Pareades.	Vipers, & c.
Cenchres.	Scorpions.	Rhaganes.
Molures.	Hornfretters.	Rot-serpents.

FRANÇOIS RABELAIS
FIVE BOOKS OF THE LIVES, HEROIC
DEEDS AND SAYINGS OF GARGANTUA
AND HIS SON PANTAGRUEL
BOOK I, CHAPTER 27 (1532-1534)

Hark you, my masters, you that love the wine, Cop's body, follow me; for Sanct Anthony burn me as freely as a faggot, if they get leave to taste one drop of the liquor that will not now come and fight for relief of the vine. Hog's belly, the goods of the church! Ha, no, no. What the devil, Sanct Thomas of England was well content to die for them; if I died in the same cause, should not I be a sanct likewise? Yes. Yet shall not I die there for all this, for it is I that must do it to others and send them a-packing." As he spake this he threw off his great monk's habit, and laid hold upon the staff of the cross, which was made of the heart of a sorbapple-tree, it being of the length of a lance, round, of a full grip, and a little powdered with lilies called flower de luce, the workmanship whereof was almost all defaced and worn out. Thus went he out in a fair long-skirted jacket, putting his frock scarfwise athwart his breast, and in this equipage, with his staff, shaft or truncheon of the cross, laid on so lustily, brisk, and fiercely upon his enemies, who, without any order, or ensign, or trumpet, or drum, were busied in gathering the grapes of the vineyard. For the cornets, guidons, and ensign-bearers had laid down their standards, banners, and colours by the wall sides: the drummers had knocked out the heads of their drums on one end to fill them with grapes: the trumpeters were loaded with great bundles of bunches and huge knots of clusters: in sum, everyone of them was out of array, and all in disorder. He hurried, therefore, upon them so rudely, without crying gare or beware, that he overthrew them like hogs, tumbled them over like swine, striking athwart and alongst, and by one means or other laid so about him, after the old fashion of fencing, that to some he beat out their brains, to others he crushed their arms, battered their legs, and bethwacked their

sides till their ribs cracked with it. To others again he unjointed the spondyles or knuckles of the neck, disfigured their chaps, gashed their faces, made their cheeks hang flapping on their chin, and so swinged and balammed them that they fell down before him like hay before a mower. To some others he spoiled the frame of their kidneys, marred their backs, broke their thigh-bones, pashed in their noses, poached out their eyes, cleft their mandibles, tore their jaws, dung in their teeth into their throat, shook asunder their omoplates or shoulder-blades, sphacelated their shins, mortified their shanks, inflamed their ankles, heaved off of the hinges their ishies, their sciatica or hip-gout, dislocated the joints of their knees, squattered into pieces the boughts or pestles of their thighs, and so thumped, mauled and belaboured them everywhere, that never was corn so thick and threefold threshed upon by ploughmen's flails as were the pitifully disjointed members of their mangled bodies under the merciless baton of the cross. If any offered to hide himself amongst the thickest of the vines, he laid him squat as a flounder, bruised the ridge of his back, and dashed his reins like a dog. If any thought by flight to escape, he made his head to fly in pieces by the lamboidal commissure, which is a seam in the hinder part of the skull. If anyone did scramble up into a tree, thinking there to be safe, he rent up his perinee, and impaled him in at the fundament. If any of his old acquaintance happened to cry out, Ha, Friar John, my friend Friar John, quarter, quarter, I yield myself to you, to you I render myself! So thou shalt, said he, and must, whether thou wouldst or no, and withal render and yield up thy soul to all the devils in hell; then suddenly gave them dronos, that is, so many knocks, thumps, raps, dints, thwacks, and bangs, as sufficed to warn Pluto of their coming and despatch them a-going. If any was so rash and full of temerity as to resist him to his face, then was it he did show the strength of his muscles, for without more ado he did transpierce him, by running him in at the breast, through the mediastine and the heart. Others, again, he so quashed and bebumped, that, with a sound bounce under the hollow of their short ribs, he overturned their stomachs so that they died immediately. To some, with a smart souse on the epigaster, he would make their midriff swag, then, redoubling the blow, gave them such a homepush on the navel that he made their puddings to gush out. To others through their ballocks he pierced their bumgut, and left not bowel, tripe, nor entrail in their body that had not felt the impetuosity, fierceness, and fury of his violence. Believe, that it was the most horrible spectacle that ever one saw. Some cried unto Sanct Barbe, others to St. George. O the holy Lady Nytouch, said one, the good Sanctess; O our Lady of Succours, said another, help, help! Others cried, Our Lady of Cunaut, of Loretto, of Good Tidings, on the other side of the water St. Mary Over. Some vowed a pilgrimage to St. James, and others to the holy handkerchief at Chamberry, which three months after that burnt so well in the fire that they could not get one thread of it saved. Others sent up their vows to St. Cadouin, others to St. John d'Angely, and to St. Eutropius of Xaintes. Others again invoked St. Mesmes of Chinon, St. Martin of Candes, St. Clouaud of Sinays, the holy relics of Laurezay, with a thousand other jolly little sancts and santrels. Some died without speaking, others spoke without dying; some died in speaking, others spoke in dying. Others shouted as loud as they could Confession, Confession, Confiteor, Miserere, In manus! So great was the cry of the wounded, that the prior of the abbey with all his monks came forth, who, when they saw these poor wretches so slain amongst the vines, and wounded to death, confessed some of them. But whilst the priests were busied in confessing them, the little monkies ran all to the place where Friar John was, and asked him wherein he would be pleased to require their assistance. To which he answered that they should cut the throats of those he had thrown down upon the ground.

VICTOR HUGO
NINETY-THREE
PART II, BOOK III, "THE CONVENTION" (1874)

He who looked upon the Assembly utterly forgot the hall. He who witnessed the drama was oblivious to the theatre. Nothing more misshapen and at the same time sublime. A crowd of heroes, a herd of cowards; wild beasts on the mountain, reptiles in the swamp. There all those combatants, the ghosts of to-day, swarmed, elbowed each other, quarrelling, threatening, fighting, and living out their lives. A convocation of Titans!

On the right the Gironde,—a legion of thinkers; on the left the Mountain,—a group of athletes. Here might be seen Brissot, to whom the keys of the Bastille had been delivered; Barbaroux, who ruled the Marseillais; Kervelegan, who had entire control of the battalion of Brest, quartered in the Faubourg Saint-Marceau; Gensonné, who had established the supremacy of representatives over generals; Gaudet, that man of ill-omen, to whom the Queen one evening at the Tuileries had shown the sleeping Dauphin: Gaudet kissed the child on the forehead, and beheaded the father; the chimerical Salles, who denounced the intrigues of the Mountain with Austria; Sillery, the cripple of the Right, and Couthon, the paralytic of the Left; Lause-Duperret, who, upon being called a "villain" by a certain journalist, invited him to dinner, saying, "Oh, 'villain' simply means a man whose opinions differ from our own;" Rabaut-Saint-Étienne, who began his almanac in 1790 with these words: "The Revolution is over;" Quinette, one of those who hastened the downfall of Louis XVI; the Jansenist Camus, who compiled the civil constitution of the clergy, believed in the miracles of the deacon of Paris, and prostrated himself every night before an image of Christ seven feet high, nailed to his chamber wall; the priest Fauchet, who, together with Camille Desmoulins, was instrumental in bringing about the 14th of July; Isnard, guilty of saying,

"Paris will be destroyed," at the very moment when Brunswick was saying, "Paris will be burned;" Jacob Dupont, who was the first man to proclaim himself "an atheist," and to whom Robespierre replied, "Atheism is aristocratic;" Lanjuinais, a stern, sagacious, and valiant Breton; Ducos, the Euryalus of Boyct-Fonfrède; Rebecqui, the Pylades of Barbaroux, who tendered his resignation because Robespierre had not as yet been guillotined; Richaud, who was opposed to the permanency of Sections; Lasource, who uttered the murderous apothegm, "Woe be unto grateful nations," and who at the foot of the scaffold was to contradict himself by those haughty words, flung to the members of the Mountain,—"We are dying because the nation slumbers; when it awakes your turn will come;" Biroteau, who in abolishing the inviolability of the crown unconsciously

forged his own axe and reared his own scaffold; Charles Villatte, who shielded his conscience behind this protest: "I will not vote beneath the axe;" Louvet, the author of "Faublas," who was to end as a librarian at the Palais Royal, with Lodoi'ska at the desk; Mereier, the author of the "Tableau de Paris," who exclaimed, "Every king felt of his neck on the 21st of January; Maree, who had the care of the "faction of ancient limits;" the journalist Carra, who at the foot of the scaffold said to the executioner: "It is provoking to die; I should like to have seen the result;" Vige'e, who called himself a grenadier of the second battalion of Maycune-et-Loire, and who when threatened by the public tribunes, cried, "I move that at the first murmur of the tribunes we all withdraw, and, sabre in hand, march upon Versailles;" Buzot, who was doomed to die of hunger, and Valaze, to fall by his own dagger;

Jacques-Louis David
Le Serment du jeu de paume (*The Tennis Court Oath*),
18th century,
Paris, Musée Carnavalet

Condorect, who was to die at Bourg-la-Ueine, or Bonrg-Kgalitc, as it was called at that time, betrayed by a volume of Horace that he carried in his pocket; Petion, whose fate it was to be adored by the populace in 1792 and devoured by the wolves in 1794; and twenty more besides,—Pontécoulant, Marboz, Lidon, Saint-Martin, Dussaulx, the translator of Juvenal, who had made the Hanover campaign; Boileau, Bertrand, Lesterp-Beauvais, Lesage, Gomaire, Gardien, Mainvielle, Duplantier, Lacaze, Antiboul, and, foremost among them all, Barnave, whom men called Vergniaud. On the other side, Antoine-Louis-Léon Florelle de Saint-Just, a youth of twenty-three, whose pallid face, low forehead, regular profile, and deep, mysterious eyes conveyed an impression of profound melancholy; Merlin de Thionville, whom the Germans called "Feuer-Teufel,"—the fire-devil; Merlin de Douai, the guilty author of the Law of the Suspects; Soubrany, whom the Parisians, in the riot of the first Prairial, demanded for their general; the former cure, Lebon, who now held a sabre in the hand that had once sprinkled holy water; Billaud-Varennes, who foresaw the magistracy of the future, when arbitrators would take the place of judges; Fabre d'Églantine, who chanced upon the happy invention of the republican calendar, and Rouget de Lisle, the composer of the Marseillaise,—no second inspiration ever visited either of these two men; Manuel, the attorney of the Commune, who had said, "A dead king is no less a man;" Goujon, who marched into Tripstadt, Newstadt, and Spire, and who witnessed the flight of the Prussian army; Lacroix, a lawyer transformed into a general and made knight of Saint-Louis six days before August 10; Fréron-Thersite, son of Fréron Zoïle; Ruth, the inexorable searcher of the iron cupboard, predestined to a great republican suicide, who was to kill himself on the day of the death of the Republic; Fouché, with the soul of a demon and the face of a corpse; Camboulas, the friend of Père Duchesne, who used to say to Guillotin, "You belong to the Club of the Feuillants, but your daughter belongs to the Club of the Jacobins;" Jagot, who replied to those who pitied the nakedness of the prisoners in those savage words: "A prison is a dress of stone;" Javogues, the frightful desecrator of the tombs of Saint-Denis; Osselin, himself a proscriber, who sheltered one of the proscribed, Madame Gharry, in his own house; Bentabolle, who while presiding over the Assembly gave the tribunes the signal for applause or disapproval; the journalist Robert, Mademoiselle Kéralio's husband, who wrote: "Neither Robespierre nor Marat comes to my house; Robespierre is welcome to come whenever he chooses, Marat never;" Garan-Coulon, who, when Spain interceded on the occasion of the trial of Louis XVI., had haughtily requested that the Assembly should not condescend to read the letter of one king pleading for another; the bishop Gregoire, who in the earlier part of his career was worthy to have belonged to the primitive church, but who afterwards, during the period of the Empire, renounced his Republican principles; Amar, who said, "The whole earth condemns Louis XVI.; to whom then shall we appeal for judgment? To the planets;" Rouyer, who on the 21st of January opposed the firing of the cannon of the Pont-Neuf, saying, "A king's head ought to make no more noise in falling than the head of any other man;" Chenier, brother of the poet Andre; Vadier, one of those who placed a pistol on the tribune; Tanis, who used to say to Momoro, "I want Marat and Robespierre to embrace at my table." "Where do you live?" "At Charenton." "It would have surprised me had you said elsewhere," was Momoro's reply; Legendre, who was the butcher of the French Revolution, as Pride had been of the English Revolution. "Come and be slaughtered!" he cried to Lanjuinais. To which the latter replied: "First pass a decree that I am an ox, if you please;" Collot d'Herbois, that gloomy comedian, wearing, as it were, the antique mask with the double mouth, one of which said "Yes," while the other said "No," approving on the one hand and blaming on the other, defaming Carrier in Nantes and deifying Chillier in Lyons, sending Robespierre to the scaffold and Marat to the Pantheon; Génissieux, who asked that the penalty of death should be imposed on whosoever should be found wearing a medal that bore the inscription, "Louis XVI. martyred:" Leonard Bourdon, the schoolmaster, who had offered his house to the old man of Mount Jura; Topsent, the sailor; Goupilleau, the lawyer; Laurient Lecointre, merchant; Duhem, the doctor; Sergent, the sculptor; David, the artist; and Joseph Égalité, the prince; and others besides,—Lecointe Puiraveau, who called for a formal decree pronouncing Marat "insane;" Robert Lindet, the troublesome author of that devilfish whose head was the Committee of Public Safety, and whose twenty-one thousand arms embraced France in the shape of revolutionary committees; Lebœuf, on whom Girey-Dupré, in his "Noel des faux-Patriotes," wrote this line:—

"Lebœuf vit Legendre et beugla."

Thomas Paine, the benevolent American; Anacharsis Cloots, the millionnaire, a German baron, who although an atheist was still a man of sincere purpose, and a follower of Hébert; the upright Lebas, a friend of the Duplays; Rovère, one of those men whom one occasionally meets, who indulge in wickedness for its own sake, a variety of amateur more common than we might imagine; Charlier, who wished to address aristocrats with the familiar "vous;" the elegiac and cruel Tallien, who was to bring about the 9th Thermidor out of pure love of it; Cambacérès, a lawyer, who finally became a prince; Carrier, another lawyer, who turned into a tiger; Laplanche, who once exclaimed, "I demand priority for the alarm-gun;" Thuriot, who wished the jurors of the Revolutionary Tribunal to vote aloud; Bourdon de l'Oise, who provoked Chambon to challenge him, denounced Paine, and in his turn was denounced by Hébert; Fayau, who proposed to despatch an incendiary army into the Vendee; Tavaux,

who on the 13th of April acted as a sort of mediator between the Gironde and the Mountain; Vernier, who suggested that the leaders of the Gironde and the Mountain should be sent to serve as common soldiers; Rewbell, who shut himself up in Mayence; Bourbotte, whose horse was killed under him at Saumur; Guimberteau and Jard-Panvilliers, the commanders of the army of the Cherbourg coast and that of La Rochelle; Lecarpentier, who was in charge of the squadron of Cancale; Roberjot, for whom the ambush of Rastadt was lying in wait; Prieur de la Marne, who wore in camp his former major's epaulettes; Levasseur de la Sarthe, who by a single word induced Serrent, commander of the Battalion of Saint-Armand, to kill himself; Reverchon, Maure, Bernard de Saintes, Charles Richard, Lequinio, and towering above them all a Mirabeau whom men called Danton.

Belonging to neither of these parties, and yet holding both in awe, rose the man Robespierre.

[...]

Below crouched dismay, which may be noble, and fear, which cannot fail to be contemptible. Beneath all these passions, this heroism and devotion, this rage, might be seen the gloomy multitude of the anonymous. The shoals of the Assembly were called the Plain, comprising the entire floating element,—men who are in doubt, who hesitate, retreat, tempoporize, mistrustfully watching one another. The Mountain and the Gironde were the chosen few, the Plain was the crowd. The Plain was summed up and expressed in Sieyès. Sieyès was a man of a naturally profound mind, full of chimerical projects. He had paused at the Third Estate, and had never been able to rise as high as the people. Certain minds are constituted to rest midway. Sieves called Robespierre a tiger, who returned the compliment by calling him a mole. He was a philosopher who had attained prudence it not wisdom. He was a courtier, rather than the servant of the Revolution. He took a spade and went to work with the people in the Champs de Mars, hauling the same cart with Alexander de Beauharnais. He urged others to energetic labors which he never performed himself. He said to the Girondists: "Put the cannon on your own side." There are philosophers who are natural wrestlers, and they like Condorcet joined the party of Vergniaud, or like Camilla Desmoulins that of Danton. There are philosophers who value their lives, and those who belonged to this class followed Sieyès.

The best vats have their dregs. Still lower even than the Plain was the Marsh, whose stagnation was hideous to look upon, revealing as it did transparent egotism. There shivered the timid in silent expectation. Nothing could be more wretched. Ignominious to the last degree, and yet feeling no shame, hiding their indignation, living in servitude, cherishing covert rebellion, possessed by a certain cynical terror, they had all the desperation peculiar to cowardice; they really preferred the Gironde, and yet they chose the Mountain; when the final result depended on them, they went over to the successful side; they surrendered Louis XVI. to Vergniaud, Danton to Robespierre, and Robespierre to Tallien. They put Marat in the pillory during his life-time, and deified him after his death. They showed themselves the partisans of the very cause which they suddenly turned against. They seemed to possess an instinct for jostling the infirm. Since they had joined the cause with the understanding that it was a strong one, any sign of wavering seemed to them equivalent to treason. They were the majority, the power, and the fear. Hence springs the audacity of the base. Hence the 31st of May, the 11th Germinal, the 9th Thermidor,—tragedies where dwarfs untied the knots of giants.

[...]

And among these passionate men were to be found others, fanciful dreamers. Utopia was there in all its varied forms,—from the warlike, which admitted the scaffold, to the mild, which would fain abolish the penalty of death; a

spectre or an angel, according as one viewed it from the throne or from the side of the common people. Men eager for the fray stood face to face with others who were contented to brood over their dreams of peace. The brain of Carnot created fourteen armies while Jean Debry was revolving in his head a scheme of universal democratic federation. Amid this furious eloquence, amid these howling and thundering voices, some men there were who preserved a fruitful silence. Lakanal was silent, preoccupied with his system for national public education; Lanthenas held his peace, absorbed in his plans for primary schools; Revelliere-Lepaux was silent, dreaming of philosophy when it should attain the dignity of religion. Others busied themselves with matters of minor importance and the details of every-day life. Guyton-Morveaux was interested in the improvement of the sanitary condition of hospitals; Main; in the abolishment of existing servitudes; Jean-Bon-Saint-André in the suppression of arrest and imprisonment for debt; Romme in Chappe's proposition; Duboë in the filing of the archives; Coreu-Fustier in the foundation of the Cabinet of Anatomy and the Museum of Natural History; Guyomard in the navigation of rivers and the damming of the Scheldt. Men were fanatical about art, even monomaniacs on the subject; on the 21st of January, at the very time when the head of monarchy was falling on the Place de la Revolution, Bézard, the representative of the Oise, went to see a picture of Rubens which had been found in a garret in the Rue Saint-Lazare. Artists, orators, and prophets, giants like Danton, and men as childlike as Cloots, gladiators and philosophers, were all straining for the same goal,—progress. Nothing disconcerted them. The greatness of the Convention consisted in its efforts to discover what degree of reality there might be in that which men call the impossible. At one end stood Robespierre with his eyes fixed upon the Law, and at the other Jondoreet gazing with equal steadiness on Duty.

RUDYARD KIPLING
REWARDS AND FAIRIES
"IF"
(1910)

If you can keep your head when all about you
Are losing theirs and blaming it on you;
If you can trust yourself when all men doubt
    you,
But make allowance for their doubting too;
If you can wait and not be tired by waiting,
Or, being lied about, don't deal in lies,
Or, being hated, don't give way to hating,
And yet don't look too good, nor talk too
    wise;

If you can dream—and not make dreams your
    master;
If you can think—and not make thoughts your
    aim;
If you can meet with triumph and disaster
And treat those two imposters just the same;
If you can bear to hear the truth you've
    spoken
Twisted by knaves to make a trap for fools,

Or watch the things you gave your life to
    broken,
And stoop and build 'em up with wornout tools;

If you can make one heap of all your
    winnings
And risk it on one turn of pitch-and-toss,
And lose, and start again at your beginnings
And never breath a word about your loss;
If you can force your heart and nerve and
    sinew
To serve your turn long after they are gone,
And so hold on when there is nothing in you
Except the Will which says to them: "Hold on";

If you can talk with crowds and keep your
    virtue,
Or walk with kings—nor lose the common
    touch;
If neither foes nor loving friends can hurt you;
If all men count with you, but none too much;
If you can fill the unforgiving minute
With sixty seconds' worth of distance run—
Yours is the Earth and everything that's in it,
And—which is more—you'll be a Man my son!

Walter Quirt
The Tranquility of Previous Existence, 1941,
New York, Museum of Modern Art

16.   COHERENT EXCESS

The excess of fearsome visions in the episode of the witches in Grimmelshausen's *Simplicissimus* or in Goethe's description of Walpurgisnacht in Part I of *Faust*, or the catalogue of witchlike and diabolic entities in Gautier's *Albertus* list for us by superabundance all that we might expect to find in the course of a sabbat. In Pernety there is wholly frenetic and minutely detailed list of all the terms alchemists used to describe First Matter, so much so that we might be tempted to file these pages under the rubric of chaotic lists: but the 17th-century alchemist limited himself to reporting existent terminology and therefore had a reason for putting all those names together. Of course we cannot avoid suspecting that in doing so he felt a pleasure we should call "literary" and exaggerated for the pleasure of immoderation—otherwise his would merely be a practical list, but made impracticable by superabundance. In short, perhaps the mind of that disturbed occultist was fairly chaotic, but no matter how excessive his list may be it is not chaotic.

Perhaps the best example of a successful blend of immoderation and coherence is the description of the flowers in the garden of Paradou in Zola's *Abbe Mouret's Transgression*. A more chaotic example would seem to be the enumeration of Lautréamont, reproduced here in the anthology, except for the fact that the list seems dominated by a dysphoric tone that confers unity, albeit a fairly paranoid one, to everything the poet dislikes. On the other hand, in the passage from Barthes, the list acquires coherence because it regards all the things that the author likes.

René Magritte
Golconda, 1953,
Houston, Menil Collection

Daniel Spoerri
Repas hongrois (*Hungarian Repast*)
from the *Tableaux-pièges* (Trap-picture) series, 1963
Paris, Musée National d'Art Moderne,
Centre Georges Pompidou

280

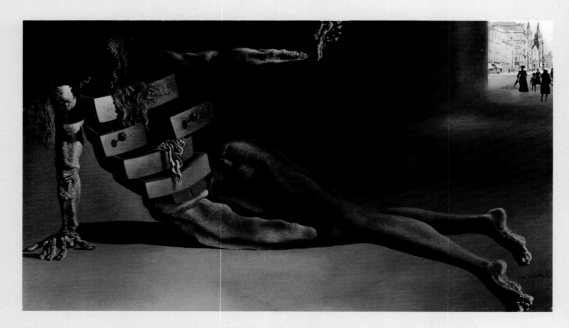

Some have seen a relationship between chaotic enumeration and the stream of consciousness: in effect, the examples of the so-called interior monologue, above all those of Joyce, would be pure collections of entirely anomalous elements were it not for the fact that, to make them a coherent whole, we assume that they emerge from the consciousness of the same character, one after another, and by associations that the author is not always required to explain. Is this example from chapter four of *Ulysses* chaotic?

He looked at the cattle, blurred in silver heat. Silvered powdered olive trees. Quiet long days: pruning ripening. Olives are packed in jars, eh? I have a few left from Andrews. Molly spitting them out. Knows the taste of them now. Oranges in tissue paper packed in crates. Citrons too. Wonder is poor Citron still alive in Saint Kevin's parade. And Mastiansky with the old cither. Pleasant evenings we had then. Molly in Citron's basketchair. Nice to hold, cool waxen fruit, hold in the hand, lift it to the nostrils and smell the perfume. Like that, heavy, sweet, wild perfume. Always the same, year

Salvador Dalí
The Anthropomorphic Cabinet, 1936,
Düsseldorf, Kunstsammlung Nordrhein-Westfalen

after year. They fetched high prices too Moisel told me. Arbutus place: Pleasant street: pleasant old times. Must be without a flaw, he said. Coming all that way: Spain, Gibraltar, Mediterranean, the Levant. Crates lined up on the quayside at Jaffa, chap ticking them off in a book, navvies handling them in soiled dungarees. There's whatdoyoucallhim out of. How do you? Doesn't see. Chap you know just to salute bit of a bore. His back is like that Norwegian captain's. Wonder if I'll meet him today. Watering cart. To provoke the rain. On earth as it is in heaven.

The "local" impression of chaos vanishes if we consider the monologue in its totality: we are in the presence of a sequence of thoughts that crowd Bloom's mind on a given morning as he reacts to a series of external stimuli.

Still with reference to Joyce, the previously mentioned case of Bloom's drawer in *Ulysses* is a different matter: basically, the list is meticulously realistic, and records what is likely to be found in a drawer. The only thing is that one does not see why the author decided to dwell at such length on those odds and ends, unless he simply wanted to enjoy and have others enjoy the incoherence of the whole. This is why this list should appear in the anthological section on chaotic enumeration, of which it has become a canonical example. On the other hand we shall consider the passage from **Pynchon** as more coherent, since he limits himself to closing Bloom's drawer in favour of examining a desk top.

Appearances to the contrary, a good example of excess that is by no means chaotic is found in the thirty-two pages of **Claude Closky**'s *Marabout*: here the author lines up terms or brief syntagms each of which begins with the syllable that ends the preceding one: we can only conclude that there is method in this madness and that the list, chaotic from the point of view of the signified, is not so from the point of view of the signifiers.

It is hard to say whether the list of all the things that **Perec** sees in a single day spent in Place Saint-Sulpice in Paris is one characterized by coherent or chaotic excess. The author meticulously registers everything: the event, time, and the part of square from where he sees it. The list can only be random and disordered, given that in all likelihood a hundred thousand other events occurred that day in the square that Perec neither noted nor wrote down; but on the other hand the fact that the lists contains only what he noticed makes it disturbingly homogeneous. We can also ascribe Perec's *Je me souviens* to this same borderline category, given that its chaos is regulated by the fact that that everything listed is that which the author does us the favour of remembering.

Among coherent lists by excess we might also include the portrayal of the slaughterhouse in **Döblin**'s *Berlin Alexanderplatz*: in principle it ought to be the ordered description of a place and the operations carried out in it, but it is hard to perceive the form of the place and the logical sequence of activities in that dense collection of details, numerical data, gouts of blood, and herds of frightened piglets. Döblin's abattoir is horrible because it is a mass of particulars so awful that they stun the reader and dissolve any possible order in the disorder of mad bestiality—prophetically alluding to future slaughterhouses.

We cannot avoid defining as coherent, even though excessive, the lists drawn up by Boltanski of the Swiss who died in Canton Valais in 1991, or of the artists who took part in the Venice Biennale between 1885 and 1995. And certain lists by Annette Messager are also disquietingly coherent.

Then there is the list that becomes chaotic by excess of ire, hatred, and rancour, accumulating cascades of insults. A typical example is that of Céline, who bursts out in a tide of abuse, not against the Jews for once but against Soviet Russia: "Bing! Badabing! They're snuffing it! Bloated! By God's guts! ... 487 million! Of impalificated cossackologists! Quid? Quid? Quod? In all the chancres of Slavonia! Quid! From the Slavigothic Baltic to the White Black Highseas? Quam? The Balkans! Slimy, Rotten as cucumbers! ... Stinking shitspreaders! Of ratshit! I don't give a flying fart ... I don't give a fuck! I'm out of here, bigtime! Cow pats! Immensely! Volgaronov! ... Tataronesque Mushymongoloids! ... Stakhanovicious! Arslikoff! Four hundred thousand versts ... of shitcrusted steppe, of Zébis-Laridon hides! ... I've come across the mother of all Vesuviuses here!

Herman de Vries
Eschenau Sutra "One and Many", 2002,
Lausanne, Musée Cantonal des Beaux-Arts

Floods! ... fungus-infected arsewipes! ... The Tsar's chamber pots for you and your filthy perverted arseholes! ... Stabilin! Voroshitsky! Limpdick leftovers! ... TransBeria! ...”

In a case such as this one it is probably worth quoting the original (which smacks curiously of Captain Haddock's furious outbursts in *Tintin*): "Dine! Paradine! Crèvent! Boursouflent! Ventre dieu! ... 487 millions! D'empalafiés cosacologues! Quid? Quid? Quod? Dans tous les chancres de Slavie! Quid? De Baltique slavigote en Blanche Altramer noire? Quam? Balkans! Visqueux! Ratagan! de concombres! ... Mornes! Roteux! de ratamerde! Je m'en pourfentre ... Je m'en pourfoutre! Gigantement! Je m'envole! Coloquinte! ... Barbatoliers? Immensément! Volgaronoff! ... mongomoleux Tartaronesques! ... Stakhanoviciants! ... Culodovitch! ... Quatre cent mille verstes myriamètres ... de steppes de condachiures, de peaux de Zébis-Laridon! ... Ventre Poultre! Je m'en gratte tous les Vésuves! ... Déluges! ... fongueux de margachiante! ... Pour vos tout sales pots fiottés d'entzarinavés! ... Stabiline! Vorokchiots! Surplus Déconfits! ... Transbérie!...”

Finally I hope that, being an aficionado of lists in all my novels, I may be permitted to quote excerpts of mine in the anthology: one where the names of swarms of vagabonds, taken from reliable historical registers (and hence coherent in themselves), are nonetheless given for the pure pleasure of the sound and a taste for hotchpotch; and another where, having to represent the Sambatyon, the river which according to Jewish tradition was not made of water but of stones, I looked up the names of hundreds of minerals in Pliny the Elder and took pleasure in imagining the flow of all possible and imaginable stones (and others again) making them debouch into the Devil's Gorge, plainly inspired by the Falls of Iguazu.

Grandville (Jean Ignace Isidore Gerard)
illustration for Honoré de Balzac's
Les amours de deux bêtes in *Les animaux peints
par eux-mêmes: vie privée et publique des animaux,*
Paris, Hetzel, 1868,
private collection

HANS JAKOB CHRISTOFFEL VON GRIMMELSHAUSEN
SIMPLICISSIMUS, II, 16 (1669)

After they had all left, I went into the room myself, thinking about what I wanted to take and where I should start looking for it. Mulling this over in my mind, I sat down astride one of the benches. Hardly was I seated than the bench, with me on it, shot out of the window. My satchel and musket, which I had put down on the floor, I left behind, as payment for the magic grease, so to speak. Sitting down, flying off, and landing all happened in a trice. At least it seemed to me that I was instantaneously transported to a large crowd of people. (Of course, it is possible I was so terrified I didn't register the time the journey took.) They were all involved in a strange dance, the like of which I have never seen before or since. They were holding hands in several rings, one inside the other, and they all had their backs to each other, as in pictures of the Three Graces, that is with their faces turned towards the outside. The innermost ring consisted of some seven or eight people, the next probably twice that many, the third more than both of them put together and so on until the outer ring which had more than two hundred in it. One ring or circle was dancing round to the left, the next to the right, making it impossible for me to see exactly how many rings there were nor what it was in the middle that they were dancing round. The way all the heads wound in and out was funny and at the same time strangely eerie. And the music was just as strange as the dance. It seemed to me that each dancer was singing his or her own song, which produced a bizarre harmony. The bench I came on had landed close to the musicians, who were standing outside the circles. Instead of pipes, flutes and shawms some of them were merrily blowing away on grass-snakes, adders and glow-worms. Others were holding cats, blowing up their backsides and fingering their tails, producing a sound like bagpipes. There were some fiddling away on horses' skulls as if they were the finest violins and others playing the harp on cows' skeletons such as you see lying around the knacker's yard, and there was even one holding a bitch under his arm, grinding away with her tail and playing on her dugs with his fingers. And all the time the demons were trumpeting through their noses so that the woods resounded with their din. As soon as the dance was over the whole hellish crew started bawling and bellowing, ranting and raging, screaming, stamping and storming as if they had all gone raving mad. You can imagine how terrified I was. In the midst of all this racket a man came up to me. He was carrying a gigantic toad under his arm, easily as big as a side drum; its intestines had been pulled out through its rear end and stuffed back into its mouth, which I found so disgusting it made me want to puke. "Come on, Simplicius," he said, "I know you can play the lute very well. Why don't you give us a nice tune?"

Jacques Callot
The Temptation of Saint Anthony, 17th century,
Nancy, Musée Historique Lorrain

JOHANN WOLFGANG VON GOETHE
FAUST
FROM "WALPURGIS NIGHT"
(1773-1774)

FAUST, MEPHISTOPHELES, JACK-O'LANTERN,
in alternate song.

Spheres of magic, dream, and vision,
Now, it seems, are opening o'er us.
For thy credit, use precision!
Let the way be plain before us
Through the lengthening desert regions.
[...]
Uhu! Schuhu! Tu-whit! Tu-whit!
Are the jay, and owl, and pewit
All awake and loudly calling?
What goes through the bushes yonder?
Can it be the Salamander—
Belly thick and legs a-sprawling?
Roots and fibres, snake-like, crawling,
Out from rocky, sandy places,
Wheresoe'er we turn our faces,
Stretch enormous fingers round us,
Here to catch us, there confound us;
Thick, black knars to life are starting,
Polypusses'-feelers darting
At the traveller. Field-mice, swarming,
Thousand-colored armies forming,
Scamper on through moss and heather!
And the glow-worms, in the darkling,
With their crowded escort sparkling,
Would confound us altogether.

But to guess I'm vainly trying—
Are we stopping? are we hieing?
Round and round us all seems flying,
Rocks and trees, that make grimaces,
And the mist-lights of the places
Ever swelling, multiplying.
[...]

Faust. How strangely through the dim
    recesses
A dreary dawning seems to glow!
And even down the deep abysses
Its melancholy quiverings throw!
Here smoke is boiling, mist exhaling;
Here from a vapory veil it gleams,
Then, a fine thread of light, goes trailing,
Then gushes up in fiery streams.
The valley, here, you see it follow,
One mighty flood, with hundred rills,
And here, pent up in some deep hollow,
It breaks on all sides down the hills.
Here, spark-showers, darting up before us,
Like golden sand-clouds rise and fall.
But yonder see how blazes o'er us,
All up and down, the rocky wall!
[...]
Mephistopheles. Must seize the rock's old ribs
    and hold on stoutly!
Else will they hurl thee down the dark
    abysses there.
A mist-rain thickens the gloom.
Hark, how the forests crash and boom!
Out fly the owls in dread and wonder;
Splitting their columns asunder,
Hear it, the evergreen palaces shaking!
Boughs are twisting and breaking!
Of stems what a grinding and moaning!
Of roots what a creaking and groaning!
In frightful confusion, headlong tumbling,
They fall, with a sound of thunder rumbling,
And, through the wreck-piled ravines and
    abysses,
The tempest howls and hisses.
Hearst thou voices high up o'er us?
Close around us—far before us?
Through the mountain, all along,
Swells a torrent of magic song.
[...]
Witches [*in chorus*]. The witches go to the
    Brocken's top,
The stubble is yellow, and green the crop.
They gather there at the well-known call,
Sir Urian sits at the head of all.
Then on we go o'er stone and stock:
The witch, she—and—the buck.

Hans Baldung Grien
Witches' Sabbath, 1510,
private collection

DOM ANTOINE-JOSEPH PERNETY
DICTIONNAIRE MYTHO-HERMÉTIQUE
"THE NAMES OF THE ALCHEMICAL PRIMA MATERIA" (1758)

Sulphur acts upon salt, agglutinating it and giving it its shape; salt acts upon sulphur, dissolving it and making it putrefy; and one united to the other in equal proportion creates a viscous, vitriolic water, which is the *prima materia*—the base material—of all nature and art.

Below are some of the names by which hermetic philosophers have called their material. The vast majority of them are explained herein because—as Morienus and Raimundus Lullus have said—the entire secret of this art lies in the comprehension of these various names. Some are from Greek, others are from Hebrew, and some from Arabic, but most are from Latin or French.

Absemir, Steel, Vinegar, Harsh Vinegar, Philosophers' Vinegar, Burning Water, Nitrogen Water, Urine Water, Water of Chaos, Water of the Art, Water of the Styx, Spring Water, Water of Blood, Water of Talc, Water of Life, Leafy Water, Heavy Water, Ponderous Water, First Water, Purifying Water, Dry Water, Simple Water, Starry Water, Viscous Water, Adam, Adarnet, Adrop, Aphrop, Lamb, Agresta, Aibathest, Alartar, Albar of Copper, Tree, Philosophical Tree, Lunar Tree, Metal Tree, Solar Tree, Albira, Alborach, Alchaest, Alcharit, Alcophil, Alembroth, Alkuphal, Allume, Almagro, Alocines, Aloeam, Aludel, Alusi, Alzernad, Alzon, Amalgra, Amizade, Anachron, Anathron and Anatron, Anathuel, Androgynous, Soul, Soul of the Elements, Soul of the World, Soul of Saturn, Antimony, Antimony of Parts of Saturn, Antybar, Ardent Water, Eagle, Philosophers' Eagle, Flying Eagle, Arémaros, Coagulated Quicksilver, Silver, Quicksilver, Argyrion, Air, Arneth or Zarnich, Arsenic, Asmarcech, Astima, Atimad, Avcafort, Vulture, Azoch, Azoth, Azure, Bath, Kings' Bath, Sun's bath, Diana's Bath, Steam Bath, Double-boiler Water Bath, Good, Diffusive Good, Whiteness, White of Black, Borax, Borteza or Bonza, Bronze, Burnt Bronze, Incombustible Bronze, Black Bronze, Butter, Cadmium, Caduceus, Rennet Milk, Armenian Bitch, Cain, Lime, Quicklime, Cambar, Camereth, Fireplace, Camel, Field, Cancer, Dog, Corascene Dog, Chaos, Caspa, Caspachaia, Ash, Tartar Ash, Fused Ash, Incombustible Ash, Black Ash, Cennus, Chai, Chaia, Ches, Chesseph, Chesseph Hai, Key of all Metals, Key of the Work, Chibur, Kilo, Heaven, Philosophers' Heaven, Middle Heaven, Peacock Tail, Colcotar, Cholera, Golden Glue, Companion, Compare, Compost, Composed, Preserve, Containing, Content, Royal Crown, White Body, Confused Body, Contrary Body, Stained Body, Imperfect Body, Improper Body, Mixed Body, Black Body, Corsufle, Raven, Tormented Thing, Vile Thing, Crystal, Crucible, Heart of the Sun, Heart of Saturn, Deeb, Dehab, Deia, Denuded, Derbel, Diabestes, December, Average Device, Sweetness of Butter, Dragon, Dragon of Babylon, High-Flying Dragon, Soaring Dragon, Duenech, Ebemeseth, Ebemich, Element, Elixir , Elsaron, Embryo, Hermaphrodite, Boars' Excrement, Metal Being, Summer, White Ethelia, Eudica, Euphrates, Eve, Fada, Falcone, Favonius, Calcinated Feces, Dissolved Feces, Female, Female Prostitute, Phoenix, Yeast, Sublimated Yeast, Iron, Gall, Blessed Son of Fire, Son of the Nile, Son of the Sun and the Moon, Saturn's Youngest Son, Fímo, Best Bronze, Flower of the Sun, Phlegm, Source, Kings' Source, Form, Human Form, Brother, Serpent Brother, Fridanus, Fruit, Fruit of the Solar Tree, White Smoke, Yellow Smoke, Red Smoke, Fire, Fire Water, Artificial Fire,

Plate from "Cabala: Mirror of Art and Nature"
in *Alchymia*,
Augsburg, 1615

Firecracker, Fire Against Nature, Corrosive-
and Non-corrosive Fire, Lamp Fire, Ash Fire,
Sand Fire, Unnatural Fire, Liquid Fire, Natural
Fire, Damp Fire, Gabertin, Gabricius, Gabrius,
Rooster, Ice, Egg Yolk, Jordan, Daylight, Jumis,
White Rubber, Red Rubber, Gold Rubber,
Gophris, Granusae, Gur, Hageralzarnad,
Hebrit, Hydra of Lerna, Inferno, Infinity,
Insipid, Winter, White Hypostasis, Iris,
Judhevophé, Karnech, Kenchel, Kibrich,
Kinna, Dried Lakebed, Boiling Lake, Eagle's
Tears, Laton, Milk, Virgin's Milk, Wood, Golden
Wood, Lignum Vitae (Wood of Life), Lion,
Red Lion, Green Lion, Vegetable Liquor, Plant
Lye, Lithargyrius, Light, Lead Light, Lucifer,
Moon, Leafy Moon, Wolf, Mother, Mother of
all Metals, Mother of Gold, Magnesia, White
Magnesia, Red Magnesia, Magnet, Evil, Right
Hand, Left Hand, Marcassite, Lead Marcassite,
Sea, Marble, Mars, Martheeka, Marthek, Male,
Coffeepot Mass, Matter, Matter of Matters,
Matter of all Forms, Lunar Material, Morning,
Fauheh Medal, Three-Tier Medicine, Medicine
of the Spirit, Melancholy, Mercury, Animal
Menstruation, Mineral Menstruation,
Vegetable Menstruation, Midday, Microcosm,
Honey, Mine, Goldmine, Ministry, Measure,
Mzzadir, Death, Bitter Death, Mozhacumia,
Nature, Fog, Enemy, Black that is Blacker
than Black, Neusis, Fish Eye, West, Oil, Oil of
Mars, Incombustible Oil, Red Oil, Olive, Ollus,
Shadow, Sun Shadow, East, Gold, Eastern
Gold, Beak Gold, Coral Gold, Rubber Gold,
Etheus Gold, Leafy Gold, Roman Gold,
Orpiment, Father, Sole Father of All Things,
Sheep, Human Hair, Danger, Physon, Stone,
Animal Stone, Burning Stone, Stone that is
not a Stone, Stone Known in the Book's
Chapters, Philosopher's Stone, Indian Stone,
Indrademene Stone, Metal Stone, Mineral
Stone, Red Stone, Starry Stone, Plant Stone,
Lead, Lead White, Philosophers' Lead,
Chicken, Powder, Ash Powder Extract, Prison,
Springtime, Prostitute, Hermogenes Chick,
Point, Purity of the Dead, Fifth Nature, Fifth
Element, Raceen, Root of all Metals, Beam of
Moonlight, Beam of Sunlight, Golden Branch,
Randerich, Rare, King, Recon, Reheson,
Residence, Risous, Little Sparrow, Rose
Among Thorns, Monkfish, Blush, Ruby, Dew,
May Dew, Sand, Saltpeter, Salamander, Brine,
Marine Brine, Salted, Alembroc Salt, Alkali
Salt, Almisadir Salt, Urine Salt, Pilgrims' Salt,
Salt of Salts, Winseman's Salt, Lunar Salt,
Fused Salt, Solar Salt, Mushroom Saliva,
Lunar Saliva, Incombustible Saliva, Valuable
Saliva, Blood, Dragon's Blood, Lion's Blood,
Salamander's Blood, Spiritual Blood, Human
Blood, Soap, Soap of Sages, Saturn, Scapula,
Pomegranate Syrup, Sebleynde, Sedena,
Secret of the School, Seed, Trail, Sepulcher,
Evening, Sericon, Serinech, Snake, Winged
Snake, Snake that Eats its Own Tail [Ouroboros],
Cadmus Snake, Wingless Snake, Servant,
Fled Servant, Red Servant, Seth, Lord of the
Stones, Smeratha, Philosophers' Soda, Sun,
Solar Eclipse, Land of the Sun, Set Solutions,
Volatile Solution, Sister, Sister of the Serpent,
Eldest Sister, Spear, Sword, Philosophers'
Semen, Metallic Semen, Mercury Sperm, Sperm
of All Things, Raw Spirit, Cooked Spirit, Spirit
of Clarity, Constructed Spirit, Penetrating
Spirit, Universal Spirit, Splendor, Splendor
of the Seas, Splendor of the Sun, Dirt of the
Corpse, Bride, Lunar Spittle, Swamp, Sealed
Star, Ostrich's Stomach, Sublifiatus, Solar
Sweat, Talc, Tamuae, Tartar, Tartar or Inferno,
Temaychum, Dusk, Teriacha, Terra, Terra
Adami, Earth's Clay, Damned Earth, Land of
Tombs, Leafy Land, Fat Land, Land of Plenty,
Putrid Earth, Leftover Earth, Red Earth, Virgin
Earth, Third, Raven's Head, Dead Crow's
Head, Tevos, Thabritis, Thelima, Theta or Thit,
Thion, Timas, Hermit's Tincture, Tincture of
Metals, Torch, Bull, Flakes, Bird of Hermes,
Humidity, Burning Humidity, White Humidity,
Radical Wet Union of Minds, Greasiness, Man,
Egg, Philosopher's Egg, Child's Urine, Steam,
Vase, Philosophers' Jar, Sealed Jar, Exhausted
Old Woman, Old Age, Poison, Poison that Dyes,
Aechineides's Poison, Deadly Poison, Venus,
Wind, Verdegris, Metal Staff, Virgin, Vitriol,
Roman Vitriol, Red Vitriol, Glass, Wiseman's
Vineyard, White Wine, Red Wine, Viper,

Virago, Virility, Virtues of the Stars, Mineral Virtues, Visitation of the Occult, Life, Fox, Vulphi, Xit, Yharit, Yle, Zaapl, Saffron, Zahav, Zaibac, Zephyr, Zibac, Zinc, Zi!, Ziva, Sulfur Ambrosia, Metal Sulfur, Nature of Sulfur, Incombustible Sulfur, Red Sulfur, Zarnet Sulfur, Zoichon, Zumech, Zumelazuli.

True philosophers can be recognized by the material they use for teaching. Those who use more than one material—that is, materials of various natures—to compose their mercury err in their ways. There is one sole material, even though it is found everywhere, and in everything ...

THÉOPHILE GAUTIER
ALBERTUS, OR THE SOUL AND SIN
(1833)

CX
Bats and owls, orfreys and vultures bald, great owls and birds of night with dun, flaming eyes; monsters of all kinds yet unknown, strygae with hooked beaks, ghouls, larvae, harpies, vampires, and were-wolves, impious spectres, mammoths and leviathans, crocodiles and boas, growling and snarling, hissing, laughing and chattering, swarming and gleaming, flying, crawling, leaping, till the ground is covered and darkened the air. Less swift is the speed of the breathless brooms, and with her gnarled fingers the bridle drawing, "This is the place," the old hag cried.

CXI
The place was lighted by a flame, a blue light casting like that of blazing punch. It was an open spot within the forest's depth. Wizards in their gowns and witches nude astride upon their goats adown the four avenues from the four corners of the world arrived at once. Investigators into sciences occult, Fausts of every land, magi of every rite, dark-faced gypsies, and rabbis red-haired, cabalists, diviners, hermeceutists black as ink and asthmatically gasping—not one of them all failed at the meeting-place.

CXII
Skeletons preserved in dissecting rooms, stuffed animals, monsters, greenish fœti, yet dripping all from their spirit bath, cripples and lamesters on slugs mounted; man hanged to death with protruding tongue grimacing; pale faces beheaded, with red-circled neck, with one hand staying their tottering heads; every creature ever put to death (a dreadful blood-stained crowd); handless parricides in black veils shrouded; heretics grouped in tunics sulphurous; wretches on the wheel broken, contused and blue; drowned ones with marbled flesh—a sight most dismal to behold!

ÉMILE ZOLA
ABBÉ MOURET'S TRANSGRESSION
FROM BOOK II, CHAPTER VII
(1875)

Deep within a clump of poplars and willows gaped a cavern, formed by rugged bits of rocks which had fallen over a basin where tiny rills of water trickled between the stones. The grotto was completely lost to sight beneath the onslaught of vegetation. Below, row upon row of hollyhocks seemed to bar all entrance with a trellis-work of red, yellow, mauve, and white-hued flowers, whose stems were hidden among colossal bronze-green nettles, which calmly exuded blistering poison. Above them was a mighty swarm of creepers which leaped aloft in a few bounds; jasmines starred with balmy flowers; wistarias with delicate lacelike leaves; dense ivy, dentated and resembling varnished metal; lithe honeysuckle, laden with pale coral sprays; amorous clematideæ, reaching out arms all tufted with white aigrettes. And among them twined yet slenderer plants, binding them more and more closely together, weaving them into a fragrant woof. Nasturtium, bare and green of skin, showed open mouths of ruddy gold; scarlet runners, tough as whipcord, kindled here and there a fire of gleaming sparks; convolvuli opened their heart-shaped leaves, and with thousands of little bells rang a silent peal of exquisite colours; sweetpeas, like swarms of settling butterflies, folded tawny or rosy wings, ready to be borne yet farther away by the first breeze. It was all a wealth of leafy locks, sprinkled with a shower of flowers, straying away in wild dishevelment, and suggesting the head of some giantess thrown back in a spasm of passion, with a streaming of magnificent hair, which spread into a pool of perfume.

"I have never dared to venture into all that darkness," Albine whispered to Serge. [...]

They wandered through a field of flowers capriciously, at random. Their feet trod a carpet of lovely dwarf plants, which had once neatly fringed the walks, and now spread about in wild profusion. In succession they passed ankle-deep through the spotted silk of soft rose catchflies, through the tufted satin of feathered pinks, and the blue velvet of forget-me-nots, studded with melancholy little eyes. Further on they forced their way through giant mignonette, which rose to their knees like a bath of perfume; then they turned through a patch of lilies of the valley in order that they might spare an expanse of violets, so delicate-looking that they feared to hurt them. But soon they found themselves surrounded on all sides by violets, and so with wary, gentle steps they passed over their fresh fragrance inhaling the very breath of springtide. Beyond the violets, a mass of lobelias spread out like green wool gemmed with pale mauve. The softly shaded stars of globularia, the blue cups of nemophila, the yellow crosses of saponaria, the white and purple ones of sweet rocket, wove patches of rich tapestry, stretching onward and onward, a fabric of royal luxury, so that the young couple might enjoy the delights of that first walk together without fatigue. But the violets ever reappeared; real seas of violets that rolled all round them, shedding the sweetest perfumes beneath their feet and wafting in their wake the breath of their leaf-hidden flowerets.

Albine and Serge quite lost themselves. Thousands of loftier plants towered up in hedges around them, enclosing narrow paths which they found it delightful to thread. These paths twisted and turned, wandered maze-like through dense thickets. There were ageratums with sky-blue tufts of bloom; woodruffs with soft musky perfume; brazen-throated mimuluses, blotched with bright vermilion; lofty phloxes, crimson and violet, throwing up distaffs of flowers for the breezes to spin; red flax with sprays as fine as hair; chrysanthemums like full golden moons, casting short faint rays, white and violet

and rose, around them. The young couple surmounted all the obstacles that lay in their path and continued their way betwixt the walls of verdure. To the right of them sprang up the slim fraxinella, the centranthus draped with snowy blossoms, and the greyish hounds-tongue, in each of whose tiny flowercups gleamed a dewdrop. To their left was a long row of columbines of every variety; white ones, pale rose ones, and some of deep violet hues, almost black, that seemed to be in mourning, the blossoms that drooped from their lofty, branching stems being plaited and goffered like crape. Then, as they advanced further on, the character of the hedges changed. Giant larkspurs thrust up their

Maximillian Lenz
Tulips, 1914,
Vienna, private collection

flower-rods, between the dentated foliage of which gaped the mouths of tawny snapdragons, while the schizanthus reared its scanty leaves and fluttering blooms, that looked like butterflies' wings of sulphur hue splashed with soft lake. The blue bells of campanulæ swayed aloft, some of them even over the tall asphodels, whose golden stems served as their steeples. In one corner was a giant fennel that reminded one of a lace-dressed lady spreading out a sunshade of sea-green satin. Then the pair suddenly found their way blocked. It was impossible to advance any further; a mass of flowers, a huge sheaf of plants stopped all progress. Down below, a mass of brank-ursine formed as it were a pedestal, from the midst of which sprang scarlet geum, rhodanthe with stiff petals, and clarkia with great white carved crosses, that looked like the insignia of some barbarous order. Higher up still, bloomed the rosy viscaria, the yellow leptosiphon, the white colinsia, and the lagurus, whose dusty green bloom contrasted with the glowing colours around it. Towering over all these growths scarlet foxgloves and blue lupins, rising in slender columns, formed a sort of oriental rotunda gleaming vividly with crimson and azure; while at the very summit, like a surmounting dome of dusky copper, were the ruddy leaves of a colossal castor-bean. [...]

They went the round of all the other basins. In the next one a number of amaranthuses had sprung up, raising monstrous crests which Albine had always shrunk from touching, such was their resemblance to big bleeding caterpillars. Balsams of all colours, now straw-coloured, now the hue of peach-blossom, now blush-white, now grey like flax, filled another basin where their seed pods split with little snaps. Then in the midst of a ruined fountain, there flourished a colony of splendid carnations. White ones hung over the moss-covered rims, and flaked ones thrust a bright medley of blossom between

the chinks of the marble; while from the mouth of the lion, whence formerly the water-jets had spurted, a huge crimson clove now shot out so vigorously that the decrepit beast seemed to be spouting blood. Near by, the principal piece of ornamental water, a lake, on whose surface swans had glided, had now become a thicket of lilacs, beneath whose shade stocks and verbenas and day-lilies screened their delicate tints, and dozed away, all redolent of perfume.

"But we haven't seen half the flowers yet," said Albine, proudly. "Over yonder there are such huge ones that I can quite bury myself amongst them like a partridge in a corn-field."

They went thither. They tripped down some broad steps, from whose fallen urns still flickered the violet fires of the iris. All down the steps streamed gilliflowers, like liquid gold. The sides were flanked with thistles, that shot up like candelabra, of green bronze, twisted and curved into the semblance of birds' heads, with all the fantastic elegance of Chinese incense-burners. Between the broken balustrades drooped tresses of stonecrop, light greenish locks, spotted as with mouldiness. Then at the foot of the steps another parterre spread out, dotted over with box-trees that were vigorous as oaks; box-trees which had once been carefully pruned and clipped into balls and pyramids and octagonal columns, but which were now revelling in unrestrained freedom of untidiness, breaking out into ragged masses of greenery, through which blue patches of sky were visible.

And Albine led Serge straight on to a spot that seemed to be the graveyard of the flower-garden. There the scabious mourned, and processions of poppies stretched out in line, with deathly odour, unfolding heavy blooms of feverish brilliance. Sad anemones clustered in weary throngs, pallid as if infected by some epidemic. Thick-set daturas spread out purplish horns, from which insects, weary of life, sucked fatal poison.

Marigolds buried with choking foliage their writhing starry flowers, that already reeked of putrefaction. And there were other melancholy flowers also: fleshy ranunculi with rusty tints, hyacinths and tuberoses that exhaled asphyxia and died from their own perfume. But the cinerarias were most conspicuous, crowding thickly in half-mourning robes of violet and white. In the middle of this gloomy spot a mutilated marble Cupid still remained standing, smiling beneath the lichens which overspread his youthful nakedness, while the arm with which he had once held his bow lay low amongst the nettles.

Then Albine and Serge passed on through a rank growth of peonies, reaching to their waists. The white flowers fell to pieces as they passed, with a rain of snowy petals which was as refreshing to their hands as the heavy drops of a thunder shower. And the red ones grinned with apoplectical faces which perturbed them. Next they passed through a field of fuchsias, forming dense, vigorous shrubs that delighted them with their countless bells. Then they went on through fields of purple veronicas and others of geraniums, blazing with all the fiery tints of a brasier, which the wind seemed to be ever fanning into fresh heat. And they forced their way through a jungle of gladioli, tall as reeds, which threw up spikes of flowers that gleamed in the full daylight with all the brilliance of burning torches. They lost themselves too in a forest of sunflowers, with stalks as thick as Albine's wrist, a forest darkened by rough leaves large enough to form an infant's bed, and peopled with giant starry faces that shone like so many suns. And thence they passed into another forest, a forest of rhododendrons so teeming with blossom that the branches and leaves were completely hidden, and nothing but huge nosegays, masses of soft calyces, could be seen as far as the eye could reach. "Come along; we have not got to the end yet," cried Albine. "Let us push on." But Serge stopped. They were now in the midst of an old ruined colonnade. Some of the columns offered inviting seats as they lay prostrate amongst primroses and periwinkles. Further away, among the columns that still remained upright, other flowers were growing in profusion. There were expanses of tulips showing brilliant streaks like painted china; expanses of calceolarias dotted with crimson and gold; expanses of zinnias like great daisies; expanses of petunias with petals like soft cambric through which rosy flesh tints gleamed; and other fields, with flowers they could not recognise spreading in carpets beneath the sun, in a motley brilliance that was softened by the green of their leaves. "We shall never be able to see it all," said Serge, smiling and waving his hand. "It would be very nice to sit down here, amongst all this perfume."

Near them there was a large patch of heliotropes, whose vanilla-like breath permeated the air with velvety softness. They sat down upon one of the fallen columns, in the midst of a cluster of magnificent lilies which had shot up there. They had been walking for more than an hour. They had wandered on through the flowers from the roses to the lilies. These offered them a calm, quiet haven after their lovers' ramble amid the perfumed solicitations of luscious honeysuckle, musky violets, verbenas that breathed out the warm scent of kisses, and tuberoses that panted with voluptuous passion. The lilies, with their tall slim stems, shot up round them like a white pavilion and sheltered them with snowy cups, gleaming only with the gold of their slender pistils. And there they rested, like betrothed children in a tower of purity; an impregnable ivory tower, where all their love was yet perfect innocence.

COMTE DE LAUTRÉAMONT
MALDOROR AND THE COMPLETE WORKS OF THE COMTE DE LAUTRÉAMONT
FROM POÉSIES I
(1846-1870)

One dreams only when one is asleep. There are words like those of dream, nothingness of life, earthly thoroughfare, the preposition perhaps, the disordered tripod, which have instilled into your souls this clammy poetry of languor, like that of putrefaction. To pass from words to ideas is but one step.
The disturbances, anxieties, depravities, death, exceptions to the physical or moral order, the spirit of negation, the brutishness, the hallucinations waited upon by the will, torments, destruction, madnesses, tears, insatiabilities, slaveries, deep-thinking imaginations, novels, the unexpected things which must not be done, the chemical peculiarities of the mysterious vulture that watches for the carcass of some dead illusion, precocious and abortive experiences, obscurities with a flea-like shell, the terrible obsession with pride, the inoculation with deep stupors, funeral orations, envies, betrayals, tyrannies, impieties, irritations, bitternesses, aggressive tirades, insanity, spleen, rational terrors, strange misgivings the reader would rather not feel, grimaces, neuroses, the cruel routes through which one forces last-ditch logic, exaggerations, lack of sincerity, the nuisances, platitudes, gloom, the dismal, the childbirths worse than murders, passions, the clique of assize-court novelists, tragedies, odes, melodramas, eternally presented extremes, reason hissed off stage with impunity, the odours of wet chicken, dulled tastes, frogs, octopi, sharks, the simoom of the deserts, whatever is clairvoyant, squinting, nocturnal, narcotic, somnambulist, slimy, talking seal, equivocal, consumptive, spasmodic, aphrodisiac, anaemic, one-eyes, hermaphrodite, bastard, albino, pederast, phenomenon of aquarium and bearded lady, the drunken hours of taciturn dejection, the fantasies, pungencies, monsters, demoralising syllogisms, the excrement, whatever is thoughtless as a child, desolation, that intellectual manchineel-tree, perfumed chancres, thighs like camellias, the guilt of a writer who rolls down the slope of nothingness and scorns himself with joyous cries, remorse, hypocrisies, the vague perspectives that grind you within their imperceptible mills, the sober gobs of spittle upon sacred axioms, the insinuating tickle of vermin, idiotic prefaces like those of Cromwell, Mlle de Maupin and Dumas *fils*, the decrepitude, impotence, blasphemies, asphyxiations, fits, rages,—before these foul charnel-houses, which I blush to name, it is time at last to react against what offends us and so imperiously bows us down. You are being incessantly driven out of your mind and caught in the trap of shadows built with coarse skill by egoism and self-esteem.

CLAUDE CLOSKY
MARABOUT
(1996)

Marabout, bout de ficelle, selle de cheval, cheval de course, course à pied, pied à terre, Terre de Feu, feu follet, lait de chèvre, chèvrefeuille, feuilleton, tonton Jules, Jules César, z'haricot, Ricoré, Rémuzat, musarder, désinvolte, volte-face, facétie, cigarette, arrété, théorie, rideaux verts, vers l'avant, avant-garde, garde-manger, géomètre, mettre au clou, clouer le bec, bec à l'oie, lois pénales, Nal Délice, Lisses de France, France Loisirs, zirconite, Nintendo, Daumesnil, Nilgiri, richissime, symétrie, trilogie, Giraudy, Digitsoft, Soft and Co, Cogistel, Téléfleurs, Fleurs du mal, mal acquis, quiproquo, Conesco, Coppola, la bonne cause, cause toujours, jour de fête, fête des mères, mercantile, antilope, l'opéra, rabatjoie, joyeuses Pâques, pack de bière, bière anglaise, glaise en sac, sac à main, main dans le sac, saccharose, rose fluo, Fluogum, gomina, minaret, raie au beurre, beurre d'anchois, choix des armes, arme à gauche, gauche caviar, caviardé, Art Déco, codéine, in situ, tu l'as dit, dix mille balles, balle perdué, du bidon, Dombrowski, Ski Open, peine de mort, Morrison, Sonatec, Technofi, fiche tricot, Caumartin, Martin Jean, Jean Gabin, bengali, Lipari, Paris-Turf, Turf-Infos, faux jeton, tomber pile, pile Wonder, wonderfull, full contact, tact exquis, Kit et Kat, catogan, gant de crin, craint la pluie, pluie des mois, moitié prix, pris en faute, faute de quoi, quoi au juste? Juste Prix, prise de sang, sans payer, payez-vous, Vougécourt, court-métrage, tragédie, édifice, fils de pute, Puttelange, Langeron, Ronsenac, Nacqueville, Villetaneuse, Neusanir, Niradeth, dettes de jeu, jeu de prince, Prince de Galles, galibot, beau discours, course de fond, fond la caisse, qu'est-ce qu'il pleut, pleut des cordes, corde au cou, coup de pot, pauvre petit, petit joint, joint de culasse, Las Vegas, gaspacho, chopping board, bored to death, death duty, duty-free, fruit séché, Chez Omar, Mario Bross, brosse à cheveux, cheveux en brosse, brosse de peintre, peintre abstrait, très profond, font la paire, perce-oreille, Rayon Vert, Vert en Ville, Ville-sur-Saulx, sauter le pas, paprika, case en moins, moins de seize ans, enkysté, Stephen King, King Kali, Ali Khan, canular, larme à l'oeil, l'oeil crevé, Velázquez, kézako? cosinus, Nussenbaum, baume au coeur, coeur fidèle, Fidèlio, Liora Fleurs, fleur de l'âge, l'âge idiot, Dioptigel, Gel Première, première fois, foie de morue, rue au pain, pince de crabe, crabotage, Agence A, Apollo, Logasoft, Softelec, Electro, trop petit, petit trot, tropical, calotin, teint ambré, bréviligne, Ligne Roset, Rosenthal, talons plats, plat pays, Pays-Bas, Banespa, spadassin, Saint-Vincent, sans répit, pisser le sang, sans façon, sont partout, Touring-club, Club 17, 7 sur 7, 707, cent sept ans, en vitesse, test sanguin, gain de cause, cause perdue.

Rosa Klein (André Rogi)
Bonnard's Palette, 1930,
Paris, Musée National d'Art Moderne,
Centre Georges Pompidou

THOMAS PYNCHON
GRAVITY'S RAINBOW
(1973)

There must be cubicles like this all over
the ETO: only three dingy scuffed-cream
fiberboard walls and no ceiling of its own.
Tantivy shares it with an American colleague,
Lt. Tyrone Slothrop. Their desks are at right
angles, so there's no eye contact but by
squeaking around some 90º. Tantivy's desk is
neat, Slothrop's is a godawful mess. It hasn't
been cleaned down to the original wood
surface since 1942. Things have fallen roughly
into layers, over a base of bureaucratic
smegma that sifts steadily to the bottom,
made up of millions of tiny red and brown
curls of rubber eraser, pencil shavings, dried
tea or coffee stains, traces of sugar and
Household Milk, much cigarette ash, very
fine black debris picked and flung from
typewriter ribbons, decomposing library
paste, broken aspirins ground to powder.
Then comes a scatter of paperclips, Zippo
flints, rubber bands, staples, cigarette butts
and crumpled packs, stray matches, pins,
nubs of pens, stubs of pencils of all colors
including the hard-to-get heliotrope and raw
umber, wooden coffee spoons, Thayer's
Slippery Elm Throat Lozenges sent by
Slothrop's mother, Nalline, all the way from

Massachusetts, bits of tape, string, chalk …
above that a layer of forgotten memoranda,
empty buff ration books, phone numbers,
unanswered letters, tattered sheets of carbon
paper, the scribbled ukulele chords to a
dozen songs including "Johnny Doughboy
Found a Rose in Ireland" ("He does have
some rather snappy arrangements," Tantivy
reports, "he's a sort of American George
Formby, if you can imagine such a thing,"
but Bloat's decided he's rather not), an
empty Kreml hair tonic bottle, lost pieces to
different jigsaw puzzles showing parts of the
amber left eye of a Weimaraner, the green
velvet folds of a gown, slate-blue veining in
a distant cloud, the orange nimbus of an
explosion (perhaps a sunset), rivets in the
skin of a Flying Fortress, the pink inner thigh
of a pouting pin-up girl … a few old Weekly
Intelligence Summaries from G-2, a busted
corkscrewing ukulele string, boxes of
gummed paper stars in many colors, pieces
of a flashlight, top to a Nugget shoe polish
can in which Slothrop now and then studies
his blurry brass reflection, any number of
reference books out of the ACHTUNG library
back down the hall—a dictionary of technical
German, an F.O. *Special Handbook* or *Town
Plan*—and usually, unless it's been pinched
or thrown away, a *News of the World*
somewhere too—Slothrop's a faithful reader.

GEORGES PEREC
TENTATIVE DE DESCRIPTION DE QUELQUES LIEUX PARISIENS "ST.-SULPICE SQUARE, DAY ONE"

Date: 18 October, 1974
Time: 10:30 a.m.
Place: Bar-Tabac Saint-Sulpice
Weather: Cool and dry. Grey sky. A few patches of sunlight.
Draft inventory for some of the strictly visible things:
—A few letters of the alphabet, a few words: *KLM* (on an envelope carried by a passer-by), an uppercase *P* that stands for "Parking;" "Hôtel Récamier," "St-Raphaël," "l'épargne à la dérive" (1), "Taxis tête de station" (2), "Rue du Vieux-Colombier," "Brasserie-bar La Fontaine Saint-Sulpice," "P ELF," "Parc Saint-Sulpice."
—A few conventional signs: two arrows beneath the parking garage's *P*, one pointing slightly downward, the other pointing toward Rue Bonaparte (on the Luxembourg side), and at least four "do not enter" signs (a fifth is reflected in the café's mirrors).
—A few numbers: 86 (at the front of a bus on the 86 line, right above the name of its terminus: Saint-Germain-des-Près), 1 (a plaque for the door of 1 Rue du Vieux-Colombier), 6 (a plaque on the square, indicating that we are in Paris' sixth arrondissement).
—A few fleeting slogans: "De l'autobus, je regarde Paris"
—A little soil: a mound of gravel and sand
—A few stones: along the edge of the sidewalk, around a fountain, a church, some houses ...
—A little asphalt
—A few trees: (with leaves, often yellowed)
—A fairly large portion of the sky (perhaps 1/6 of my field of vision)
—A swarm of pigeons that suddenly land on the traffic divider in the middle of the square, between the church and the fountain
—A few automobiles (yet to be inventoried)

—A few human beings
—Some type of dachshund
—A little bread (baguette)
—A little salad (frisée?) sticking out of a shopping basket

Trajectories :
The 96 goes to Gare Montparnasse
The 84 goes to Porte de Champerret
The 70 goes to Place du Dr Hayem, to Maison de l'O.R.T.F. 4 [*Office de Radiodiffusion Télévision Française*, the national radio and television headquarters]
The 86 goes to Saint-Germain-des-Près
Exigez le Roquefort Société le vrai dans son ovale vert
The water doesn't spurt from the fountain. A few pigeons are perched on the edge of one of the fountain's pools.
On the traffic-dividing median are a few benches, double-seated benches with a single shared back. From where I am, I count six of them. Four are empty. On the sixth one are three bums making the usual gestures (drinking a little red straight from the bottle).
The 63 goes to Porte de la Muette
The 86 goes to Saint-Germain-des-Près
Nettoyer c'est bien ne pas salir c'est mieux
A German bus
A Brinks armored car
The 87 goes to Champ-de-Mars
The 84 goes to Porte de Champerret
Colors: red (a Fiat, a dress, St.-Raphaël, "no admittance" signs)
a blue purse
green shoes
a green raincoat
a blue taxi
a blue, 2-HP motorbike
The 70 goes to Place du Dr. Hayem, to Maison de l'O.R.T.F.
A green Citroën Méhari
The 86 goes to Saint-Germain-des-Près
Danone: yoghurts and desserts
Exigez le Roquefort Société le vrai dans son ovale vert
Most people have at least one hand busy:

they're carrying a purse, a little valise, a
shopping basket, a cane, a leash with a dog
on the other end, a child's hand.
A truck is delivering beer in metal kegs
(*Kanterbraü, la bière de Maître Kanter*)
The 86 goes to Saint-Germain-des-Près
The 63 goes to Porte de la Muette
A two-storey "Cityrama" bus
A blue Mercedes truck
A brown Printemps Brummell truck
The 84 goes to Porte de Champerret
The 87 goes to Champ-de-Mars
The 70 goes to Place du Dr Hayem,
to the Maison de l'O.R.T.F.

The 96 goes to Gare Montparnasse
Darty Réal
The 63 goes to Porte de la Muette
Casimir maître traiteur. Trasports Charpentier.
Berth France S.A.R.L.
Le Goff tirage à bière
The 96 goes to Gare Montparnasse
A car from the driving school
Coming from Rue du Vieux-Colombier,
an 84 turns onto Rue Bonaparte (toward
Luxembourg)
Walon déménagements
Fernand Carrascossa déménagements
Wholesale potatoes

Jean Dubuffet
Apartment Houses, 1946,
New York, Metropolitan Museum of Art

It looks like a Japanese is taking my picture from a tour bus.
An old man with his half baguette, a woman with a box of desserts shaped like a little pyramid.
The 86 goes to Saint-Mandé (it doesn't turn onto Rue Bonaparte, and instead goes down Rue du Vieux-Colombier)
The 63 goes to Porte de la Muette
The 87 goes to Champ-de-Mars
The 70 goes to Place du Dr Hayem, to the Maison de l'O.R.T.F
Coming from Rue du Vieux-Colombier, an 84 turns onto Rue Bonaparte (toward Luxembourg)
A bus, empty.
More Japanese, on another bus
The 86 goes to Saint-Germain-des-Près
Braun reproductions d'art
A moment of calm (tiredness?)
Pause.

GEORGES PEREC
JE ME SOUVIENS
(1978)

I remember that all numbers that add up to nine are divisible by nine (sometimes I'd spend an entire afternoon checking …).

I remember a time it was rare to see any trousers without turned-up cuffs.

I remember Profirio Rubirosa (Trujillo's son-in-law?).

I remember that "Caran d'Ache" is a Frenchified transcription of the Russian word (*Karandach*?) for "pencil."

I remember the two Contrescarpe cabarets *Le cheval d'or* ("The Golden Horse") and *Le cheval vert* ("The Green Horse").

I remember Bob Azzam and his orchestra's version of *Chérie je t'aime, chérie je t'adore* ("I Love You Dear, I Adore You Dear," also known by the title *Moustapha*).

I remember the first movie I saw starring Jerry Lewis and Dean Martin was called *Sailor Beware!*

I remember the hours I spent—in my senior year of high school, I think—trying to retrofit three houses for electricity, gas, and water without having all the pipes cross (as long as you're in two-dimensional space, there's no solution; that's one of the most elementary examples of topology, just like Koenigsberg's bridges or playing-cards' colors).

I remember:
Is one supposed to say "Six et quatre font tonze,"
or "Six et qatre font honze"?
And:
What color is Henry IV's white horse?

Peter Blake
Les Tuileries, 2004

I remember that the name of the hero in *L'Etranger* was Antoine (?) Meursault: a lot of people have noticed that no one ever remembers his name.

I remember cotton candy at fairgrounds.

I remember *Baiser*-brand lipstick, "The lipstick that lets you kiss."

I remember terracotta marbles that would split in half if they struck too hard, and agate marbles, and large glass marbles that sometimes had little air bubbles in them.

I remember the Front-Wheel Drive Gang.

I remember the Bay of Pigs.

I remember the Three Stooges, and Bud Abbott and Lou Costello; and Bob Hope, Dorothy Lamour, and Bing Crosby; and Red Skelton.

I remember that Sidney Bechet wrote an opera—or was it a ballet?—entitled *La nuit est une sorcière* ("The Night is a Sorceress").

I remember Hermès purses, with their tiny clasps.

I remember the "Enrich Your Vocabulary" game column in *Reader's Digest*.

I remember *Burma*-brand jewelry (but wasn't there also a jewelry line called "Murat"?).

I remember:
Lundi matin
L'Empereur, sa femme et le P'tit Prince
Sont venus chez moi
Pour me serrer la pince
Comme j'étais parti
Le P'tit Prince a dit:
Puisque c'est ainsi nous reviendrons mardi.
Etc.

I remember:
Pourquoi les filles du Nord sont-elle précoes?
Parce-que le concerto en sol mineur.

I remember the teacher saying, "'Nabuchadnazar,' write it all in two syllables!" and the students' response, "'It all': *it*, dash, *all*."

I remember "*Mon pin ballot dans mon culot.*"

[...]

I remember Ivan Labibine Osouzoff and Yamamoto Kakapoté, and Harry Cover.

I remember that Jean-Paul Sartre wrote a series of articles on Cuba titled *Ouragan sur le sucre* ("A Hurricane Over Sugar") for *France-Soir*.

I remember Bourvil.
I remember one of Bourvil's sketches in which he repeated "Alcohol, no, rusty water, yes!" over and over, ending each paragraph of his pseudo-lecture with that little ditty.
I remember *Pas si bête*, and Madame Husson's *Rosier*.

I remember the Wakouwa "The Wonder Dog" toy.

I remember there was an anti-submarine frigate called Georges Leygues.

I remember how happy I was when I learned a lot of words deriving from *caput*: *capitaine, capot, chef, chete, caboche, capitale, Capitole, chapitre, caporal* ...

ROLAND BARTHES
ROLAND BARTHES BY ROLAND BARTHES
"J'AIME, JE N'AIME PAS—I LIKE, I DON'T LIKE"
(1975)

I like: salad, cinnamon, cheese, pimento, marzipan, the smell of new-cut hay (why doesn't someone with a "nose" make such a perfume), roses, peonies, lavender, champagne, loosely held political convictions, Glenn Gould, too-cold beer, flat pillows, toast, Havana cigars, Handel, slow walks, pears, white peaches, cherries, colors, watches, all kinds of writing pens, desserts, unrefined salt, realistic novels, the piano, coffee, Pollock, Twombly, all romantic music, Sartre, Brecht, Verne, Fourier, Eisenstein, trains, Médoc wine, having change, *Bouvard and Pécuchet*, walking in sandals on the lanes of southwest France, the bend of the Adour seen from Doctor L.'s house, the Marx Brothers, the mountains at seven in the morning leaving Salamanca, etc.

I don't like: white Pomeranians, women in slacks, geraniums, strawberries, the harpsichord, Miró, tautologies, animated cartoons, Arthur Rubinstein, villas, the afternoon, Satie, Bartók, Vivaldi, telephoning, children's choruses, Chopin's concertos, Burgundian branles and Renaissance dances, the organ, Marc-Antoine Charpentier, his trumpets and kettledrums, the politico-sexual, scenes, initiatives, fidelity, spontaneity, evenings with people I don't know, etc.

I like, I don't like: this is of no importance to anyone; this, apparently, has no meaning. And yet all this means: *my body is not the same as yours*. Hence, in this anarchic foam of tastes and distastes, a kind of listless blur, gradually appears the figure of a bodily enigma, requiring complicity or irritation. Here begins the intimidation of the body, which obliges others to endure me *liberally*, to remain silent and polite confronted by pleasures or rejections which they do not share.

(A fly bothers me, I kill it: you kill what bothers you. If I had not killed the fly, it would have been *out of pure liberalism*: I am liberal in order not to be a killer.)

ALFRED DÖBLIN
BERLIN ALEXANDERPLATZ
"FOR IT HAPPENS ALIKE WITH MAN
AND BEAST; AS THE BEAST DIES,
SO MAN DIES, TOO"
(1929)

The slaughter-house in Berlin. In the northeast part of the city, from Eldenaer Strasse across Thaerstrasse across Landsberger Allee as far as Cotheniusstrasse along the Belt Line Railway, run the houses, halls, and stables of the slaughter- and stock-yards.
They cover an expanse of 47.88 hectares, equal to 118.31 acres. Not counting the structures behind Landsberger Allee, 27,083,492 [Deutsch]marks were sunk into this construction, of which sum the cattle-yards cost 7,682,844 marks, and the slaughter-house 19,410,648 marks.
The cattle-yard, slaughter-house, and wholesale meat-market form an inseparable economic whole. The administrative body is the municipal committee for stock-yards and slaughter-houses, and consists of two members of the city administration, a member of the district office, 11 councillors and three citizen-deputies. There are 258 employees in the organization: among them are veterinaries, inspectors, branders, assistant veterinaries, assistant inspectors, permanent employees and laborers. Traffic ordinance of October 4, 1900: General Regulations governing the cattle-driving, delivery of fodder, scale of fees, market fees, boxing fees, slaughter fees, fees for the removal of fodder-troughs from the pork-market hall.
Along Eldenaer Strasse run the dirty-gray walls topped with barbed wire. The trees outside are bare, it is winter, the trees have sent their sap into the roots, to wait for spring. Slaughter wagons roll up at a smart gallop, with yellow and red wheels, prancing horses in front. A skinny horse runs along behind a wagon, from the sidewalk somebody calls "Emil," they bargain about the old nag, 50 marks and a round for the eight of us, the horse turns, trembles, nibbles at a tree, the driver tears it away, 50 marks and a round, Otto, otherwise we'll let it drop. The man on the sidewalk slaps the horse: All right! Yellow administration headquarters, an obelisk for the war dead. And to the right and left longish halls with glass roofs, these are stables and waiting-rooms. Outside black signboards: property of the Berlin Union of Wholesale Butchers, Incorporated. No bill posting without proper authority. The Board of Directors. In the long halls there are doors, black openings through which the animals are driven, numbered 26, 27, 28. The cattle-hall, the pork-room, the slaughter-rooms: death tribunals for the animals, swinging hatchets, you won't get out of here alive. Peaceful streets nearby, Strassmannstrasse, Liebigstrasse, Proskauer, Public Gardens in which people are strolling about. They dwell snugly side by side, the doctor comes running when one of them gets sick and has a sore throat. But on the other side, the tracks of the Belt Line Railway stretch over a distance of 10 miles. Live-stock comes rolling up from the provinces, specimens of the genus sheep, hog, ox, from East Prussia, Pomerania, Brandenburg, West Prussia. They bleat and low over the railings of their pens. The hogs grunt and sniff the ground, they can't see where they're going, the drivers follow them with sticks. They lie down in the stables, white and fat, side by side, snorting and sleeping. They have been driven a long time, then well shaken up in the cars; now there's nothing vibrating beneath them, only the flagstones are cold. They wake up and huddle close together. They lie piled one on top of the other. Two of them are fighting, there is room in the pen, they butt their heads together, snap at each other's necks and ears, turn around in a circle, snort, then at times become quite still, just biting each other. One of them grows afraid and climbs over the bodies of the others, its adversary climbs after it, gives a snarl, and while those underneath grub themselves up again, the

two plump down, looking for each other. A man in a linen smock ambles through the corridor, the pen opens, he steps in between the animals with a stick; then, once the door is open, they rush out, squealing, grunting, and screaming. They crowd along the corridors. Across the courtyards, between the halls, he drives them up, those funny creatures with their jolly fat hams, their jolly little tails, and the green and red stripes on their backs. Here you have light, dear little pigs, and here you have dirt, just give a sniff, go ahead and grub a while, for how many minutes longer will it be? No, you are right, one should not work by the clock, just go on sniffing and grubbing. You are going to be slaughtered, there you are, take a look at the slaughter-house, at the hog slaughter-house. There exist old houses, but you get a new

model. It is bright, built of red brick, from the outside you might take it for a locksmith's workshop, for a machine-shop, an office-room, or a drafting-room. I am going to walk the other way, dear little pigs, for I'm a human being, I'll go through this door, we'll meet again, inside. A push against the door, it rebounds, swings to and fro. Whew, what a lot of steam! What are they steaming? It's like a bath, all that steam, the hogs are taking a Turkish bath, perhaps. You can't see where you're walking. Your glasses are covered with vapor, you could go naked, sweat out your rheumatism, cognac alone won't do, the slippers go clattering about. Nothing can be seen, the steam is too thick. But a continuous noise of squealing, snorting, clattering, men's voices calling back and forth, tools being dropped, slamming of lids. Somewhere around here are

English School
Butcher's Shop, 19th century,
private collection

the hogs, they came in from across the way, from the door at the side. This thick white steam! Here they are, the hogs, some of them are hanging up, already dead, they've been cut up, almost ripe for guzzling. A man with a hose is squirting water on the white halves of the hogs. They are hanging on iron posts, head downward: some of the hogs are still whole, their legs are locked in a cross-beam above, a dead animal can't do anything at all, nor can it run. Pigs' feet, hacked off, lie in a pile. Two men arrive out of the fog carrying something, an animal on an iron bar, gutted and slit open. They lift the bar up and put it through the rings. Many of its comrades are dangling there, staring at the flagstones.
You walk through the room in a fog. The flagstones are grooved, damp, covered with blood. Between the posts are rows of white eviscerated animals. Behind there must be the slaughter-pens, there is a sound of smacking, clattering, squealing, screaming, rattling, grunting. Steaming boilers and vats send vapors into the room. The dead animals are dipped in the boiling water, then scalded and taken out very white, a man scrapes off the epidermis with a knife, the animal grows whiter still, becomes quite smooth. Quite soft and white, relaxed as though after a tiring bath, after a successful operation or a massage, the hogs lie in rows, on benches or planks, they lie quite still in their replete tranquility, in their new white shirts. They all lie on their sides, on some of them can be seen a double row of teats, a sow has many breasts, they must be fertile animals. But they all have a straight red slit at their throats right down the middle, that's very suspicious.
The cracking sound starts up again, a door is opened in back, the vapor vanishes, they drive in a new lot of hogs, there you run while I walk in front through the sliding door, funny rosy creatures, jolly hams, jolly little curly tails, backs with motley colored stripes. And they sniff in the new pen. It's cold as the old one, but there is still something wet on the floor, something unknown, a red lubricity.

They sniff at it with their snouts.
A pallid young man with slick blond hair has a cigar in his mouth. Look here, that's the last man who will occupy himself with you. Don't think ill of him, he is doing his official duty. He has to settle an administrative matter with you. He is dressed only in his boots, trousers, shirt and suspenders, the boots come up over his knees. That's his official garb, he takes his cigar out of his mouth, lays it on a shelf on the wall, takes a long hatchet out from the corner. It is the sign of his official dignity, of his rank over you, like the brass badge of a detective. He'll soon flash it at you. The young man takes a long wooden pole, lifts it up to the height of his shoulders over the squeaking little pigs which are rooting, sniffing and grunting undisturbed down below. The man walks around, looking down, searching, searching. The problem at stake is an inquiry against John Doe, John Doe in the case of X *vs.* Y.—Bing, one of them has run in front of his feet, bing, another one. The man is quick, he has given an account of himself, the hatchet had whizzed down, plunged into the lot of them with its blunt side, first on one head, then on another. That was a great moment! Kicking, writhing. Flinging from side to side. No longer conscious. Just lying there. What are those legs and heads doing? But the pig isn't doing that, it's the legs that do it, on their own, you might say. And already two men have begun to look across from the scalding room; it's time for them now, they lift a slide onto the killing-pen, drag out the animal, they sharpen their long knives on the stone and kneel down, slash, slash, they thrust them into the throat, zzing, a long slit, a very long slit in the throat, the animal is opened up like a bag, deep, plunging cuts, the animal twitches, kicks, thrashes about, it is unconscious, no more than unconscious now, more's to come, it squeals, and now for the opening of the veins in the throat. It is profoundly unconscious, we have stepped into metaphysics, into theology, my child, you no longer walk on earth, we're

wandering now on the clouds. Hurry up with the pan now, the black warm blood streams into it, foams and bubbles in the pan, stir it quickly. The blood coagulates in the body, forms clots and stops up wounds. Now it has left the body, and it still wants to coagulate. Like a child that keeps on crying Mama, Mama, when it lies on the operating table, but there is no question of Mama, and Mama does not come, but it's suffocating under the mask with the ether, it goes on crying till it can cry no longer: Mama. Zzing, zzing, the veins, right and left. Stir it quickly. That's it. Now the twitching stops. Now you are still. We are through with physiology and theology, physics begins.

The man who was kneeling gets up. His knees hurt him. The pig has to be scalded, gutted, then hacked up; this is done step by step. The boss, looking well-fed, wanders up and down through the steam, puffing at his pipe, glancing from time to time at an open belly. On the wall next to the swinging door hangs a poster: Annual Ball, First Section of Live-Stock Shippers, Saalbau, Friedrichshain, Kermbach Orchestra. Outside are posters announcing boxing matches. Germania Halls, Chausseestrasse 110, Entrance from 1.50 to 10 marks, 4 Qualification Matches.

Supply at the cattle-market: 1399 steers, 2700 calves, 4654 sheep, 18,864 hogs. Market conditions: prime steers firm, otherwise quiet. Calves firm, sheep quiet, hogs opening firm, closing weak, overweights lagging. The wind blows through the driveway it is raining. The cattle bleat as several men drive a big, roaring, horned herd into the place. The animals close in on each other, they stop in their tracks, then run in the wrong direction while the drivers chase them with sticks. A bull jumps up on a cow in the middle of the bunch, the cow runs right and left, the bull is after her, hugely he rises up on her again and again.
A big, white steer is driven into the slaughter-hall. Here there is no vapor, no pen like they

have for the swarming pigs. The big strong animal, the steer, steps in alone, between its drivers through the gate. The blood-bespattered hall lies open before it with the chopped-up bones, and the halves and quarters hanging about. The big steer has a broad forehead. With sticks and thrusts it is driven up to the butcher. In order to make it stand still, he gives it a slight blow on the hind leg with the flat part of the hatchet. One of the drivers seizes it from below around the neck. The animal stands for a moment, then yields, with a curious ease, as if it agreed and was willing, after having seen everything and understood that this is its fate, and that it cannot do anything against it. Perhaps it thinks the gesture of the driver is a caress, it looks so friendly. The animal follows the tug of the driver's arms, turns its head obliquely to one side, mouth upward.
But then the butcher stands behind it with his hammer uplifted. Don't look around! The hammer lifted by the strong man with both his fists is behind you, above you, and then: zoom, down it comes! The muscular force of a strong man like an iron wedge in its neck! And a second later—the hammer has not yet been lifted—the animal's four legs give a spring, the whole heavy body seems to fly up with a jerk. And then as though it had no legs, the beast, the heavy body, falls down on the floor with a thud, onto its rigidly cramped legs, lies like this for a moment, drops on its side. The executioner walks around the animal from left to right, cracks it over the head, and on the temples, with another mercifully stunning blow: you will not wake up again. Then another man beside him removes the cigar from his mouth, blows his nose, sharpens his knife, it is half as long as a sword, and kneels behind the animal's head; its legs have already stopped their convulsive movements. With short twitching jerks it tosses the hind part of its body back and forth. The butcher searches for something on the floor and before using the knife, he calls for the basin to catch the blood. The blood is still circulating quietly

inside, little disturbed, under the impulses of a mighty heart. To be sure, the spine is crushed, but the blood still flows quietly through the veins. The lungs breathe, the intestines move. Now he applies the knife, the blood will gush out, I can see it now, in a stream as thick as your arm, black, beautiful, jubilating blood. Then the whole merry party will leave the house, the guests will dance out into the open, a tumult, and gone are the happy pastures, the warm stable, the fragrant fodder, everything gone, blown away, an empty hole, darkness, a new cosmos emerges! Haha! Suddenly we see a gentleman who has bought the house, new streets being laid out, better business conditions, going to tear down everything. They bring the big basin, shove it up to him, the huge animal throws its hind legs in the air. The knife is thrust into its neck near the gullet, look carefully for the veins, they are covered with a tough skin, well safeguarded. And now it's open, another one too, it spurts forth, hot steaming blackness, black red, the blood bubbles out over the knife, over the butcher's arm, jubilant blood, hot blood, the guests are coming, the transformation act proceeds, from the sun came your blood, the sun hid in your body, now it surges forth again. The animal breathes with huge efforts, it amounts to suffocation, a huge irritation, it snorts and rattles. Yes, the beams are cracking. The flanks heave so fearfully that one of the men helps the beast. If you want a stone to fall, give it a push. A man jumps on top of the animal, on its body, with both legs, he stands up there, bouncing, steps on the entrails, bobs up and down, the blood should come out more quickly, all of it. And the snorting grows louder, it is a long drawn-out panting, panting away, with light defensive blows of the hind legs. The legs quiver gently. Life is going out with a snort, the breathing begins to die down. The hind quarters turn over heavily. That's the earth, that's gravity. The man bobs upward. The other man underneath is already preparing to turn back the hide of the neck.

UMBERTO ECO
THE NAME OF THE ROSE
(1980)

Salvatore wandered through the world, begging, pilfering, pretending to be ill, entering the temporary service of some lord, then again taking to the forest or the high road. From the story he told me, I pictured him among those bands of vagrants that in the years that followed I saw more and more often roaming about Europe: false monks, charlatans, swindlers, cheats, tramps and tatterdemalions, lepers and cripples, jugglers, invalid mercenaries, wandering Jews escaped from the infidels with their spirit broken, lunatics, fugitives, under banishment, malefactors with an ear cut off, sodomites, and along with them ambulant artisans, weavers, tinkers, chair-menders, knife-grinders, basket-weavers, masons, and also rogues of every stripe, forgers, scoundrels, cardsharps, rascals, bullies, reprobates, recreants, frauds, hooligans, simoniacal and embezzling canons and priests, people who lived on the credulity of others, counterfeiters of bulls and papal seals, peddlers of indulgences, false paralytics who lay at church doors, vagrants fleeing from convents, relic-sellers, pardoners, soothsayers and fortunetellers, necromancers, healers, bogus alms-seekers, fornicators of every sort, corruptors of nuns and maidens by deception and violence, simulators of dropsy, epilepsy, hemorrhoids, gout, and sores, as well as melancholy madness. There were those who put plasters on their bodies to simulate incurable ulcerations, others who filled their mouths with a blood-colored substance to feign accesses of consumption, rascals who pretended to be weak in one of their limbs, carrying unnecessary crutches and imitating the falling sickness, scabies, buboes, swellings, while applying bandages, tincture of saffron, carrying irons on their hands, their heads swathed, slipping into the churches stinking, and suddenly fainting in the squares, spitting saliva and popping their

eyes, making the nostrils spurt blood concocted of blackberry juice and vermilion, to wrest food or money from the frightened people who recalled the church fathers' exhortations to give alms: Share your bread with the hungry, take the homeless to your hearth, we visit Christ, we house Christ, we clothe Christ, because as water purges fire so charity purges our sins.

Long after the events I am narrating, along the course of the Danube I saw many, and I still see some, of these charlatans who had their names and their subdivisions in legions, like the devils.
It was like a mire that flowed over the paths of our world, and with them mingles preachers in good faith, heretics in search of new victims, agitators of discord.

Flemish School
The Blind Men, 1643,
Basel, Kunstmuseum

UMBERTO ECO
BAUDOLINO
(2000)

As they advanced they heard first a distant sound, then a crackling, a noise that became increasingly audible and distinct, as if someone were throwing a great number of boulders and pebbles from the peaks, and the avalanche were dragging with it earth and rubble, rumbling downwards. Then they made out a cloud of dust, like a mist or brume; but, unlike a great mass of humidity, which would have darkened the rays of the sun, this gave off myriad glints, as if the sun's rays were striking against a fluttering of mineral atoms.

At a certain point Rabbi Solomon was the first to understand. "It's the Sambatyon," he shouted, "so we are close to our goal!" It was indeed the river of stone, as they realized when they arrived at its banks, dazed by the great din that almost prevented them from hearing one another's words. It was a majestic course of rocks and clods, flowing ceaselessly, and in that current of great shapeless masses could be discerned irregular slabs, sharp as blades, broad as tombstones, and between them, gravel, fossils, peaks, and crags.

Moving at the same speed, as if driven by an impetuous wind, fragments of travertine rolled over and over, great faults sliding above, then, their impetus lessening, they bounced off streams of spall, while little chips now round, smoothed as if by water in their sliding between boulder and boulder, leaped up, falling back with sharp sounds, to be caught in those same eddies they themselves had created, crashing and grinding. Amid and above this overlapping of mineral, puffs of sand were formed, gusts of chalk, clouds of lapilli, foam of pumice, rills of mire.

Here and there sprays of shards, volleys of coals, fell on the bank, and the travelers had to cover their faces so as not to be scarred.

[...]

They rode for six days, seeing that the river's bed did, indeed, narrow, becoming first a stream and then a creek, but they arrived at the source only towards the fifth day. By then, for two days they had seen above the horizon an impervious chain of high mountains, which loomed over the travelers, almost blocking their view of the sky, crammed as they were in an ever narrower passage, with no exit, from which, way, way above, could now be seen only a great cloud barely luminescent, that gnawed the top of those peaks.

Here, from a fissure, like a wound between two mountains, they saw the Sambatyon springing up: a roiling of sandstone, a gurgling of tuff, a dripping of muck, a ticking of shards, a grumbling of clotted earth, an overflowing of clods, a rain of clay, all gradually transformed into a steady flow, which began its journey towards some boundless ocean of sand.

[...]

Until, after almost five days' travel, and nights as sultry as the days, they realized that the continuous churn of that tide was changing. The river had assumed a greater speed, in its flow something like currents were visible, rapids that dragged along shreds of basalt like straws, a distant thunder was heard ... Then, more and more impetuous, the Sambatyon subdivided into myriad streamlets, which penetrated among mountainous slopes like the fingers of a hand in a clump of mud; at times a wave was swallowed by a grotto, then, from a sort of rocky passage that seemed impassable, it emerged with a roar and flung itself angrily towards the valley. Abruptly, after a vast curve, they were forced to make because the banks had become impervious, lashed by granite whirlwinds, the friends reached the top of a plateau, and saw the Sambatyon below them, annihilated in a sort of maw of Hell.

There were cataracts that plunged down from dozens of rocky eaves arranged like an amphitheater, into a boundless final vortex, an incessant retching of granite, an eddy of bitumen, a sole undertow of alum, a churning of schist, a clash of orpiment against the banks. And on the matter that the vortex erupted towards the sky, but low with respect to the eyes of those who looked down as if from the top of a tower, the sun's rays formed on those silicious droplets an immense rainbow that, as every body reflected the rays with varying splendor according to its own nature, had many more colors than those usually formed in the sky after a storm, and, unlike them, seemed destined to shine eternally, never dissolving. It was a reddening of haematrites and cinnabars, a glow of blackness as if it were steel, a flight of crumbs of aureopigment from yellow to bright orange, a blueness of armenium, a whiteness of calcinated shells, a greening of malachite, a fading of liothargirium into saffrons ever paler, a blare of risigallam, a belching of greenish earth that faded into dust of crisocolla and then transmigrated into nuances of indigo and violet, a triumph of aurum musivum, a purpling of burnt white lead, a flaring of sandracca, a couch of silvered clay, a single transparence of alabaster.

No human voice could make itself heard in that clangor, nor did the travelers have any desire to speak. They witnessed the death agony of the Sambatyon enraged at having to vanish into the bowels of the earth, trying to take with it all that surrounded it, clenching its stones to express all its impotence.

Yves Tanguy
Multiplication of the Arcs, 1954,
New York, Museum of Modern Art

17.   CHAOTIC ENUMERATION

L et us move now to chaotic enumeration, where we delight in introducing the absolutely heterogeneous. As we have seen, the early examples are in Rabelais, but we could find older precedents. For example, one is that *jocus monacorum* called **Coena Cypriani** (The Supper of Cyprianus) in which many biblical characters get involved in some entirely absurd goings on in the course of a dinner. There is no point in knowing whether the text was really the work of Saint Cyprianus (who lived in the 3rd century A.D.) or whether it was more likely to have been written a few centuries after that. Nor do we know if it had a mnemonic function, to help young monks to remember the episodes from the Bible, or if it was purely for amusement (some think it was a game, a parody). The fact is that the succession of events must not have seemed absurd to contemporary readers because each character does something that in some way connects him to the biblical account. But for those who read it now the list appears as delightfully chaotic and is reminiscent of (and who knows if it did not inspire) the film *Hellzapoppin'*.

A principal example of chaotic enumeration, which anticipates the unsettling lists of the Surrealists, is in **Rimbaud**'s *Bateau Ivre*. In fact, a propos of Rimbaud it is worth dusting off the distinction between *conjunctive* and *disjunctive* enumeration.[1] Conjunctive enumeration (and there are a great many examples of this in our anthology) brings together different things giving the whole a coherence insofar as they are seen by the same person or considered in the same context;

Hannah Höch
Cut with the Dada Kitchen Knife through the Last
Weimar Beer-Belly Cultural Epoch in Germany, 1919,
Berlin, Staatliche Museen zu Berlin, Nationalgalerie

contrariwise, disjunctive enumeration expresses a shattering, a kind of schizophrenia of the person who becomes aware of a sequence of disparate impressions without managing to confer any unity upon them. In this sense, Spitzer, in the aforementioned essay, was inspired by the notion of disjunctive enumeration for his concept of chaotic enumeration, and in fact he cited by way of example these verses from Rimbaud's *Illuminations*:

In the wood there is a bird, his song stops you and makes you blush.
There is a clock that does not chime
There is a swamp with a nest of white beasts
There is a descending cathedral and an ascending lake.
There is a little carriage abandoned in the undergrowth, or which runs
    down the path, beribboned.
There is a company of little actors in costume, glimpsed on the road
    through the edge of the wood.
Finally, when you are hungry and thirsty, there is someone who drives you
    out

Literature offers an embarrassment of choice. In order to avoid making endless lists of lists we shall restrict ourselves to anthologizing a passage from **Neruda** as an example of the many chaotic lists found in Latin American literature.[2] **Prévert** cannot be denied a mention, and there must also be an excerpt from **Calvino** where, in the course of his "Cosmicomic" fantasies, on imagining the random formation of the earth's surface by meteoric detritus, the author himself frequently defines his list as an "absurd hotchpotch" and notes: "I had fun imagining that among these terribly incongruous objects there ran a mysterious bond whose nature I would have to guess." At first sight, it is difficult to imagine the mysterious bond that links the attributes Cole Porter confers upon his beloved in *You are the Top*!: "You're the top!—You're the Coliseum.—You're the top!—You're the Louver Museum.—You're a melody from a symphony by Strauss—

Combs, hairpins and other toiletries
from Pompeii, 1st century A.D.,
Naples, Museo Archeologico Nazionale

You're a Bendel bonnet,—A Shakespeare's sonnet,—You're Mickey
Mouse.—You're the Nile,—You're the Tower of Pisa, ..."

It is interesting to compare Porter's song with **Breton**'s eulogy to
his woman and **Balestrini**'s praise of Miss Richmond. The
comparison refers us to the opposition between lists based on the
signified and those based on the *signifier*. Evidently in Balestrini all
that counts are the alliterations, created even at the cost of coining
non-Italian adjectives, whereas in both Porter and Breton the
intention is also to call up precise images, wholly surreal in the
former and in a more accessible "musical" style in the latter.

Two authors are fully entitled to join the number of masters of
chaotic enumeration (and have always been cited as such) even though
most of their enumerations have an undoubted coherence. See in the
anthology the excerpts from **Gadda** and **Arbasino**. Gadda lists the
furnishings in the Cavenaghi household and what happens during
the fire in via Keplero; in the first case one would say that the house
was in a really chaotic state, and that a really chaotic state was caused
by the fire; but this would be a matter of metaphors, because that
house contains all the furnishings it contains and could in all likelihood
be there, and the sequence of events in the course of the fire in via
Keplero follows a precise chronological order. For his part Arbasino
describes presumably real places, characters and events (some Roman
churchmen visit the house) according to a chronological sequence of
events. Yet what seizes the reader in these cases is the vertigo created
by the author's voracious glance, which through a sort of verbal
bulimia makes chaotic what originally was not. In short, in these two
authors (with Arbasino always having held up Gadda as his model)
we witness the "chaoticization" of order.

Similarly, all the things listed in Szymborska's "Birthday" really
exist in this world but the list is conceived in order to praise the
marvellous chaos in which we live.

We shall finish with the greatest example of the incongruous list
(to the point that it can permit itself the luxury of brevity) and that
is the list of animals in the Chinese encyclopaedia called the "Celestial
Emporium of Benevolent Knowledge" invented by Borges and then

Robert Rauschenberg
Untitled, 1964,
Private collection

Giacomo Balla
Girl Running on a Balcony, 1912
Milan, Galleria d'Arte Moderna

mentioned by Michel Foucault as an exergue in *The Order of Things*,[3] whereby the animals would be divided into: (a) those that belong to the emperor; (b) embalmed ones; (c) those that are trained; (d) suckling pigs; (e) mermaids; (f) fabulous ones; (g) stray dogs; (h) those that are included in this classification; (i) those that tremble as if they were mad; (j) innumerable ones; (k) those drawn with a very fine camel-hair brush; (l) etcetera; (m) those that have just broken the flower vase; (n) those that at a distance resemble flies.[4]

On considering both coherent excesses and chaotic enumerations we realize that, compared to the lists of antiquity, something different has happened. As we have seen, Homer fell back on the list because he lacked words, tongue and mouth, and the topos of the ineffable dominated the poetics of lists for many centuries. But, on looking at the lists drawn up by Joyce or Borges it is clear that they did not make lists because they did not know what to say, but because they wanted to say things out of a love of excess, hubris and a greed for words, for the joyous (and rarely obsessive) science of the plural and the unlimited. The list becomes a way of reshuffling the world, almost putting into practice Tesauro's invitation to accumulate properties in order to bring out new relationships between distant things, and in any case to cast doubt on those accepted by common sense. In this way the chaotic list becomes one of the modes of that breakdown of form set in motion in different ways by Futurism, Cubism, Dadaism, Surrealism, or by New Realism.

1. Cf. Detlev W. Schumann "Enumerative Style and its Significance in Whitman, Rilke, Werfel" in *Modern Langauge Quarterly*, June 1942.
2. A propos of Neruda, see A. Alonso in *Poésia y estilo de Pablo Neruda* (Buenos Aires, 1940) quoted in Spitzer, p. 23, in a chaper entitled "Disjecta membra y objetos heterogéneos" where he talks of "enumeraciones desarticulatas".
3. *Les mots et les choses* (Paris, Gallimard, 1966), English tr. *The Order of Things* (London, Tavistock Publications, 1970).
4. "John Wilkins' Analytical Language", translated by Eliot Weinberger; included in *Jorge Luis Borges: Selected Non-fictions*, ed. Eliot Weinberger (London, Penguin Books, 1999). The essay was originally published as "El idioma analítico de John Wilkins", *La Nación*, 8 February 1942, and republished in *Otras inquisiciones*.

THE SUPPER OF CYPRIANUS
(V-VI CENT.)

A certain king, who went by the name of Joel,
celebrated his marriage in the East, at Cana
in Galilee, and invited many to the wedding
feast.
Solomon prepared the table
and everyone gathered 'round.
Thus, the first to be seated were:
Adam front and center,
Eve upon the leaves,
Cain upon the plow,
Abel atop a milk pail,
Noah on the ark,
Japheth atop some bricks,
Abraham under the tree,
Isaac upon the altar,
Jacob atop a stone,
Lot near the door,
Moses upon a boulder,
Elias upon a hide,
Daniel upon the tribunal chair, Tobias upon
the bed,
Joseph atop a bushel of grain,
Benjamin atop a sack,
David atop a mound of earth,
John upon the ground,
Pharaoh upon some sand,
Lazarus upon the table,
Jesus at the well, Zachariah upon a sycamore,
Matthew upon a stool, Rebecca upon an urn,
Raab atop the oakum, Ruth atop the straw,
Techla upon the windowsill,
Susanna in the garden,
Absalom amid the branches,
Judah atop the coin purse,
Peter at the desk,
James atop the net,
Samson atop the column,
Elias upon the saddle,
Rachel atop her bundle.
Paul stood by waiting,
and Esau mumbled
while Job complained,
as he was the only one seated amidst dung.

Veronese (Paolo Caliari)
The Marriage at Cana, 1563,
Paris, Musée du Louvre

ARTHUR RIMBAUD
THE DRUNKEN BOAT
(1871)

I watched the lightning tear the sky apart,
Watched waterspouts, and streaming undertow,
And Dawn like Dove-People rising on wings—
I've seen what men have only dreamed they
   saw!

I saw the sun with mystic horrors darken
And shimmer through a violet haze;
With a shiver of shutters the waves fell
Like actors in ancient, forgotten plays!

I dreamed of green nights and glittering
   snow,
Slow kisses rising in the eyes of the Sea,
Unknown liquids flowing, the blue and yellow
Stirring of phosphorescent melody!

For months I watched the surge of the sea,
Hysterical herds attacking the reefs;
I never thought the bright feet of Mary
Could muzzle up the heavy-breathing waves!

I have jostled—you know?—unbelievable
   Floridas
And seen among the flowers the wild eyes
Of panthers in the skins of men! Rainbows
Bridling blind flocks beneath the horizons!

In stinking swamps I have seen great hulks:
A leviathan that rotted in the reeds!
Water crumbing in the midst of calm
And distances that shatter into foam!

Glaciers, silver suns, waves of pearl, fiery skies,
Giant serpents stranded where lice consume
Them, falling in the depths of dark gulfs

From twisted trees, bathed in black perfume!
I wanted to show to children these fishes
   shining
In the blue wave, the golden fish that sing—
A froth of flowers cradled my wandering
And delicate winds tossed me on their wings.

Sometimes, a martyr of poles and latitudes,
The sea rocked me softly in sighing air,
And brought me shadow-flowers with yellow
   stems—
I remained like a woman, kneeling ...

Almost an island, I balanced on my boat's sides
Rapacious, blond-eyed birds, their dung, their
   screams.
I drifted on. Through fragile tangled lines
Drowned men, still staring up, sank down
   to sleep.

Now I, a little lost boat, in swirling debris,
Tossed by the storm into the birdless upper
   air
—All the Hansa Merchants and Monitors
could not fish up my body drunk with the sea;

Free and soaring, trailing a violet haze,
Shot through the sky, a reddening wall
Wet with the jam of poets' inspiration,
Lichens of sun, and snots of bright blue sky;

Lost branch spinning in a herd of hippocamps,
Covered over with electric animals,
An everlasting July battering
The glittery sky and its fiery funnels;

Shaking at the sound of monsters roaring,
Rutting Behemoths in thick whirlpools,
Eternal weaver of unmoving blues,
I thought of Europe and its ancient walls!

Max Ernst
Thirty-three Girls Chasing White Butterflies, 1958,
Madrid, Museo Thyssen-Bornemisza

PABLO NERUDA
ODE TO FEDERICO GARCÍA LORCA
(1936)

If I could fill the town halls with soot
and, sobbing, tear down clocks,
it would be to see when to your house
comes summer with its broken lips,
come many people with dying clothes,
come regions of sad splendor,
come dead plows and poppies,
come gravediggers and horsemen,
come planets and maps with blood,
come buzzards covered with ashes,
come masked men dragging damsels
pierced by great knives,
come roots, veins, hospitals,
springs, ants,
comes night with the bed where
a solitary Hussar is dying among the spiders,
comes a rose of hatred and pins,
comes a yellowish vessel,
comes a windy day with a child,
come I with Oliverio, Norah,
Vicente Aleixandre, Delia,
Maruca, Malva Marina, María Luisa, and Larco,
The Blond, Rafael Ugarte,
Cotapos, Rafael Alberti,
Carlos, Bebé, Manolo Altolaguirre,
Molinari,
Rosales, Concha Méndez,
and others that slip my mind.

Come, let me crown you, youth of health
and butterflies, youth pure
as a black lightningflash perpetually free,
and just between you and me,
now, when there is no one left among the
rocks,
let us speak simply, man to man:
what are the verses for if not for the dew?

Federico,
you see the world, the streets,
the vinegar,
the farewells in the stations
when the smoke lifts its decisive wheels
toward where there is nothing but some
separations, stones, railroad tracks.

There are so many people asking questions
everywhere.
There is the bloodied blindman, and the
angry one, and the
disheartened one,
and the wretch, the thorn tree,
the bandit with envy on his back.

That's the way life is, Federico, here you have
the things that my friendship can offer you,
the friendship of a melancholy manly man.
By yourself you already know many things,
and others you will slowly get to know.

JACQUES PRÉVERT
"TENTATIVE DE DESCRIPTION D'UN DÎNER DE TÊTES À PARIS-FRANCE" (1946)

Ceux qui pieusement ...
Ceux qui copieusement ...
Ceux qui tricolorent
Ceux qui inaugurent
Ceux qui croient
Ceux qui croient croire
Ceux qui croa-croa
Ceux qui ont des plumes
Ceux qui grignotent
Ceux qui andromaquent
Ceux qui dreadnoughtent
Ceux qui majusculent
Ceux qui chantent en mesure
Ceux qui brossent à reluire
Ceux qui ont du ventre
Ceux qui baissent les yeux
Ceux qui savent découper le poulet
Ceux qui sont chauves à l'intérieur de la tête
Ceux qui bénissent les meutes
Ceux qui font les honneurs du pied
Ceux qui debout les morts
Ceux qui baionnette ... on
Ceux qui donnent des canons aux enfants
Ceux qui donnent des enfants aux canons
Ceux qui flottent et ne sombrent pas
Ceux qui ne prennent pas Le Pirée pour un
    homme
Ceux que leurs ailes de géants empêchent de
    voler
Ceux qui plantent en rêve des tessons de
    bouteille sur la grande muraille de Chine
Ceux qui mettent un loup sur leur visage
    quand ils mangent du mouton
Ceux qui volent des oeufs et qui n'osent pas
    les faire cuire
Ceux qui ont quatre mille huit cent dix
    mètres de Mont-Blanc, trois cents de Tour
    Eiffel, vingt-cinq Centimetres de tour de
    poitrine et qui en sont fiers

Ceux qui mamellent de la France
Ceux qui courent, volent et nous vengent,
tous ceux-là, et beaucoup d'autres, entraient
fièrement à l'Élysée en faisant craquer les
graviers, tous ceux-là se bousculaient, se
dépéchaient, car il y avait un grand diner de
têtes et chacun s'était fait celle qu'il voulait.
L'un une tête de pipe en terre, l'autre une tête
d'amiral anglais; il y en avait avec des têtes
de boule puante, des têtes de Galliffet, des
têtes d'animaux malades de la tête, des têtes
d'Auguste Comte, des têtes de Rouget de
Lisle, des têtes de sainte Thérèse, des têtes
de fromage de tête, des têtes de pied, des
têtes de monseigneur et des têtes de crémier.
Quelques-uns, pour faire rire le monde,
portaient sur leurs épaules de charmants
visages de veaux, et ces visages étaient si
beaux et si tristes, avec les petites herbes
vertes dans le creux des oreilles comme le
goémon dans le creux des rochers, que
personne ne les remarquait.
Une mère à tête de morte montrait en riant
sa fille à tête d'orpheline au vieux diplomate
ami de la famille qui s'était fait la tête de
Soleilland.
C'était véritablement délicieusement
charmant et d'un goût si sûr que lorsque
arriva le Président avec une somptueuse tête
d'oeuf de Colomb ce fut du délire. [...]
Le soleil brille pour tout le monde, il ne brille
pas dans les prisons, il ne brille pas pour ceux
qui travaillent dans la mine,
ceux qui écaillent le poisson
ceux qui mangent la mauvaise viande
ceux qui fabriquent les épingles à cheveux
ceux qui soufflent vides les bouteilles que
    d'autres boiront pleines
ceux qui coupent le pain avec leur couteau
ceux qui passent leurs vacances dans les usines
    ceux qui ne savent pas ce qu'il faut dire
ceux qui traient les vaches et ne boivent pas
    le lait

ceux qu'on n'endort pas chez le dentiste ceux
  qui crachent leurs poumons dans le métro
ceux qui fabriquent dans les caves les stylos
  avec lesquels d'autres écríront en plein air
  que tout va pour le mieux
ceux qui en ont trop à dire pour pouvoir le dire
ceux qui ont du travail
ceux qui n'en ont pas
ceux qui en cherchent
ceux qui n'en cherchent pas
ceux qui donnent à boire aux chevaux
ceux qui regardent leur chien mourir
ceux qui ont le pain quotidien relativement
  hebdomadaire
ceux qui l'hiver se chauffent dans les églises
ceux que le suisse envoie se chauffer dehors
ceux qui croupissent
ceux qui voudraient manger pour vivre
ceux qui voyagent sous les roues
ceux qui regardent la Seine couler
ceux qu'on engage, qu'on remercie, qu'on
  augmente, qu'on diminue, qu'on manipule,
  qu'on fouille, qu'on assomme
ceux dont on prend les empreintes
ceux qu'on fait sortir des rangs au hasard
  et qu'on fusille
ceux qu'on fait défiler devant l'Arc
ceux qui ne savent pas se tenir dans le
  monde entier
ceux qui n'ont jamais vu la mer
ceux qui sentent le lin parce qu'ils travaillent
  le lin
ceux qui n'ont pas l'eau courante
ceux qui sont voués au bleu horizon
ceux qui jettent le sel sur la neige moyennant
  un salaire absolument dérisoire
ceux qui vieillissent plus vite que les autres
ceux qui ne sont pas baissés pour ramasser
  l'épingle
ceux qui crèvent d'ennui le dimanche après-
  midi
parce qu'ils voient venir le lundi
et le mardi, et le mercredi, et le jeudi, et le
  vendredi
et le samedi
et le dimanche après-midi.

JACQUES PRÉVERT
"CORTÈGE" (1949)

Un vieillard en or avec une montre en deuil
Une reine de peine avec un homme
  d'Angleterre
Et des travailleurs de la paix avec des
  gardiens de la mer
Un hussard de la farce avec un dindon de
  la mort
Un serpent à café avec un moulin à lunettes
Un chasseur de corde avec un danseur de têtes
Un maréchal d'écume avec une pipe en retraite
Un chiard en habit noir avec un gentleman au
  maillot
Un compositeur de potence avec un gibier
  de musique
Un ramasseur de conscience avec un
  directeur de mégots
Un repasseur de Coligny avec un amiral
  de ciseaux
Une petite soeur du Bengale avec un tigre
  de Saint-Vincent-de-Paul
Un professeur de porcelaine avec un
  raccommodeur de philosophie
Un contrôleur de la Table Ronde avec des
  chevaliers de la Compagnie du Gaz de Paris
Un canard à Sainte-Hélène avec un Napoléon
  à l'orange
Un conservateur de Samothrace avec une
  Victoire de cimetière
Un remorqueur de famille nombreuse avec
  un père de haute mer
Un membre de la prostate avec une
  hypertrophie de l'Académie française
Un gros cheval in partibus avec un grand
  évêque de cirque
Un contrôleur à la croix de bois avec un petit
  chanteur d'autobus
Un chirurgien terrible avec un enfant dentiste
Et le général des huîtres avec un ouvreur de
  Jésuites.

JACQUES PRÉVERT
"LA BATTEUSE" (1946)

La batteuse est arrivée
la batteuse est repartie

Ils ont battu le tambour
ils ont battu les tapis
ils ont tordu le linge
ils l'ont pendu
ils l'ont repassé
ils ont fouetté la crème et ils l'ont renversée
ils ont fouetté un peu leurs enfants aussi
ils ont sonné les cloches
ils ont égorgé le cochon
ils ont grillé le café
ils ont fendu le bois
ils ont cassé les oeufs
ils ont fait sauter le veau avec les petits pois
ils ont flambé l'omelette au rhum
ils ont découpé la dinde
ils ont tordu le cou aux poulets
ils ont écorché les lapins

ils ont éventré les barriques
ils ont noyé leur chagrin dans le vin
ils ont claqué les portes et les fesses des femmes
ils se sont donné un coup de main
ils se sont rendu des coups de pied
ils ont basculé la table
ils ont arraché la nappe
ils ont poussé la romance
ils se sont étranglés étouffés tordus de rire
ils ont brisé la carafe d'eau frappée
ils ont renversé la crème renversée
ils ont pincé les filles
ils les ont culbutées dans le fossé
ils ont mordu la poussière
ils ont battu la campagne
ils ont tapé des pieds
tapé des pieds tapé des mains
ils ont crié et ils ont hurlé ils ont chanté
ils ont dansé
ils ont dansé autour des granges où le blé
    était enfermé
Où le blé était enfermé moulu fourbu vaincu
    battu.

page 339: *Rain of Fireballs*
an illustration from *La fin du monde* (*The End of the World*)
by Nicolas Camille Flammarion, Paris, 1894

ITALO CALVINO
"METEORITES" (1968)

According to the latest theories, in the beginning Earth was a tiny, cold mass that gradually grew larger as it successively englobed meteorites and meteor dust. Early on, we fooled ourselves by thinking we could keep it [the Earth] clean—old Qfwfq continued—because it was so small, and you could sweep and dust it every day. And a lot of stuff sure rained down on it: you'd have thought the Earth did all that circling 'round solely for the purpose of picking up all the dust and garbage floating through space. It's all different now, there's an atmosphere, you look up at the sky and say, " Oh, how clear it is, how pure;" but you should've seen the stuff that flew by overhead when the planet, just following its orbit, ran into one of those meteor clouds and couldn't get out. It was a white dust like naphthalene that left minute grains on everything, and sometimes deposited larger, crystalline slivers, as if some glass lamp had shattered to bits and come raining down from the sky. And in the middle there were even some larger pebbles, scattered pieces of other planetary systems, cores of eaten pears, faucets, Ionic capitals, back issues of the *Herald Tribune* and *Paese Sera* newspapers: universes are created and destroyed, but its always the same material getting recycled over and over. Because it was small and rather nimble (it moved a lot faster back then than it does nowadays), the Earth managed to dodge a lot of stuff: we'd see some object coming at us from the depths of space, flitting about like some bird—and it turned out to be a sock; or we'd see something navigating at a slight pitch—that was a grand piano that flew by; things like that would come within a half meter of us, only to continue on their way, their trajectories not quite brushing up against ours. Then they'd be lost—maybe forever—in the dark, empty void we left behind us. [...] Those were the brief contemplative moments we allowed ourselves—but they never lasted long. Each morning we'd get up early, only to discover that our few hours of sleep left the Earth enough time to get covered up anew by all the detritus. "Hurry up, Qfwfq, we've not a moment to lose!" Xha would yell, thrusting the broom at me, and off I'd go to do my usual rounds as the dawn began to brighten on the plain's thin, bare horizon. As I went along, here and there I came across piles of scraps and junk; as the day grew lighter, I became aware of the opaque dusting that veiled the planet's otherwise sparkling ground. With each stroke of the broom I gathered all I could into the litter bin or sack I dragged with me, but first I'd pause to inspect the odd objects the night had brought with it: the skull of an ox; a cactus; the wheel of a cart; a golden nugget; a movie projector. I'd weigh them in my hands, suck on the finger I pricked on the cactus, and daydream, imagining there was some mysterious connecting linking all these objects, and I had to find out what it was. [...] In the hemisphere I had to take care of, sometimes I didn't throw everything out right away—especially the heavier stuff—and I'd pile it all in a corner, to collect it so I could come back later with a wheelbarrow. So sometimes there was a little build-up, some stacks and piles here and there: carpets; sand dunes; copies of various editions of the Koran; oil wells; an absurd jumble of various clutter. Naturally, Xha would never have approved of my system— but, in truth, I took a fair amount of pleasure seeing all these composite shadows towering on the horizon. Sometimes I happened to leave the piles I'd collected from one day to the next (the Earth had finally grown so large that Xha couldn't circle the whole thing in one single day), and was surprised each morning to see how many new things had latched on to all the old stuff. [...] And thus, little by little, the Earth took on the forms you're now familiar with. The meteoric rain of little bits continues to this day, adding new details: it frames things with a window, a tent, a network of telephone wires; it fills

the empty spaces with random pieces that fit together as best they can—stoplights, obelisks, bars and tobacconists, church apses, floods, dentists' offices, a cover of the *Domenica del Corriere* magazine showing a hunter biting a lion. And there's always a bit of excess in the conclusion of superficial details—like all the pigment in butterflies' wings, for example—as well as a few incongruous elements, like a war in Kashmir; and I always get the feeling there's still something missing that's about to arrive—maybe just some Saturnian verses by Cnaeus Naevius to fill the gap between two poetic fragments, or the formula regulating the transformation deoxyribonucleic acid undergoes in the chromosomes—and then the picture will be complete …

Paul Delvaux
The Acropolis, 1966,
Paris, Musée National d'Art Moderne,
Centre Georges Pompidou

ANDRÉ BRETON
FREE UNION (1931)

My love whose hair is woodfire
Her thoughts heat lightning
Her waist an hourglass
My love an otter in the tiger's jaws
Her mouth a rosette bouquet of stars of the
 highest magnitude
Her teeth footprints of white mice on white
 earth
Her tongue smooth as amber and as glass
My love her tongue a sacred host stabbed
 through
Her tongue a doll whose eyes close and open
Her tongue a fantastic stone
Each eyelash traced by a child's hand
Her eyebrows the edge of a swallow's nest
My love her temples slates of a greenhouse
 roof
And their misted panes
My love whose shoulders are champagne
And the dolphin heads of a fountain under ice
My love her wrists thin as matchsticks
Whose fingers are chance and the ace of hearts
Whose fingers are mowed hay
My love with marble and beechnut beneath
 her arms
Of Midsummer night
Of privet and the nests of angel fish
Whose arms are sea foam and river locks
And the mingling of wheat and mill
My love whose legs are fireworks
Moving like clockwork and despair
My love her calves of elder tree marrow

My love whose feet are initial letters
Are key rings and sparrows drinking
My love her neck pearled with barley
My love her throat of a golden valley
Rendez-vous in torrent's very bed
Her breasts of night
My love her breasts molehills beneath the sea
Crucibles of rubies
Spectre of the dew-sparkled rose
My love whose belly unfurls the fan of every day
Its giant claws
Whose back is a bird's vertical flight
Whose back is quicksilver
Whose back is light
The nape of her neck is crushed stone and
 damp chalk
And the fall of a glass where we just drank
My love whose hips are wherries
Whose hips are chandeliers and feathers
And the stems of white peacock plumes
Imperceptible in their sway
My love whose buttocks are of sandstone
Of swan's back and amianthus
And of springtime
My love whose sex is gladiolus
Is placer and platypus
Algae and sweets of yore
Is mirror
My love her eyes full of tears
Of violet panoply and magnetic needle
My love of savanna eyes
My love her eyes of water to drink in prison
My love her eyes of wood always to be
 chopped
Eyes of water level earth and air and fire

NANNI BALESTRINI
"OH COMME ELLE EST BELLE
MADEMOISELLE RICHMOND"
(1974-1977)

Oh comme elle est bartavelle
balancelle bagatelle attelle
ascensionelle artificielle artérielle
comme elle est aquarelle Mademoiselle
    Richmond

oh comme elle est anticonstitutionelle
annuelle aisselle airelle
aguelle actuelle accidentelle
comme elle est voyelle Mademoiselle
    Richmond

oh comme elle est visuelle
virtuelle violoncelle villanelle
vervelle vermicelle varicelle
comme elle est vaisselle Mademoiselle
    Richmond

oh comme elle est usuelle
universelle unisexuelle unipersonelle
tutelle truelle trimestrielle
comme elle est temporelle Mademoiselle
    Richmond

oh comme elle est traditionelle
touselle tourterelle tourelle
torrentjelle tonnelle textuelle
comme elle est temporelle Mademoiselle
    Richmond

oh comme elle est tarentelle
surelle surnaturelle superficielle
substantielle spirituelle spinelle
comme elle est soutanelle Mademoiselle
    Richmond

oh comme elle est solennelle
soldanelle sexuelle séquelle
sentinelle sensuelle sensationelle
comme elle est sempiternelle Mademoiselle
    Richmond

oh comme elle est semestrielle
semelle selle sauterelle
sautelle sarcelle saltarelle
comme elle est sacramentelle Mademoiselle
    Richmond

oh comme elle est ruelle
rondelle rituelle ritournelle
ridelle ribambelle révérencielle
comme elle est réelle Mademoiselle
    Richmond

oh comme elle est rebelle
rationelle radicelle querelle
quenelle pucelle prunelle
comme elle est providentielle Mademoiselle
    Richmond

oh comme elle est proportionelle
professionelle présidentielle préjudicielle
poutrelle poubelle potentielle
comme elle est ponctuelle Mademoiselle
    Richmond

oh comme elle est pommelle
polichinelle piurielle pimprenelle
piloselle pestilentielle personnelle
comme elle est perpétuelle Mademoiselle
    Richmond

oh comme elle est péronelle
pénitentielle pelle pédicelle
paumelle paternelle .patelle
comme elle est pastourelle Mademoiselle
    Richmond

oh comme elle est passionelle
passerelle partielle parcelle
originelle ombelle oiselle
comme elle est officielle Mademoiselle
    Richmond

oh comme elle est ocelle
occasionelle nouvelle noctuelle
nivelle nielle naturelle
oh comme elle est nacelle Mademoiselle
    Richmond

oh comme elle est mutuelle
mortelle mortadelle morelle
mistelle missibelle mirabelle
cmnme elle est ministérielle Mademoiselle
    Richmond

oh comme elle est mercurielle
mensuelle menstruelle maternelle
matérielle margelle marelle
comme elle est maquerelle Mademoiselle
    Richmond

oh comme elle est manuelle
manivelle mamelle magnanarelle
lumachelle libelle lamelle
comme elle est jumelle Mademoiselle
    Richmond

oh comme elle est jouvencelle
javelle jarretelle isabelle
irrationelle intentionelle intemporelle
comme elle est intellectuelle Mademoiselle
    Richmond

oh comme elle est insurrectionnelle
institutionnelle industrielle individuelle
incorporelle impersonelle immatérielle
comme elle est immortelle Mademoiselle
    Richmond

oh comme elle est hirondelle
haridelle habituelle gravelle
gratterelle graduelle glabelle
comme elle est gazelle Mademoiselle
    Richmond

oh comme elle est gamelle
gabelle fraxinelle fraternelle
formelle fonctionnelle flanelle
comme elle est flagelle Mademoiselle
    Richmond

oh comme elle est filoselle
ficelle femelle exponentielle
excrémentielle exceptionelle excelle
comme elle est éventuelle Mademoiselle
    Richmond

oh comme elle est étincelle
éternelle essentielle escarcelle
escabelle écuelle échelle
comme elle est donzelle Mademoiselle
    Richmond

oh comme elle est différentielle
dentelle cruelle criminelle
crécerelle crécelle coupelle
comme elle est correctionnelle Mademoiselle
    Richmond

oh comme elle est corporelle
conventuelle contractuelle continuelle
consubstantielle constitutionnelle confidentielle
comme elle est conditionnelle Mademoiselle
    Richmond

oh comme elle est colonelle
colombelle coéternelle coccinelle
citronelle citadelle circonstancielle
comme elle est cervelle Mademoiselle
    Richmond

oh comme elle est chamelle
chandelle chanterelle chapelle
charnelle cicatricielle cascatelle
comme elle est casuelle Mademoiselle
    Richmond

oh comme elle est caravelle
cannelle brocatelle bretelle
boute-selle bisexuelle bielle
comme elle est belle Mademoiselle
    Richmond

Benjamin Walter Spiers
Armour, Prints, Paintings, Pipes, China (all Crack'd),
Old Rickety Tables and Chairs Broken Back'd, 1882,
private collection

CARLO EMILIO GADDA
THE CAVENAGHI FAMILY'S HOUSE, IN L'ADALGISA (1944)

[...] In a flash, they'd turned the whole house upside down: stools, pillows, side tables, beds; all the knick-knacks in the sitting room, the bazaar that was the lounge, and the polar-bear pelt with its muzzle laid out and its curved claws (which used to scratch the polish as soon as they were stepped on) and the end table and the canapés and Luciano's rocking horse and the plaster bust of great-grandfather Cavenaghi that was always teeteringly perched atop a spiraling column; bags of bon-bons, Laris, lionesses, grandfather clocks, jars of liquor-infused cherries, urinals full of dried chestnuts, Grandmother Bertagnoni's lace-making cushion, rolled-up carpets and veritable troops of slippers flushed out from under the beds, pretty much all the ingredients and trappings of domestic dementia and prudence.

CARLO EMILIO GADDA
THE FIRE ON KEPLER STREET, IN ACCOPPIAMENTI GIUDIZIOSI (1963)

All sorts of crazy stories were being told about the fire at 14 Kepler Street; but the truth is, not even His Excellency Filippo Tommaso Marinetti would've been able to synthesize the simultaneity of all that had happened in three minutes' time in that howling rat nest as swiftly as the fire managed to: it immediately spewed out all the female tenants, half-naked in the mid-August heat, alongside their litters of countless children, from the stench and sudden terror raging through the building; then a few men, then a number of poor women—it seemed each of them had bad legs, and were bony and pallid and unkempt— in lacey white lingerie, instead of the sober black they usually wore on their way to church; then a number of men, also in pretty sad shape, then Italian-American poet Rotunno Anacarsi; then the maid tending to the Garibaldi veteran who was already in the throes of death up on the sixth floor; then Achilles,

carrying a little girl and a parrot; then the Balossi kid, in his skivvies, carrying Mrs. Carpioni in his arms—no, no, I'm wrong, it was Mrs. Maldifassi, and she was shrieking so much you'd have thought the devil was on her tail, plucking out all her feathers. Then, finally, amid endless shouts, screams, tears, little kids, and huge wails of anguish, and the thumping and crashing of all the valuables and bundles thrown from the windows hitting the ground, when you heard the fire trucks arriving full-speed and two trucks were already unloading three dozen police officers in white uniform, and the Green Cross ambulance was pulling up; then, at last, from the two right-hand windows up on the fourth floor, and a second later from the fifth floor, the fire couldn't help but let loose its own fearful sparks—so eagerly awaited!—and twisting red serpent-tongues of fire came in sudden spurts, darting here and there, with roiling, blackberry-like plumes of dark smoke, pitchy and thick as if it came from some infernal roast, billowing out in puffs and coiling itself up like a soot-black python rising from the depths with sinister scintillations; and blazing butterflies, or so they seemed, perhaps of fine paper or more likely swaths of cloth or charred pleather fluttering all over a sky utterly befouled with ashes, adding to the disheveled women's fright, some standing barefoot in the dust of the unpaved street; others in slippers, with no worry about stepping in all the horse piss and dog-logs strewn about amidst the screams and cries of their thousands of offspring. They already felt their heads, and their vainly permed coifs, ablaze in that frightful, blazing torch.

[...]

"A fire," everyone echoed later, "is one of the most terrible things there is." And it's true:

amid the selfless sacrifice of those magnificent firefighters, amid all that confusion, amid countless cataracts of drinking water sent down over the piss-stained, discolored green ottomans—though this time menaced by a truly hideous red—and over the sideboards and cupboards, which perhaps housed a hundred-off grams of oozing gorgonzola, but were already licked by tongues of fire, like a python might taste its coiled-up prey; with spurting, hydrous needles, out of the swollen, sodden serpents of hemp fire-hose and long, piercing javelins of the brass nozzles ending up in white plumes and clouds under a torrid August sky; and pieces of partly scorched porcelain insulators, fallen and shattered to bits—*pattatraff!*—on the sidewalk below; and melted phone wires, detached from the iron-hot brackets that had held them in place, fluttering in the evening sky, with black airborne peninsulas of charred cardboard and veritable montgolfiers of smoldering upholstery and smoking wallpaper, and below, amid the firemen's feet, behind the fire ladders, bends and coils and hoses reared back, spewing parabolic streams from every part of the crowded street, jagged shards of shattered windowpanes immersed in a swamp of water and muck, enameled iron chamber pots full of carrot-shaped poop, thrown from the windows—even now!—slopping over the rescuers' high boots, against the leg-protectors of the engineers and *carabinieri* and fire-chiefs leading the men; and the insolent and uninterrupted *click-clack, click-click, click-a-clack* of the women's old wooden clogs as they ran about picking up pieces of comb, fragments of mirrors, and beatific images of San Vincenzo de' Liguori amidst the splashes and spills of the catastrophic laundromat.

Firemen intervening at a fire in a hospital near Rennes,
illustration from "Le Petit Journal", 1906

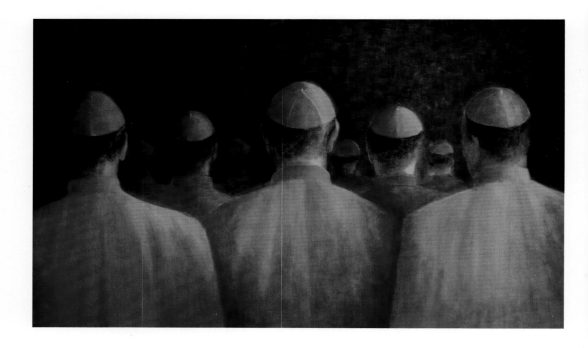

ALBERTO ARBASINO
LUNCHTIME GATHERING OF THE
MONSIGNORI, IN FRATELLI D'ITALIA
(1963)

Early on, I hadn't been invited to lunch—only the coffee break. But Ferdinando had called Antonio the previous evening, telling him to bring me with him. And so, at 1:15 p.m. on the dot, we showed up at the Palazzo Opprandini. The little courtyard was a thicket of fig trees and ferns, magnolias, paradise palms, and dwarf euphorbias, with arms, hands, and fingers from a gigantic monumental sculpture pointing the way toward a cool elevator covered in vine branches and cascades depicted in ornate intarsia. It was very expensive—twenty-five lire—and inside there was a prie-dieu covered in gilt chinoiseries. It stopped at the penultimate floor, then went up to the top floor, and on to the covered roof terrace just above the attic. From the arched windows of the loggia one saw a span of white oleanders and a pair of little towers, topped by golden roosters, reminiscent of

Moscow's towers. There were tent-coverings and benches on the landings, all made of the same emerald green brocade with spiral and shell patterns, and horses' hooves garlanded by acanthus. On the red lacquer door were two enormous, highly polished lions' heads, with a ring in their noses and a cittern between their perked-up ears.
The interior was straight out of *Sunset Boulevard*: zebra pelts on the floor; black- and white-striped wall covering just like the Siena's main cathedral, with some gold- and white stripes as well; long white divans as huge as boats; massive gilt lampshades. We walk past vitrines full of stuffed Staffordshires, eighteenth-century barbers' basins, brass bed-warmers from the Napoleonic era; antique yellow marble-topped consoles—their surface "four fingers thick!"—decorated with densely arranged red marble obelisks between large black marble cannonballs; collections of opals and filigrees inside low-lit display cases, and Catalonian and Sicilian votive paintings on glass, hung one next to the other, like in a sanctuary.

There were neo-gothic niches lined with authentic William Morris tapestries, full of out-of-season daffodils and tulips with long white beard-like roots hanging down in their blue glass vases. There were mooresque tables encrusted in mother-of-pearl and topped with orderly stacks of *Time* and *The New Yorker*, plus a few odd copies of *The Yellow Book*. All around were goofy nylon poufs in faux otter and broadtail pelts with fringed borders. There was even a corner filled with Dugento decorations: forged-iron guardsmen's badges; a Provençal chest decorated with scenes from the story of Saint Madina among the Sardinians, and a picture of Saint Marinella receiving the silver shower in a gold-leaf background and grand red coral frame—she is depicted between two donors who Ferdinand says look just like Alcibiades and Talleyrand. An impressive greenhouse lay behind the wall of glass enclosing the dining room, almost like the wings of a theatrical stage. It housed gigantic succulents and cacti that looked like demented Japanese bushes that had evaded the gardener's watch and devoured him. "Various species and genera— *splendens, fulgens, potens, patiens, impatiens, dolorosa, lachrimosa, vergognosa, semper fidelis, parvula*—and atop *pulcherrima* Lady Brett's Indian parrot was perched." There were broken columns and pediments in fragments, strewn about on the gravel. "The last epigraph commemorates the great battle between the Charleston and the Fox-Trot, in 1928." And in the bluish shadows, it all seemed made of ceramic. Little squirrels played with white mice. And at the back of the third sitting-room—formerly Cardinal Somerset's chapel—was a large hearth with brightly colored Vietri tiles; in front of it stood an enormous Victorian-Shakespearean sofa upholstered in a gros-point needlework pattern; above it stood a one-and-a-half-meter statuette of Topo Gigio in bright *pannolenci* felt, pipe in mouth.

"It's too bad the Vanvitelli canvases are out on loan today." (Indeed, one of the walls is half bare.) Father Zermatt and Father Klosters, the men of the house, step forward: both are smiling; both have a pleasant scent of aftershave about them; both have closely cropped platinum blonde hair; both have broad shoulders below their frocks, and perfectly white collars. Father Zermatt is Ferdinand's friend, and must be the older of the two; he's already earned the purple lining around his buttons and cuffs, indicating a solid start to his career. Giulio and Ferdinando are already there, and look like two little devils wearing the red and green plastic glasses they got yesterday evening when they went to the movies to see some 3-D horror flick—"A veritable Grünewald." Together they lead us onto the terrace, which gives a splendid view out over the Portico d'Ottavia and the Synagogue, the Theater of Marcellus, the Palazzo Mattei, the Tiber Island and, up above, the Capitoline Hill. Everyone's seated, Aperol-colored cocktails in hand, and we're introduced: first, to Cardinal Santacecilia; then, to Monsignor Igitur, who's also American; finally, to a rather large, friendly young guy with super-white, tusk-like teeth— Father Poldi-Pezzoli, from Ajaccio, coadjutor of the Bishop of Ephesus and Pergamon, who's here on sabbatical leave. The Cardinal doesn't say a word, and just lounges on a chaise-longue that looks like it came straight off a steamer; he must be at least ninety. We're all snacking on cocktail nuts, and Father Zermatt shows us the intentionally chaotic, mismatched planters brimming with zinnias, roses, snap-dragons, buttercups— "Just like the little garden of some country parish, where one worshipper brings some sage, another brings tagete flowers." "Not to be confused with *cebete*!"

Lincoln Seligman
Cardinals, 2005,
private collection

WISŁAWA SZYMBORSKA
"BIRTHDAY" (1972)

So much world all at once—how it rustles and
bustles!
Moraines and morays and morasses and mussels,
the flame, the flamingo, the flounder, the
feather—
how to line them all up, how to put them
together?
All the tickets and crickets and creepers and
creeks!
The beeches and leeches alone could take weeks.
Chinchillas, gorillas, and sarsaparillas—
thanks do much, but all this excess of kindness
could kill us.
Where's the jar for this burgeoning burdock,
brooks' babble,
rooks' squabble, snakes' squiggle, abundance,
and trouble?
How to plug up the gold mines and pin down
the fox,
how to cope with the lynx, bobolinks, streptococs!
Tale dioxide: a lightweight, but mighty in deeds:
what about octopodes, what about centipedes?
I could look into prices, but don't have the nerve:
these are products I just can't afford, don't
deserve.
Isn't sunset a little too much for two eyes
that, who knows, may not open to see the
sun rise?
I am just passing through, it's a five-minute stop.
I won't catch what is distant: what's too
close, I'll mix up.
While trying to plumb what the void's inner
sense is,
I'm bound to pass by all these poppies and
pansies.
What a loss when you think how much effort
was spent
perfecting this petal, this pistil, this scent
for the one-time appearance, which is all
they're allowed,
so aloofly precise and so fragilely proud.

Gino Severini
Dynamic Hieroglyphic of the Bal Tabarin, 1912,
New York, Museum of Modern Art

18.   MASS MEDIA LISTS

The poetics of the list also pervades many aspects of mass culture, but with intentions different to those of avant-garde art. We need only think of that model of the visual list which is the parade of girls adorned with ostrich feathers coming down the staircase in the *Ziegfield Follies*, or the renowned water ballet in *Bathing Beauty*, or the multiple parades in *Footlight Parade*, the models who file past in *Roberta*, or the modern fashion shows of the great designers.

Here the succession of bewitching creatures is intended merely to suggest abundance, a need to satisfy the desire for the blockbuster, to show not only one glamorous image but a great many of them, to provide the user with an inexhaustible reserve of voluptuous appeal, just as potentates of old adorned themselves with cascades of jewels, or as in certain American restaurants you pay a fixed price on entry and then can eat as much as you wish from a gigantic buffet. The technique of the list is not intended to cast doubt on any order in the world; on the contrary its purpose is to reiterate that the universe of abundance and consumption, available to all, represents the only model of ordered society.

Providing lists of different beauties has something to do with the characteristics of the society that generated the mass media. It is reminiscent of Marx, who at the beginning of *Das Kapital* says: "the wealth of those societies in which the Capitalist mode of production prevails presents itself as an immense accumulation of commodities". This global accumulation has its various symbolic loci: one is the

Viva le donne! (Footlight Parade)
directed by Lloyd Bacon, 1933

shop window, which displays an occasionally excessive series of objects but effectively has us understand that it shows only one example of what we might find inside; another is the trade fair, which showcases a greater number of different objects than any museum and systematically announces through its very name that the exhibition is only partial and the number of objects to which it refers is infinite; a third place is represented by the "galleries" celebrated by Walter Benjamin, which a 19th-century Parisian guidebook defined as "corridors covered with glass and inlaid marble walls" where there are series of "the most elegant shops, so that a gallery of this kind is a city, in fact a world in miniature"; and finally there is the department store, extolled by Zola in his *Au Bonheur de dames* (The Ladies' Delight), a true list of itself.

On the other hand Spitzer had already talked of a "bazaar spirit" with regard to some of Balzac's enumerations contemporary with the first Parisian department stores, as in this text from *Croquis et fantaisies*: "It was an odd house, a panorama, a genuine physiognomic gallery, a bazaar of figures, fortunes and opinions: Glamorous women, cultivated women, innocent women, God-fearing women, parvenu women, coquettish women, authors, actors, orators, prose writers, poets, magistrates, lawyers, diplomats, academics, stockbrokers, Gallicans, ultramontanists, republicans, monarchists, papists, Bonapartists, Chartists, Orleanists, anarchists, alarmists, short-story writers, writers of feuilletons, pamphleteers, publicists, journalists, artists, they all meet here, shoulder to shoulder, they dump one another, abuse one another ..."

Mass media lists are substitutes for the *Wunderkammern* and the treasuries of the past. One example would be the museums of marvels particularly widespread in the United States, such as the various "Ripley's Believe it or Not" museums, where they display shrunken heads from Borneo, a violin made entirely out of matchsticks, a calf with two heads, a mermaid found in 1842, a guitar made from a 19th-

Ziegfield Follies: The Ziegfield Girls on Stage
Broadway shows, c. 1921-1931,
Iron Mountain, Pennsylvania, Bettmann Collection

An American in Paris
directed by Vincente Minnelli, 1951

Andy Warhol
Campbell's Soup Cans, 1962,
New York, Museum of Modern Art

Raymond Depardon
New York, USA, 2006

Don Jacot
Garbo's, 2001,
New York, Louis K. Meisel Gallery

century French bidet, a collection of unusual tombstones, an instrument of torture similar to the Virgin of Nuremberg, a statue of a fakir who lived covered in chains or a Chinese with two irises. What makes the set of these marvels coherent is that none of these relics are *authentic*, because there are several Ripley's museums, all identical. Then there is the museum devoted to the late American president Lyndon Johnson, which boasts forty thousand red boxes containing all the documents of his political life, half a million photos, mementoes of his schooldays, honeymoon photos, a series of films constantly projected for visitors that record the trips abroad made by the presidential couple, waxwork statues that show the wedding dresses worn by his daughters Lucy and Linda, a life-size reproduction of the Oval Office in the White House, the red pumps worn by the dancer Maria Tallchief, a score autographed by the pianist Van Cliburn, the plumed hat worn by Carol Channing in *Hello Dolly!* (all mementoes justified by the fact that the artists in question had performed in the White House), gifts made by representatives of various states, a feathered Indian headdress, portraits made with matchsticks, commemorative panels in the form of cowboy hats, doilies embroidered with the American flag, the sword given by the king of Thailand, and some rocks from the moon brought home by the astronauts.

Finally we come to the Mother of all Lists, infinite by definition because it is in constant evolution, the World Wide Web, which is both web and labyrinth, not an ordered tree, and which of all infinities promises us the most mystical, almost totally virtual one, and really does offer us a catalogue of information that makes us feel wealthy and omnipotent, the only snag being that we do not know which of its elements refers to data from the real world and which does not; there is no longer any distinction between truth and error.

Ilya Kabakov
The Man Who Flew into Space from His Apartment,
from the *Ten Characters* series, 1985,
Paris, Musée National d'Art Moderne,
Centre Georges Pompidou

19.   LISTS OF INFINITIES

Both narrative and philosophy have evoked the infinity of lists without attempting to draw up any list: they simply conceived of *containers* of infinite lists, or devices for *producing* an infinite list of elements.

The literary model is that of Borges' Library of Babel, which contains infinite volumes kept in an unlimited and periodic expanse of rooms. Thomas Pavel, in his book *Fictional Worlds* (Harvard University Press, 1986), draws inspiration from this idea of Borges when he invites us to conduct a fascinating mental experiment: let us suppose that an omniscient being is able to write or read a Magnum Opus, which contains all true statements about both the real world and all possible worlds. Naturally, since it is possible to talk of the universe in diverse languages, and each language defines it in a different way, there exists a Maximal Collection of Magnum Opuses. The collection of Daily Books by a given individual must be shown on the Day of Judgement, together with that of the Books that evaluate the lives of families, tribes and nations.

But the angel who writes a Daily Book does not line up only true statements: he connects them, assesses them, and builds them into a system. And since on Judgement Day individuals and groups will each have a defending angel, for each one the defenders will rewrite another astronomical series of Daily Books where the same statements will be linked up differently, and compared differently to the statements in some of the Magnum Opuses.

Heinrich Johann Vogeler
Baku (Agitationstafel), 1927,
Berlin, Staatliche Museen zu Berlin, Nationalgalerie

Since infinite alternative worlds are part of each of the infinite
Magnum Opuses, the angels will write infinite Daily Books in which
they mix statements that are true in one world and false in another.
If we consider that some angels are clumsy, and mix statements that
a single Magnum Opus records as mutually contradictory, in the end
we would have a series of Compendia, of Miscellanies, and of Compendia
of Fragments of Miscellanies, which will amalgamate strata of books
of different origins, and at that point it will be very difficult to say
which books are true and which are fictitious, and with respect to
which original book.

Joaquín Torres-García
New York Street Scene, 1920,
New Haven, Yale University Art Gallery

Maria Helena Vieira da Silva
The Library, 1949,
Paris, Musée National d'Art Moderne,
Centre Georges Pompidou

We will have an astronomic infinity of books each of which straddles different worlds, and stories that some have considered to be true will be seen as fictitious by others.

Pavel writes these things to make us understand that we already live in a universe of this kind, except that the books were not written by archangels but by us, from Homer to Borges; and he suggests that the legend he recounts is a very good portrayal of our situation with regard to the universe of statements that we are accustomed to accept as "true". So the *frisson* with which we perceive the ambiguous confines between fiction and reality is not only equal to the one that seizes us when faced with the books written by angels, but also to that which should seize us when faced with the series of books that represent, authoritatively, the real world.

One of the properties of Borges' Library is also that of displaying books that contain all the possible combinations of twenty-five orthographical symbols, so that we cannot imagine any combination of characters that the Library has not foreseen. This was the old dream of the cabalists, because only by making infinite combinations of a finite series of letters could we hope one day to formulate the secret name of God.

In 1622 Pierre Guldin (*Problema arithmeticum de rerum combinationibus*) calculated how many words could have been produced with the twenty-three letters of the alphabet used at the time, combining them two by two, three by three, and so on, until he got to words twenty-three letters long, without taking into account repetitions and without worrying whether the words that could be engendered made sense or were pronounceable, and he came to a number in excess of seventy thousand billion billion (which would have taken more than a million billion billion letters to write). If we were to write all these words in registers of one thousand pages, at 100 lines per page and 60 characters per line, we would need 257 million billion registers of this kind; and if we wished to put them in a library equipped with cubic constructions measuring 432 feet per side, each capable of housing 32 million volumes, then we would need 8,052,122,350 such libraries. But what realm could contain all these buildings? If we calculate the surface available on the entire planet, we could house only 7,575,213,799 of them!

The same combinatorial enthusiasm persuaded Marin Mersenne (*Harmonie universelle*, 1636) to consider not only the words *pronounceable* in French, Greek, Hebrew, Arabic, Chinese and all other possible tongues, but also the number of possible musical sequences. Mersenne shows that to note all the *melodies* producible would require more reams of paper than those needed to span the distance between the earth and the sky and, if each sheet contained 720 melodies of 22 notes apiece and if each ream were compressed to less than one inch in thickness, since the melodies producible with 22 notes are over twelve thousand billion billion, by dividing this figure by the 362,880 melodies that can be contained in a ream, we would still get a sixteen-figure number, while the inches spanning the centre of the earth and

Salvador Dalí
Fifty Abstract Paintings Which Seen from Two Yards Change into Three Lenins Masquerading as Chinese and Seen from Six Yards Appear as the Head of a Royal Tiger, 1962, Figueres, Fundació Gala-Salvador Dalí

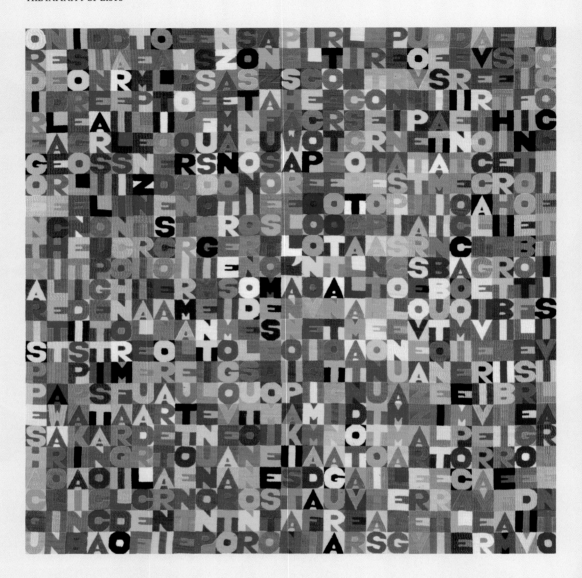

Alighiero Boetti,
Untitled, 1987,
Kassel, Museumslandschaft Hessen Kassel,
Neue Galerie

the stars are only a fourteen-figure number. And if we wished to write down all these melodies, one thousand per day, we would need almost twenty-three thousand million years.

In his brief text *Horizon de la doctrine humaine*, Leibniz wondered what might be the maximum number of statements, true, false and even non-existent, that could be formulated using a finite alphabet of twenty-four letters. Given that one can make words thirty-one letters long (of which Leibniz found examples in Greek and Latin), with the alphabet it is possible to produce 24^{32} thirty-one-letter words. But how long can a statement be? Given that it is possible to imagine statements as long as a book, the sum of statements, true or false, that a man can read in a lifetime (calculating that he reads one hundred pages per day and that each page contains one thousand letters), is 3,650,000,000. And even if this man lived a thousand years "the longest sentence utterable, or the biggest book a man can manage to read, will amount to 3,650,000,000,000 [letters], and the number of all the truths, falsehoods, utterable or, rather, readable sentences, pronounceable or not pronounceable, meaningful or less so, comes to $24^{365,000,000,0001} - 24/23$ [letters]".

These are fantasies where mathematics verges on metaphysics. But basically contemporary literature has tried to take these combinatory possibilities and to use them to draw up real lists, or induce the reader to do so, and this is the case with *Cent mille milliards de poèmes* by Raymond Queneau (Paris, Gallimard, 1961), a book whose pages are divided into horizontal bands which, upon leafing through, we can combine in different ways the fourteen lines of a sonnet, so as to compose one hundred thousand billion poems. The author points out that the texts producible are 10^{14} (and hence a finite number) but even if you read them twenty-four hours a day it would take two hundred million years to finish the task.

20. EXCHANGES BETWEEN PRACTICAL AND POETIC LISTS

The voraciousness of the list often prompts us to interpret practical lists as if they were poetic lists—and in effect what often distinguishes a poetic list from a practical one is only the intention with which we contemplate it.

It is not impossible to read a poetic list as if it were a practical one. Let us take Borges' list of animals: in a Latin-American literature exam it would be the (practical) list of animals to be remembered in order to quote Borges' text correctly. Likewise, it is possible to read a practical list as if it were a poetic one: for many people this series—Bacigalupo, Ballarin, Maroso, Grezar or Martelli, Rigamonti, Castigliano, Menti, Loik, Gabetto, Mazzola, Ossola—would appear to be a hotchpotch of names; others will see it as a (practical) list of the members of Torino soccer team who were wiped out in a tragic air crash in 1949; but for a great many nostalgic fans it has become a poetic list, a kind of mantra to be recited with emotion.

It has been pointed out[1] that the two lists that follow would seem to be very similar to Borges' list of animals. The first includes a counter, a rigid piece of metal or wood, musical notation for a repeating pattern of musical beats, the act of preventing, a unit of pressure equal to a million dynes per square centimetre, a submerged (or partly submerged) ridge in a river, the legal profession, a stripe, and a block of a solid substance. The second list assigns to the same set a tight cluster of people or things, any of various fastenings formed by looping and tying a rope (or cord) upon itself or to another rope

Jacques-Louis David
*Consecration of the Emperor Napoleon I
and Coronation of the Empress Josephine*, 1807,
Paris, Musée du Louvre

or to another object, a hard cross-grained piece of wood, something twisted and tight and swollen, a unit of length used in navigation, a soft lump or unevenness in a yarn, a sandpiper that breeds in the Arctic, and the embedding of a circle in three-dimensional Euclidean space,

If we consult a dictionary, we see that the first set embraces most of the possible meanings of the word *bar*, while the second refers to most of the possible meanings of the word *knot*.

A restaurant menu is a practical list. But in a book on culinary matters a list of the diverse menus of the most renowned restaurants would already acquire a poetic value. And in the same way one might daydream about the abundance of an exotic cuisine on reading (not with a view to ordering, but for aesthetic reasons) the menu of a Chinese restaurant with its pages and pages of numbered dishes.

It is unlikely that in painting the *Wedding at Cana* Veronese intended to portray one by one the participants at that event (given that he no information about them), but in painting the coronation of Napoleon I, David certainly included in the picture all the persons he believed to have been present at the ceremony; but this does not prevent their number (and the difficulty of counting them all) from making us feel a hint of dizziness at this perhaps incomplete plurality.

This possibility of reading a practical list as a poetic one or vice-versa also occurs in literature. See the gigantic portrayal of the Convention made by Hugo in *Ninety-Three*. He wanted to represent the titanic dimensions (in an ideal and moral sense) of the Revolution through the physical proportions of its assembly. It is conceivable that what takes up page after page may serve the function of a practical list; yet no one can fail to see the effect of incompleteness it creates, as if it were the representation, through the abridged example of those few hundred names, of the immense tide that was sweeping over France in that fateful year.

Félix Vallotton
The Library, 1885-1925,
Saint-Germain-en-Laye,
Musée Maurice Denis - Le Prieuré

Imaginary portrait of Pliny the Younger
(Gaius Plinius Caecilius Secundus), 1684-1692,
Kremsmünster, Benediktinerstift, Library

But the most convincing examples are the catalogues of the great libraries, such as the Bibliothèque Nationale de France, or the Library of Congress in Washington: their purpose is certainly practical but the bibliophile attempting to read all those titles and murmur them like a litany would find himself in the same situation as Homer faced with his warriors. In any case this is what happens when we read the catalogue of the works of **Theophrastus** drawn up by Diogenes Laërtius (*Life of Theophrastus*, 42–50), where the titles of books (most of which are lost) now appear to us not so much as an inventory but as an incantation. Perhaps **Rabelais** was thinking of endless lists of this type when he invented the catalogue of books kept in the Abbey of Saint Victor. Apparently practical, nonetheless Rabelais' list is poetic because the books do not exist and it is not clear whether it is the incongruousness of the titles or the size of the list that affords us a glimpse of the infinity of bestiality.

The appetite for lists about books has fascinated many writers, from **Cervantes** to **Huysmans** and **Calvino**; moreover it is well known that bibliophiles read the catalogues of antiquarian bookshops (which are certainly meant to be practical lists) as fascinating portrayals of a land of Cockaigne or desires, and they get as much pleasure out of this as a reader of Jules Verne gets from exploring the deeps of the silent oceans and encountering terrifying sea monsters.

Another lover of old books, Mario Praz, in a text for catalogue 15 of the 1931 Libreria della Fiera Letteraria, observed how bibliophiles read antiquarian bookshop catalogues with the same pleasure as others read thrillers. "You can be sure," he said, "that no reading has ever generated such swift, moving action as that of an interesting catalogue." But immediately after this he gives us an idea of how even uninteresting catalogues can be read in the same way.

1. Claudio Paolucci, a personal communication.

DIOGENES LAËRTIUS (180-240 A.D.) THE LIVES AND OPINIONS OF EMINENT PHILOSOPHERS FROM "THEOPHRASTUS", BOOK XIII

Three books of the First Analytics; seven of the Second Analytics; one book of the Analysis of Syllogisms; one book, an Epitome of Analytics; two books, Topics for referring things to First Principles; one book, an Examination of Speculative Questions about Discussions; one on Sensations; one addressed to Anaxagoras; one on the Doctrines of Anaxagoras; one on the Doctrines of Anaximenes; one on the Doctrines of Archelaus; one on Salt, Nitre, and Alum; two on Petrifactions; one on Indivisible Lines; two on Hearing; one on Words; one on the Differences between Virtues; one on Kingly Power; one on the Education of a King; three on Lives; one on Old Age; one on the Astronomical System of Democritus; one on Meteorology; one on Images or Phantoms; one on Juices, Complexions, and Flesh; one on the Description of the World; one on Men; one, a Collection of the Sayings of Diogenes; three books of Definitions; one treatise on Love; another treatise on Love; one book on Happiness; two books on Species; on Epilepsy, one; on Enthusiasm, one; on Empedocles, one; eighteen books of Epicheiremes; three books of Objections; one book on the Voluntary; two books, being an Abridgment of Plato's Polity; one on the Difference of the Voices of Similar Animals; one on Sudden Appearances; one on Animals which Bite or Sting; one on such Animals as are said to be Jealous; one on those which live on Dry Land; one on those which Change their Colour; one on those which live in Holes; seven on Animals in General; one on Pleasure according to the Definition of Aristotle; seventy-four books of Propositions; one treatise on Hot and Cold; one essay on Giddiness and Vertigo and Sudden Dimness of Sight; one on Perspiration; one on Affirmation and Denial; the Callisthenes, or an essay on Mourning, one; on Labours, one; on Motion, three; on Stones, one; on Pestilences, one; on Fainting Fits, one; the Megaric Philosopher, one; on Melancholy, one; on Mines, two; on Honey, one; a collection of the Doctrines of Metrodorus, one; two books on those Philosophers who have treated of Meteorology; on Drunkenness, one; twenty-four books of Laws, in alphabetical order; ten books, being an Abridgment of Laws; one on Definitions; one on Smells; one on Wine and Oil; eighteen books of Primary Propositions; three books on Lawgivers; six books of Political Disquisitions; a treatise on Politicals, with reference to occasions as they arise, four books; four books of Political Customs; on the best Constitution, one; five books of a Collection of Problems; on Proverbs, one; on Concretion and Liquefaction, one; on Fire, two; on Spirits, one; on Paralysis, one; on Suffocation, one; on Aberration of Intellect, one; on the Passions, one; on Signs, one; two books of Sophisms; one on the Solution of Syllogisms; two books of Topics; two on Punishment; one on Hair; one on Tyranny; three on Water; one on Sleep and Dreams; three on Friendship; two on Liberality; three on Nature; eighteen on Questions of Natural Philosophy; two books, being an Abridgment of Natural Philosophy; eight more books on Natural Philosophy; one treatise addressed to Natural Philosophers; two books on the History of Plants; eight books on the Causes of Plants; five on Juices; one on Mistaken Pleasures; one, Investigation of a proposition concerning the Soul; one on Unskilfully Adduced Proofs; one on Simple Doubts; one on Harmonics; one on Virtue; one entitled Occasions or Contradictions; one on Denial; one on Opinion; one on the Ridiculous; two called Soirees; two books of Divisions; one on Differences; one on Acts of Injustice; one on Calumny; one on Praise; one on Skill; three books of Epistles; one on Self-produced Animals; one on Selection; one entitled the Praises of the Gods; one on Festivals; one on Good Fortune; one on Enthymemes; one on Inventions; one on Moral Schools; one book of Moral Characters; one treatise on Tumult; one on History; one on the Judgment Concerning Syllogisms; one

on Flattery; one on the Sea; one essay, addressed to Cassander, Concerning Kingly Power; one on Comedy; one on Meteors; one on Style; one book called a Collection of Sayings; one book of Solutions; three books on Music; one on Metres; the Megades, one; on Laws, one; on Violations of Law, one; a collection of the Sayings and Doctrines of Xenocrates, one; one book of Conversations; on an Oath, one; one of Oratorical Precepts; one on Riches; one on Poetry; one being a collection of Political, Ethical, Physical, and amatory Problems; one book of Proverbs; one book, being a Collection of General Problems; one on Problems in Natural Philosophy; one on Example; one on Proposition and Exposition; a second treatise on Poetry;

one on the Wise Men; one on Counsel; one on Solecisms; one on Rhetorical Art, a collection of sixty-one figures of Oratorical Art; one book on Hypocrisy; six books of a Commentary of Aristotle or Theophrastus; sixteen books of Opinions on Natural Philosophy; one book, being an Abridgment of Opinions on Natural Philosophy; one on Gratitude; one called Moral Characters; one on Truth and Falsehood; six on the History of Divine Things; three on the Gods; four on the History of Geometry; six books, being an Abridgment of the work of Aristotle on Animals; two books of Epicheiremes; three books of Propositions; two on Kingly Power; one on Causes; one on Democritus; one on Calumny; one on Generation.

The Library of St. Gallen, 1761,
St. Gallen, Benedictine abbey

FRANÇOIS RABELAIS
FIVE BOOKS OF THE LIVES, HEROIC DEEDS AND SAYINGS OF GARGANTUA AND HIS SON PANTAGRUEL
BOOK II, CHAPTER 7 (1564)

How Pantagruel came to Paris, and of the choice books of the Library of St. Victor.

In his abode there he found the library of St. Victor a very stately and magnific one, especially in some books which were there, of which followeth the Repertory and Catalogue, Et primo,

The for Godsake of Salvation.
The Codpiece of the Law.
The Slipshoe of the Decretals.
The Pomegranate of Vice.
The Clew-bottom of Theology.
The Duster or Foxtail-flap of Preachers, composed by Turlupin.
The Churning Ballock of the Valiant.
The Henbane of the Bishops.
Marmotretus de baboonis et apis, cum Commento Dorbellis.
Decretum Universitatis Parisiensis super gorgiasitate muliercularum ad placitum.
The Apparition of Sancte Geltrude to a Nun of Poissy, being in travail at the bringing forth of a child.
Ars honeste fartandi in societate, per Marcum Corvinum (Ortuinum).
The Mustard-pot of Penance.
The Gamashes, alias the Boots of Patience.
Formicarium artium.
De brodiorum usu, et honestate quartandi, per Sylvestrem Prioratem Jacobinum.
The Cosened or Gulled in Court.
The Frail of the Scriveners.
The Marriage-packet.
The Cruizy or Crucible of Contemplation.
The Flimflams of the Law.
The Prickle of Wine.
The Spur of Cheese.
Ruboffatorium (Decrotatorium) scholarium.
Tartaretus de modo cacandi.

The Bravades of Rome.
Bricot de Differentiis Browsarum.
The Tailpiece-Cushion, or Close-breech of Discipline.
The Cobbled Shoe of Humility.
The Trivet of good Thoughts.
The Kettle of Magnanimity.
The Cavilling Entanglements of Confessors.
The Snatchfare of the Curates.
Reverendi patris fratris Lubini, provincialis Bavardiae, de gulpendis lardslicionibus libri tres.
Pasquilli Doctoris Marmorei, de capreolis cum artichoketa comedendis, tempore Papali ab Ecclesia interdicto.
The Invention of the Holy Cross, personated by six wily Priests.
The Spectacles of Pilgrims bound for Rome.
Majoris de modo faciendi puddinos.
The Bagpipe of the Prelates.
Beda de optimitate triparum.
The Complaint of the Barristers upon the Reformation of Comfits.
The Furred Cat of the Solicitors and Attorneys.
Of Peas and Bacon, cum Commento.
The Small Vales or Drinking Money of the Indulgences.
Praeclarissimi juris utriusque Doctoris Maistre Pilloti, &c., Scrap-farthingi de botchandis glossae Accursianae Triflis repetitio enucidi-luculidissima.
Stratagemata Francharchiaeri de Baniolet.
Carlbumpkinus de Re Militari cum Figuris Tevoti.
De usu et utilitate flayandi equos et equas, authore Magistro nostro de Quebecu.
The Sauciness of Country-Stewards.
M.N. Rostocostojambedanesse de mustarda post prandium servienda, libri quatuordecim, apostillati per M. Vaurillonis.
The Covillage or Wench-tribute of Promoters.
(Jabolenus de Cosmographia Purgatorii.)
Quaestio subtilissima, utrum Chimaera in vacuo bonbinans possit comedere secundas intentiones; et fuit debatuta per decem hebdomadas in Consilio Constantiensi.
The Bridle-champer of the Advocates.

Smutchudlamenta Scoti.

The Rasping and Hard-scraping of the Cardinals.

De calcaribus removendis, Decades undecim, per M. Albericum de Rosata.

Ejusdem de castramentandis criminibus libri tres.

The Entrance of Anthony de Leve into the Territories of Brazil.

(Marforii, bacalarii cubantis Romae) de peelandis aut unskinnandis blurrandisque Cardinalium mulis.

The said Author's Apology against those who allege that the Pope's mule doth eat but at set times.

Prognosticatio quae incipit, Silvii Triquebille, balata per M.N., the deep-dreaming gull Sion.

Boudarini Episcopi de emulgentiarum profectibus Aeneades novem, cum privilegio Papali ad triennium et postea non.

The Shitabranna of the Maids.

The Bald Arse or Peeled Breech of the Widows.

The Cowl or Capouch of the Monks.

The Mumbling Devotion of the Celestine Friars.

The Passage-toll of Beggarliness.

The Teeth-chatter or Gum-didder of Lubberly Lusks.

The Paring-shovel of the Theologues.

The Drench-horn of the Masters of Arts.

The Scullions of Olcam, the uninitiated Clerk.

Magistri N. Lickdishetis, de garbellisiftationibus horarum canonicarum, libri quadriginta.

Arsiversitatorium confratriarum, incerto authore.

The Gulsgoatony or Rasher of Cormorants and Ravenous Feeders.

The Rammishness of the Spaniards supergivuregondigaded by Friar Inigo.

The Muttering of Pitiful Wretches.

Dastardismus rerum Italicarum, authore Magistro Burnegad.

R. Lullius de Batisfolagiis Principum.

Calibistratorium caffardiae, authore M. Jacobo Hocstraten hereticometra.

Codtickler de Magistro nostrandorum Magistro nostratorumque beuvetis, libri octo galantissimi.

The Crackarades of Balists or stone-throwing Engines, Contrepate Clerks, Scriveners, Brief-writers, Rapporters, and Papal Bull-despatchers lately compiled by Regis.

A perpetual Almanack for those that have the gout and the pox.

Manera sweepandi fornacellos per Mag. Eccium.

The Shable or Scimetar of Merchants.

The Pleasures of the Monachal Life.

The Hotchpot of Hypocrites.

The History of the Hobgoblins.

The Ragamuffinism of the pensionary maimed Soldiers.

The Gulling Fibs and Counterfeit shows of Commissaries.

The Litter of Treasurers.

The Juglingatorium of Sophisters.

Antipericatametanaparbeugedamphicribrationes Toordicantium.

The Periwinkle of Ballad-makers.

The Push-forward of the Alchemists.

The Niddy-noddy of the Satchel-loaded Seekers, by Friar Bindfastatis.

The Shackles of Religion.

The Racket of Swag-waggers.

The Leaning-stock of old Age.

The Muzzle of Nobility.

The Ape's Paternoster.

The Crickets and Hawk's-bells of Devotion.

The Pot of the Ember-weeks.

The Mortar of the Politic Life.

The Flap of the Hermits.

The Riding-hood or Monterg of the Penitentiaries.

The Trictrac of the Knocking Friars.

Blockheadodus, de vita et honestate bragadochiorum.

Lyrippii Sorbonici Moralisationes, per M. Lupoldum.

The Carrier-horse-bells of Travellers.

The Bibbings of the tippling Bishops.

Dolloporediones Doctorum Coloniensium adversus Reuclin.

The Cymbals of Ladies.

The Dunger's Martingale.

Whirlingfriskorum Chasemarkerorum per Fratrem Crackwoodloguetis.

Manufacture of Playing Cards in a House
in Place Dauphine, c. 1680,
Paris, Musée Carnavalet

MIGUEL DE CERVANTES
DON QUIXOTE
FROM CHAPTER VI (1615)

OF THE DIVERTING AND IMPORTANT SCRUTINY
WHICH THE CURATE AND THE BARBER
MADE IN THE LIBRARY OF OUR INGENIOUS GENTLEMAN

He was still sleeping; so the curate asked the niece for the keys of the room where the books, the authors of all the mischief, were, and right willingly she gave them. They all went in, the housekeeper with them, and found more than a hundred volumes of big books very well bound, and some other small ones. The moment the housekeeper saw them she turned about and ran out of the room, and came back immediately with a saucer of holy water and a sprinkler, saying, "Here, your worship, señor licentiate, sprinkle this room; don't leave any magician of the many there are in these books to bewitch us in revenge for our design of banishing them from the world."

The simplicity of the housekeeper made the licentiate laugh, and he directed the barber to give him the books one by one to see what they were about, as there might be some to be found among them that did not deserve the penalty of fire.

"No," said the niece, "there is no reason for showing mercy to any of them; they have every one of them done mischief; better fling them out of the window into the court and make a pile of them and set fire to them; or else carry them into the yard, and there a bonfire can be made without the smoke giving any annoyance." The housekeeper said the same, so eager were they both for the slaughter of those innocents, but the curate would not agree to it without first reading at any rate the titles.

The first that Master Nicholas put into his hand was "The four books of Amadis of Gaul." "This seems a mysterious thing," said the curate, "for, as I have heard say, this was the first book of chivalry printed in Spain, and from this all the others derive their birth and origin; so it seems to me that we ought inexorably to condemn it to the flames as the founder of so vile a sect."

"Nay, sir," said the barber, "I, too, have heard say that this is the best of all the books of this kind that have been written, and so, as something singular in its line, it ought to be pardoned."

"True," said the curate; "and for that reason let its life be spared for the present. Let us see that other which is next to it."

"It is," said the barber, "the 'Sergas de Esplandian,' the lawful son of Amadis of Gaul."

"Then verily," said the curate, "the merit of the father must not be put down to the account of the son. Take it, mistress housekeeper; open the window and fling it into the yard and lay the foundation of the pile for the bonfire we are to make."

The housekeeper obeyed with great satisfaction, and the worthy "Esplandian" went flying into the yard to await with all patience the fire that was in store for him.

"Proceed," said the curate.

"This that comes next," said the barber, "is 'Amadis of Greece,' and, indeed, I believe all those on this side are of the same Amadis lineage."

"Then to the yard with the whole of them," said the curate; "for to have the burning of Queen Pintiquiniestra, and the shepherd Darinel and his eclogues, and the bedevilled and involved discourses of his author, I would burn with them the father who begot me if he were going about in the guise of a knight-errant."

"I am of the same mind," said the barber.

"And so am I," added the niece.

"In that case," said the housekeeper, "here, into the yard with them!"

They were handed to her, and as there were many of them, she spared herself the staircase, and flung them down out of the window.

"Who is that tub there?" said the curate.

"This," said the barber, "is 'Don Olivante de Laura.'"

"The author of that book," said the curate, "was the same that wrote 'The Garden of Flowers,' and truly there is no deciding which of the two books is the more truthful, or, to put it better, the less lying; all I can say is, send this one into the yard for a swaggering fool."

"This that follows is 'Florismarte of Hircania,'" said the barber.

"Señor Florismarte here?" said the curate; "then by my faith he must take up his quarters in the yard, in spite of his marvellous birth and visionary adventures, for the stiffness and dryness of his style deserve nothing else; into the yard with him and the other, mistress housekeeper."

"With all my heart, señor," said she, and executed the order with great delight.

"This," said the barber, "is 'The Knight Platir.'"

"An old book that," said the curate, "but I find no reason for clemency in it; send it after the others without appeal;" which was done.

Another book was opened, and they saw it was entitled, "The Knight of the Cross."

"For the sake of the holy name this book has," said the curate, "its ignorance might be excused; but then, they say, 'behind the cross there's the devil;' to the fire with it."

Taking down another book, the barber said, "This is 'The Mirror of Chivalry.'"

"I know his worship," said the curate; "that is where Señor Reinaldos of Montalvan figures with his friends and comrades, greater thieves than Cacus, and the Twelve Peers of France with the veracious historian Turpin;

however, I am not for condemning them to more than perpetual banishment, because, at any rate, they have some share in the invention of the famous Matteo Boiardo, whence too the Christian poet Ludovico Ariosto wove his web, to whom, if I find him here, and speaking any language but his own, I shall show no respect whatever; but if he speaks his own tongue I will put him upon my head."

"Well, I have him in Italian," said the barber, "but I do not understand him."

"Nor would it be well that you should understand him," said the curate, "and on that score we might have excused the Captain if he had not brought him into Spain and turned him into Castilian. He robbed him of a great deal of his natural force, and so do all those who try to turn books written in verse into another language, for, with all the pains they take and all the cleverness they show, they never can reach the level of the originals as they were first produced. In short, I say that this book, and all that may be found treating of those French affairs, should be thrown into or deposited in some dry well, until after more consideration it is settled what is to be done with them; excepting always one 'Bernardo del Carpio' that is going about, and another called 'Roncesvalles;' for these, if they come into my hands, shall pass at once into those of the housekeeper, and from hers into the fire without any reprieve."

To all this the barber gave his assent, and looked upon it as right and proper, being persuaded that the curate was so staunch to the Faith and loyal to the Truth that he would not for the world say anything opposed to them. Opening another book he saw it was "Palmerin de Oliva," and beside it was another called "Palmerin of England," seeing which the licentiate said, "Let the Olive be made firewood of at once and burned until no ashes even are left; and let that Palm of England be kept and preserved as a thing that stands alone, and let such another case be made for it as that which Alexander found among the spoils of Darius and set aside for

the safe keeping of the works of the poet Homer. This book, gossip, is of authority for two reasons, first because it is very good, and secondly because it is said to have been written by a wise and witty king of Portugal. All the adventures at the Castle of Miraguarda are excellent and of admirable contrivance, and the language is polished and clear, studying and observing the style befitting the speaker with propriety and judgment. So then, provided it seems good to you, Master Nicholas, I say let this and 'Amadis of Gaul' be remitted the penalty of fire, and as for all the rest, let them perish without further question or query."

"Nay, gossip," said the barber, "for this that I have here is the famous 'Don Belianis.'"

"Well," said the curate, "that and the second, third, and fourth parts all stand in need of a little rhubarb to purge their excess of bile, and they must be cleared of all that stuff about the Castle of Fame and other greater affectations, to which end let them be allowed the over-seas term, and, according as they mend, so shall mercy or justice be meted out to them; and in the mean time, gossip, do you keep them in your house and let no one read them."

"With all my heart," said the barber; and not caring to tire himself with reading more books of chivalry, he told the housekeeper to take all the big ones and throw them into the yard. It was not said to one dull or deaf, but to one who enjoyed burning them more than weaving the broadest and finest web that could be; and seizing about eight at a time, she flung them out of the window.

In carrying so many together she let one fall at the feet of the barber, who took it up, curious to know whose it was, and found it said, "History of the Famous Knight, Tirante el Blanco."

"God bless me!" said the curate with a shout, "'Tirante el Blanco' here! Hand it over, gossip, for in it I reckon I have found a treasury of enjoyment and a mine of recreation. Here is Don Kyrieleison of Montalvan, a valiant knight, and his brother Thomas of Montalvan, and the knight Fonseca, with the battle the bold Tirante fought with the mastiff, and the witticisms of the damsel Placerdemivida, and the loves and wiles of the widow Reposada, and the empress in love with the squire Hipolito—in truth, gossip, by right of its style it is the best book in the world. Here knights eat and sleep, and die in their beds, and make their wills before dying, and a great deal more of which there is nothing in all the other books. Nevertheless, I say he who wrote it, for deliberately composing such fooleries, deserves to be sent to the galleys for life. Take it home with you and read it, and you will see that what I have said is true."

"As you will," said the barber; "but what are we to do with these little books that are left?"

"These must be, not chivalry, but poetry," said the curate; and opening one he saw it was the "Diana" of Jorge de Montemayor, and, supposing all the others to be of the same sort, "these," he said, "do not deserve to be burned like the others, for they neither do nor can do the mischief the books of chivalry have done, being books of entertainment that can hurt no one."

"Ah, señor!" said the niece, "your worship had better order these to be burned as well as the others; for it would be no wonder if, after being cured of his chivalry disorder, my uncle, by reading these, took a fancy to turn shepherd and range the woods and fields singing and piping; or, what would be still worse, to turn poet, which they say is an incurable and infectious malady."

"The damsel is right," said the curate, "and it will be well to put this stumbling-block and temptation out of our friend's way. To begin, then, with the 'Diana' of Montemayor. I am of opinion it should not be burned, but that it should be cleared of all that about the sage Felicia and the magic water, and of almost all the longer pieces of verse: let it keep, and welcome, its prose and the honour of being the first of books of the kind."

"This that comes next," said the barber, "is the 'Diana,' entitled the 'Second Part, by the Salamancan,' and this other has the same title, and its author is Gil Polo."

"As for that of the Salamancan," replied the curate, "let it go to swell the number of the condemned in the yard, and let Gil Polo's be preserved as if it came from Apollo himself: but get on, gossip, and make haste, for it is growing late."

"This book," said the barber, opening another, "is the ten books of the 'Fortune of Love,' written by Antonio de Lofraso, a Sardinian poet."

"By the orders I have received," said the curate, "since Apollo has been Apollo, and the Muses have been Muses, and poets have been poets, so droll and absurd a book as this has never been written, and in its way it is the best and the most singular of all of this species that have as yet appeared, and he who has not read it may be sure he has never read what is delightful. Give it here, gossip, for I make more account of having found it than if they had given me a cassock of Florence stuff."

He put it aside with extreme satisfaction, and the barber went on, "These that come next are 'The Shepherd of Iberia,' 'Nymphs of Henares,' and 'The Enlightenment of Jealousy.'"

"Then all we have to do," said the curate, "is to hand them over to the secular arm of the housekeeper, and ask me not why, or we shall never have done."

"This next is the 'Pastor de Filida.'"

"No Pastor that," said the curate, "but a highly polished courtier; let it be preserved as a precious jewel."

"This large one here," said the barber, "is called 'The Treasury of various Poems.'"

"If there were not so many of them," said the curate, "they would be more relished: this book must be weeded and cleansed of certain vulgarities which it has with its excellences; let it be preserved because the author is a friend of mine, and out of respect for other more heroic and loftier works that he has written."

"This," continued the barber, "is the 'Cancionero' of Lopez de Maldonado."

"The author of that book, too," said the curate, "is a great friend of mine, and his verses from his own mouth are the admiration of all who hear them, for such is the sweetness of his voice that he enchants when he chants them: it gives rather too much of its eclogues, but what is good was never yet plentiful: let it be kept with those that have been set apart. But what book is that next it?"

"The 'Galatea' of Miguel de Cervantes," said the barber.

"That Cervantes has been for many years a great friend of mine, and to my knowledge he has had more experience in reverses than in verses. His book has some good invention in it, it presents us with something but brings nothing to a conclusion: we must wait for the Second Part it promises: perhaps with amendment it may succeed in winning the full measure of grace that is now denied it; and in the mean time do you, señor gossip, keep it shut up in your own quarters."

"Very good," said the barber; "and here come three together, the 'Araucana' of Don Alonso de Ercilla, the 'Austriada' of Juan Rufo, Justice of Cordova, and the 'Montserrate' of Christobal de Virues, the Valencian poet."

"These three books," said the curate, "are the best that have been written in Castilian in heroic verse, and they may compare with the most famous of Italy; let them be preserved as the richest treasures of poetry that Spain possesses."

The curate was tired and would not look into any more books, and so he decided that, "contents uncertified," all the rest should be burned; but just then the barber held open one, called "The Tears of Angelica."

"I should have shed tears myself," said the curate when he heard the title, "had I ordered that book to be burned, for its author was one of the famous poets of the world, not to say of Spain, and was very happy in the translation of some of Ovid's fables."

JORIS-KARL HUYSMANS
AGAINST THE GRAIN
FROM CHAPTER 3 (1884)

The second half of the fifth century had arrived, the horrible epoch when frightful motions convulsed the earth. The Barbarians sacked Gaul. Paralyzed Rome, pillaged by the Visigoths, felt its life grow feeble, perceived its extremities, the occident and the orient, writhe in blood and grow more exhausted from day to day. In this general dissolution, in the successive assassination of the Caesars, in the turmoil of carnage from one end of Europe to another, there resounded a terrible shout of triumph, stifling all clamors, silencing all voices. On the banks of the Danube, thousands of men astride on small horses, clad in rat-skin coats, monstrous Tartars with enormous heads, flat noses, chins gullied with scars and gashes, and jaundiced faces bare of hair, rushed at full speed to envelop the territories of the Lower Empire like a whirlwind.

Everything disappeared in the dust of their gallopings, in the smoke of the conflagrations. Darkness fell, and the amazed people trembled, as they heard the fearful tornado which passed with thunder crashes. The hordes of Huns razed Europe, rushed toward Gaul, overran the plains of Chalons where Aetius pillaged it in an awful charge. The plains, gorged with blood, foamed like a purple sea. Two hundred thousand corpses barred the way, broke the movement of this avalanche which, swerving, fell with mighty thunderclaps, against Italy whose exterminated towns flamed like burning bricks.

The Occidental Empire crumbled beneath the shock; the moribund life which it was pursuing to imbecility and foulness, was extinguished. For another reason, the end of the universe seemed near; such cities as had been forgotten by Attila were decimated by famine and plague. The Latin language in its turn, seemed to sink under the world's ruins. Years hastened on. The Barbarian idioms began to be modulated, to leave their vein-

stones and form real languages. Latin, saved in the debacle by the cloisters, was confined in its usage to the convents and monasteries. Here and there some poets gleamed, dully and coldly: the African Dracontius with his *Hexameron*, Claudius Memertius, with his liturgical poetry; Avitus of Vienne; then, the biographers like Ennodius, who narrates the prodigies of that perspicacious and venerated diplomat, Saint Epiphanius, the upright and vigilant pastor; or like Eugippus, who tells of the life of Saint Severin, that mysterious hermit and humble ascetic who appeared like an angel of grace to the distressed people, mad with suffering and fear; writers like Veranius of Gevaudan who prepared a little treatise on continence; like Aurelianus and Ferreolus who compiled the ecclesiastical canons; historians like Rotherius, famous for a lost history of the Huns.

Des Esseintes library did not contain many works of the centuries immediately succeeding. Notwithstanding this deficiency, the sixth century was represented by Fortunatus, bishop of Poitiers, whose hymns and *Vexila regis*, carved out of the old carrion of the Latin language and spiced with the aromatics of the Church, haunted him on certain days; by Boethius, Gregory of Tours, and Jornandez. In the seventh and eighth centuries since, in addition to the low Latin of the Chroniclers, the Fredegaires and Paul Diacres, and the poems contained in the Bangor antiphonary which he sometimes read for the alphabetical and mono-rhymed hymn sung in honor of Saint Comgill, the literature limited itself almost exclusively to biographies of saints, to the legend of Saint Columban, written by the monk, Jonas, and to that of the blessed Cuthbert, written by the Venerable Bede from the notes of an anonymous monk of Lindisfarn, he contented himself with glancing over, in his moments of tedium, the works of these hagiographers and in again reading several extracts from the lives of Saint Rusticula and Saint Radegonda, related, the one by Defensorius, the other by the modest and ingenious Baudonivia, a nun of Poitiers.

But the singular works of Latin and Anglo-Saxon literature allured him still further. They included the whole series of riddles by Adhelme, Tatwine and Eusebius, who were descendants of Symphosius, and especially the enigmas composed by Saint Boniface, in acrostic strophes whose solution could be found in the initial letters of the verses. His interest diminished with the end of those two centuries. Hardly pleased with the cumbersome mass of Carlovingian Latinists, the Alcuins and the Eginhards, he contented himself, as a specimen of the language of the ninth century, with the chronicles of Saint Gall, Freculfe and Reginon; with the poem of the siege of Paris written by Abbo le Courbe; with the didactic *Hortulus*, of the Benedictine Walafrid Strabo, whose chapter consecrated to the glory of the gourd as a symbol of fruitfulness, enlivened him; with the poem in which Ermold the Dark, celebrating the exploits of Louis the Debonair, a poem written in regular hexameters, in an austere, almost forbidding style and in a Latin of iron dipped in monastic waters with straws of sentiment, here and there, in the unpliant metal; with the *De viribus herbarum*, the poem of Macer Floridus, who particularly delighted him because of his poetic recipes and the very strange virtues which he ascribes to certain plants and flowers; to the aristolochia, for example, which, mixed with the flesh of a cow and placed on the lower part of a pregnant woman's abdomen, insures the birth of a male child; or to the borage which, when brewed into an infusion in a dining room, diverts guests; or to the peony whose powdered roots cure epilepsy; or to the fennel which, if placed on a woman's breasts, clears her water and stimulates the indolence of her periods.

Apart from several special, unclassified volumes, modern or dateless, certain works on the Cabbala, medicine and botany, certain odd tomes containing undiscoverable Christian poetry, and the anthology of the minor Latin poets of Wernsdorf; apart from *Meursius*, the manual of classical erotology of Forberg, and the diaconals used by confessors, which he dusted at rare intervals, his Latin library ended at the beginning of the tenth century.

And, in fact, the curiosity, the complicated naivete of the Christian language had also foundered. The balderdash of philosophers and scholars, the logomachy of the Middle Ages, thenceforth held absolute sway. The sooty mass of chronicles and historical books and cartularies accumulated, and the stammering grace, the often exquisite awkwardness of the monks, placing the poetic remains of antiquity in a ragout, were dead. The fabrications of verbs and purified essences, of substantives breathing of incense, of bizarre adjectives, coarsely carved from gold, with the barbarous and charming taste of Gothic jewels, were destroyed. The old editions, beloved by Des Esseintes, here ended; and with a formidable leap of centuries, the books on his shelves went straight to the French language of the present century.

Jean-Charles Cazin
Interior of the Study of Doctor X, 19th century,
Arras, Musée des Beaux-Arts

ITALO CALVINO
IF ON A WINTER'S NIGHT A TRAVELER
FROM CHAPTER 1 (1979)

So, then, you noticed in a newspaper that *If on a winter's night a traveler* had appeared, the new book by Italo Calvino, who hadn't published for several years. You went to the bookshop and bought the volume. Good for you.

In the shop window you have promptly identified the cover with the title you were looking for. Following this visual trail, you have forced your way through the shop past the thick barricade of Books You Haven't Read, which were frowning at you from the tables and shelves, trying to cow you. But you know you must never allow yourself to be awed, that among there extend for acres and acres the Books You Needn't Read, the Books Made For Purposes Other Than Reading, Books Read Even Before You Open Them Since They Belong To The Category Of Books Read Before Being Written. And thus you pass the outer girdle of ramparts, but then you are attacked by the infantry of the Books That If You Had More Than One Life You Would Certainly Also Read But Unfortunately Your Days Are Numbered. With a rapid maneuver you bypass them and move into the phalanxes of the Books You Mean To Read But There Are Others You Must Read First, the Books Too Expensive Now And You'll Wait Till They're Remaindered, the Books ditto When They Come Out In Paperback, Books You Can Borrow From Somebody, Books That Everybody's Read So It's As If You Had Read Them, Too. Eluding these assaults, you come up beneath the towers of the fortress, where other troops are holding out:

the Books You've Been Planning To Read For Ages,

the Books You've Been Hunting for Years Without Success,

the Books Dealing With Something You're Working On At The Moment,

the Books You Want To Own So They'll Be Handy Just In Case,

the Books You Could Put Aside Maybe To Read This Summer,

the Books You Need To Go With Other Books On Your Shelves,

the Books That Fill You With Sudden, Inexplicable Curiosity, Not Easily Justified.

Now you have been able to reduce the countless embattled troops to an array that is, to be sure, very large but still calculable in a finite number; but this relative relief is then undermined by the ambush of Books Read Long Ago Which It's Now Time To Reread and the Books You've Always Pretended To Have Read And Now It's Time To Sit Down And Really Read Them.

With a zigzag dash you shake them off and leap straight into the citadel of the New Books Whose Author Or Subject Appeals To You. Even inside this stronghold you can make some breaches in the ranks of the defenders, dividing them into New Books By Authors Or On Subjects Not New (for you or in general) and New Books By Authors Or On Subjects Completely Unknown (at least to you), and defining the attraction they have for you on the basis of your desires and needs for the new and the not new (for the new you seek in the not new and for the not new you seek in the new).

All this simply means that, having rapidly glanced over the titles of the volumes displayed in the bookshop, you have turned toward a stack of *If on a winter's night a traveler* fresh off the press, you have grasped a copy, and you have carried it to the cashier so that your right to own it can be established.

Bob Lescaux
Writing, 1999,
private collection

21.   A NON-NORMAL LIST

Let us go back to Borges' list of animals and repeat it because it needs to be re-read carefully: animals would therefore be "belonging to the emperor, embalmed, trained, suckling pigs, mermaids, fabulous, stray dogs, included in the present classification, those who struggle like madmen, countless, drawn with a very fine camel-hair brush, etcetera, those who have broken the vase, those that look like flies from a distance". Foucault observed that the monstrosity brought into circulation by Borges in his enumeration "consists of the fact that precisely the common space of the encounters to be found therein is reduced to nothing. That which is impossible is not the nearness of things, but the very site in which they could exist."[1] The list, in point of fact, defies any reasonable criterion of set theory because there can be countless mermaids, fabulous stray dogs, and suckling pigs belonging to the emperor which have broken the vase, and above all one cannot understand what sense there may be in putting that *etcetera* not at the end, in the place of other elements, but *among* the elements of the list itself. But this is not the only problem. The thing that makes the list really disquieting is that, among the elements it classifies, it also includes those already classified.

Here, at most, the ingenuous reader will feel bewildered. But the expert reader of the logic of sets perceives the vertigo that had once stunned Frege faced with the objection made by the young Russell. Let us establish that a set is normal when it does not also include itself. The set of all cats is not a cat, but a concept, and we might

Claudio Parmiggiani
Salita della memoria (Memory's Ascent), 1977,
Brescia, Collection Campiani

represent the situation as in Figure 1, where the capital *G* is the concept of cat that brings together all the individuals *g*, real cats that exist or that never existed or will exist. But there are also sets (called non-normal) that are elements of themselves. For example the set of all concepts is a concept and the set of all infinite sets is an infinite set. Hence (taking *X* as the set and *x* as its elements) we ought to represent this situation as in Figure 2.

(Figure 1)   (Figure 2)

G

g, g, g, g, g, g, g, g, g   x, x, x, x, X, x, x, x

Now, how is the set of all normal sets? If it were a normal set and if it looked like Figure 1, we would have an incomplete set, because it does not also classify itself. If it were a non-normal set and it looked like Figure 2 we would have an illogical set, because among all the normal sets we would have also classified a non-normal set. Hence the paradox that ensues from this.

All Borges did was to play with this paradox. Either that of the animals is a normal set and hence it must not also contain itself, but this is what happens in Borges' list. On the other hand, if it were a non-normal set, the list would be incongruent because something would appear among the animals that is not an animal, because it is a set.

With Borges' classification the poetics of the list reaches the acme of heresy and blasphemes all preconstituted logical order. And it makes us think of Apollinaire's prayer and challenge in *La jolie rousse*:

You whose mouth is made in the image of God's
Mouth that is order in itself
Be indulgent in comparing us
With those who were the perfection of order
We who seek adventure everywhere

Salvador Dalí
Head Bombarded with Grains of Wheat
(*Particle Head over the Village of Cadaqués*), 1954,
private collection

We are not your enemies
We wish to give you vast and strange territories
Where the mystery in bloom offers itself to he who would pluck it
With fires new and colours never seen
With a thousand imponderable phantasms
Requiring an infusion of reality

[...]

Pity for us who always battle on the frontiers
Of the boundless and the future
Pity for our errors and pity for our sins

[...]

Many things there are I dare not tell you
Many things you would not let me say
Have pity on me.

1. Michel Foucault, *Prefazione*, in *Le parole e le cose* (Milan, Rizzoli, 1967).

APPENDIX

BIOGRAPHICAL REFERENCES OF TRANSLATIONS AND OTHER SOURCES

Alighieri, Dante
The Divine Comedy
Translated by Henry Wadsworth Longfellow
London: George Routledge & Sons, 1886

Ariosto, Ludovico
Orlando Furioso
Translated by William Stewart Rose
London: John Murray, 1828

Aristotle
The Works of Aristotle
Translated and edited by J. A. Smith and W. D. Ross
Oxford: The Clarendon Press, 1909

Ausonius, Decimus Magnus
The Mosella
Translated by F. S. Flint
London: The Egoist (Poets' Translation Series, no. 6), 1926

Bacon, Francis
Essays, Civil and Moral: And The New Atlantis
London: Folio Society, 2002

Barthes, Roland
Roland Barthes by Roland Barthes
Translated by Richard Howard
Berkeley: University of California Press, 1994

Borges, Jorge Luis
The Aleph and Other Stories
Translated by Norman Thomas di Giovanni
London: Penguin Books, 2004

Breton, André
The Yale Anthology of Twentieth-Century French Poetry
Edited by Mary Ann Caws, translated by Mary Ann Caws and Patricia Terry
London: Yale University Press, 2004

Burton, Robert
The Anatomy of Melancholy, vol. III
Oxford: The Clarendon Press, 1994

Calvino, Italo
Invisible Cities
Translated by William Weaver
London: Vintage, 1997

If On a Winter's Night a Traveller
Translated by William Weaver
London: Vintage, 2007

Cervantes, Miguel de
Don Quixote
Translated by John Ormsby
London: Smith, Elder & Co., 1885

Dickens, Charles
Bleak House
Oxford: Oxford University Press, 2008

Diogenes Laërtius
The Lives and Opinions of Eminent Philosophers
Translated by C. D. Yonge
London: Henry G. Bohn, 1853

Döblin, Alfred
Berlin Alexanderplatz
Translated by Eugene Jolas
New York: Continuum, 2004

Eco, Umberto
The Name of the Rose
Translated by William Weaver
London: Secker & Warburg, 1983

Baudolino
Translated by William Weaver
London: Secker & Warburg, 2002

Ezekiel
The King James Bible

Gautier, Théophile
The Works of Théophile Gautier
Translated and edited by F. C. De

Sumichrast
New York: George D. Sproul, 1903

Goethe, Johann Wolfgang von
Faust
Translated by Charles T. Brooks
Boston: Ticknor and Fields, 1864

Gospel According to Saint Matthew
The King James Bible

Grimmelshausen, Hans von
Simplicissimus
Translated by Mike Mitchell
Cambridge: Dedalus Books, 1999

Hesiod
Hesiod: the Homeric Hymns and Homerica
Translated by Hugh G. Evelyn-White
Cambridge, MA: Harvard University Press (Loeb Classical Library, vol. 57), 1914

Homer
The Iliad of Homer
Translated by Alexander Pope
London: Penguin Books, 1996

Hugo, Victor
Ninety-Three
Boston: Little, Brown and Company, 1888

Huysmans, Joris-Karl
Against the Grain (À Rebours)
Translated by John Howard
New York: Lieber and Lewis, 1922

Isidore of Seville
The Etymologies of Isidore of Seville
Edited and translated by Stephen A. Barney et al.
Cambridge: Cambridge University Press, 2006

Joyce, James
Ulysses
London: Penguin Books, 2000

Finnegans Wake
London: Penguin Books, 2000

Kipling, Rudyard
Rewards and Fairies

Toronto: Macmillan Company of Canada, Ltd., 1910

Lautréamont, Comte de
Maldoror and the Complete Works of the Comte de Lautréamont
Translated by Alexis Lykiard
Cambridge, MA: Exact Change, 1994

Mann, Thomas
Doctor Faustus
Translated by H. T. Lowe-Porter
London: Random House, 1997

Masters, Edgar Lee
The Spoon River Anthology
London: Dover Publications, 2000

Milton, John
Paradise Lost
Oxford: Oxford University Press, 2008

Montale, Eugenio
Collected Poems, 1920–1954
Translated by Jonathan Galassi
Manchester: Carcanet Press, 1999

Neruda, Pablo
Residence on Earth
Translated by Donald D. Walsh
London: Souvenir Press Ltd, 1976

Poe, Edgar Allan
Tales and Sketches
London: George Routledge & Sons, 1852

Pynchon, Thomas
Gravity's Rainbow
London: Jonathan Cape, 1973

Proust, Marcel
Swann's Way
Translated by C. K. Scott Moncrieff
London: Chatto & Windus, 1992

Rabelais, François
Five Books of the Lives, Heroic Deeds and Sayings of Gargantua and his Son Pantagruel
Translated by Sir Thomas Urquhart of Cromarty and Peter

Antony Motteux
London: A. H. Bullen, 1904

Rimbaud, Arthur
Arthur Rimbaud: Complete Works
Translated by Paul Schmidt
New York: Harper & Row, 1975

Rostand, Edmond
Cyrano de Bergerac
Translated by Gladys Thomas and Mary F. Guillemard
New York: G. W. Dillingham Company, 1898

Shakespeare, William
Macbeth
Philadelphia: J. B. Lippincott & Co., 1878

Richard II
London: Chiswick Press, 1898

Sidonius Apollinaris
Sidonius: Poems and Letters
Translated by W. B. Anderson
Cambridge, MA: Harvard University Press (Loeb Classical Library), 1936

Song of Songs
The King James Bible

Süskind, Patrick
Perfume
Translated by John E. Woods
London: Hamish Hamilton, 1986

Szymborska, Wisława
Nothing Twice
Translated by Stanisław Barańczak and Clare Cavanagh
Warsaw: Wydawnictwo Literackie, 1997

View with a Grain of Sand
Translated by Stanisław Barańczak and Clare Cavanagh
London: Faber & Faber, 1996

Twain, Mark
The Writings of Mark Twain, vol. XII
New York: Harper & Brothers Publishers, 1903

Villon, François
Ballads from François Villon

Portland, ME: Thomas B. Mosher, 1916.

Virgil
The Æneid of Virgil
Translated by Theodore C. Williams
Boston and New York: Houghton Mifflin Company, 1908

Whitman, Walt
Leaves of Grass
Philadelphia: David McKay, 1884

Wilde, Oscar
The Picture of Dorian Gray
London: Ward, Lock & Co., 1891

Zola, Émile
Abbé Mouret's Transgression
Translated and edited by Ernest Alfred Vizetelly
London: Chatto & Windus, 1911

Note on translation of the anthology

For passages previously unpublished in English and not mentioned in this bibliography, the translations herein are my own; all are based on the original-language versions named in the headings of each excerpt. Given the nature of Closky's, Prévert's, and Balestrini's poetic texts—all of which rely on alphabetic, syllabic, and other strictly language-based devices—I preferred to leave them in French rather than try to render their meanings in a translation that would lose the list-like sense of the original. Although every effort was made to create an accurate, fluid rendition of all selections, in certain cases content necessarily took precedence over form, in order to provide readers with an English version that clearly conveys the list-driven character of these particular texts. Reflecting on his own work as reader, writer, and translator, Nabokov once concluded, "The clumsiest literal translation is a thousand times more useful than the prettiest paraphrase." While I aimed to keep clumsiness to a minimum, it is in a similarly utilitarian spirit that I present these various excerpts. Naturally, any and all inaccuracies are my own.

—Alta L. Price

CREDITS